A&P TECHNICIAN
POWERPLANT
STUDY GUIDE

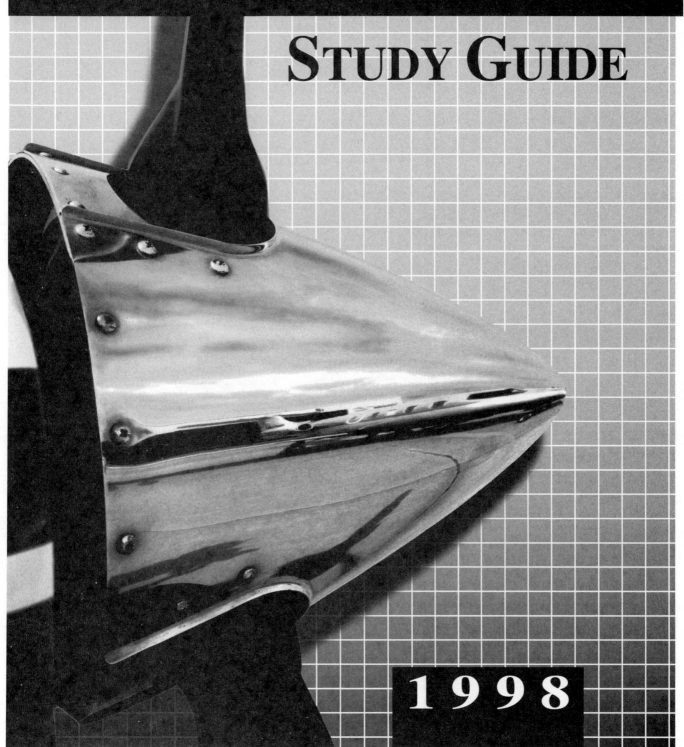

1998

JS312695A

PREFACE

Thank you for purchasing this *Aviation Mechanic Powerplant Knowledge Study Guide*. This Study Guide will help you understand the answers to the test questions so you can take the FAA computer test with confidence. It contains all the FAA Aviation Mechanic Powerplant test questions. Included are the correct answers and explanations, along with study references. Explanations of why the other choices are wrong have been included where appropriate. Questions are organized by topic, with explanations conveniently located adjacent to each question. Figures identical to those on the FAA test are included, plus our unique sliding mask for self-testing. Please note that this Study Guide is intended to be a supplement to your training, not a stand alone learning tool.

THE JEPPESEN SANDERSON TRAINING PHILOSOPHY

Maintenance training in the developing years of aviation was characterized by the separation of academics from maintenance training on the aircraft. For years, the training of theory and practice were not integrated. There were lots of books on different subjects, written by different authors, which produced a general lack of continuity in training material. The introduction of **Jeppesen Sanderson Training Products** changed all this. Our proven, professionally integrated training materials include extensive research on teaching theory and principles of how people learn best and most efficiently. Effective instruction includes determining objectives and completion standards. We employ an important principle of learning a complex skill using a step-by-step sequence known as the **building block principle**. Another important aspect of training is the principle of **meaningful repetition**, whereby each necessary concept or skill is presented several times throughout the instructional program. Jeppesen training materials incorporate these principles in our syllabi, textbooks, videos, exercises, exams, and this Study Guide. When these elements are combined with an instructor's class discussion and the skills learned in the shop, you have an ideal integrated training system, with all materials coordinated.

Observation and research show that people tend to retain 10% of what they read, 20% of what they hear, 30% of what they see, and 50% of what they both hear and see together. These retention figures can be increased to as high as 90% by including active learning methods. Videos and textbooks are generally considered passive learning materials. Exercises, stage exams, student/instructor discussions, and skills in the shop are considered to be active learning methods. Levels of learning include rote, understanding, application, and correlation. One of the major drawbacks with test preparation courses that concentrate only on passing the test is that they focus on rote learning, the lowest level of learning. Students benefit from Jeppesen's professional approach through standardized instruction, a documented training record, increased learning **and** increased passing rates. Our materials are challenging and motivating, while maximizing knowledge and skill retention. Thousands of technicians have learned aviation maintenance using our materials, which include:

MANUALS — Our training manuals contain the answers to many of the questions you may have as you begin your training program. They are based on the **study/review** concept of learning. This means detailed material is presented in an uncomplicated way, then important points are summarized through the use of bold type and color. The best results can be obtained when the manual is studied as an integral part of the coordinated materials. The manual is the central component for academic study and is cross-referenced to video presentations.

SUPPORT COMPONENTS — Supplementary items include an exercise book, stage and final exams, FAR handbook, Aircraft Technical Dictionary, and a Standard Aviation Maintenance Handbook. In addition, Jeppesen offers in-depth guidebooks on individual aviation maintenance subject areas. Jeppesen Sanderson's training products are the most comprehensive technician materials available. In conjunction with your instructor, they help you prepare for the FAA exam and practical test; and, more importantly, they help you become a more proficient and safer technician.

You can purchase our products and services through your Jeppesen dealer. For product, service, or sales information call **1-800-621-JEPP, 303-799-9090, or FAX 303-784-4153**. If you have comments, questions, or need explanations about any component of our Technician Training System, we are prepared to offer assistance at any time. If your dealer does not have a Jeppesen catalog, please request one and we will promptly send it to you. Just call the above telephone number, or write:

Marketing Manager, Training Products
Jeppesen Sanderson, Inc.
55 Inverness Drive East
Englewood, CO 80112-5498

Please direct inquiries from Europe, Africa, and the Middle East to:

Jeppesen & Co., GmbH
P.O. Box 70-05-51
Walter-Kolb-Str. 13
6000 Frankfurt/Main 70
Germany
Tel: 011-49-69-961240
Fax: 011-49-69-96124898

TABLE OF CONTENTS

INTRODUCTION _____

The *Aviation Mechanic Powerplant Knowledge Study Guide* is designed to help you prepare for the FAA Aviation Mechanic Powerplant Computer Test. It covers FAA exam material that applies to powerplant knowledge related to aircraft maintenance.

We recommend that you use this Study Guide in conjunction with the Jeppesen Sanderson A&P Technician Powerplant textbook. The Study Guide follows the FAA Aviation Mechanic Powerplant subject matter knowledge codes, with a total of 15 chapters. Questions are covered in the Study Guide in the same general sequence as the material in the textbook. References to applicable page numbers in the textbook are included along with the answers.

FAA test questions appear in the left column of the Study Guide. The question number, as well as the associated FAA subject matter knowledge code appear in bold type preceding each question. Answers are in the right column. The first line of the answer for each question is in bold type with the question number, the answer, and the abbreviation for an FAA or other authoritative source document.

> Example: **8273 Answer B. AC 65-15A**

Next is a brief explanation of the correct answer, followed by an explanation of why the other answers are wrong. In some cases, the incorrect answers are not explained. Examples include instances where the answers are calculated, or when the explanation of the correct answer obviously eliminates the wrong answers.

Abbreviations used in the Study Guide are as follows:

AC	—	Advisory Circulars
AC 65-9A	—	Airframe and Powerplant Mechanics General Handbook
AC 65-12A	—	Airframe and Powerplant Mechanics Powerplant Handbook
AC 65-15A	—	Airframe and Powerplant Mechanics Airframe Handbook
APC	—	Jeppesen Sanderson Aircraft Propellers and Controls
ASTM	—	American Society for Testing and Materials
DSA-25	—	Aircraft Powerplant Fundamentals
FAR	—	Federal Aviation Regulations
ITP-A2	—	Jeppesen Sanderson A&P Technician Airframe Textbook
ITP-P2	—	Jeppesen Sanderson A&P Technician Powerplant Textbook
TCAS	—	Jeppesen Sanderson Transport Catagory Aircraft Systems
JSGT	—	Jeppesen Sanderson A&P Technician General Textbook
TEP2	—	Aircraft Gas Turbine Powerplants

The answers in this Study Guide are based on official reference documents and, in our judgment, are the best choice of the available answers. Some questions which were valid when the FAA test was developed may no longer be appropriate due to ongoing changes in regulations or official operating procedures. However, with the computer test format, timely updating and validation of questions is anticipated. Therefore, when taking the FAA test, it is important to answer the questions according to the latest regulations or official operating procedures.

Two appendices from the FAA test materials are included in the back of the Study Guide. Appendix 1, Subject Matter Knowledge Codes, lists reference material and Appendix 2 contains a numerical listing of all powerplant questions. Included in this listing is a tabulation with the answer and the page number where the question appears in the Study Guide.

Figures in the Study Guide are the same as those that are used in the FAA Computerized Testing Supplement. These figures, that are referred to in many of the questions, are placed throughout the Study Guide as close as practical to the applicable questions. When a figure is not on the same page or facing page, a note will indicate the page number where you can find that figure. In addition, pages in this Study Guide are three-hole punched and perforated to allow you to easily remove any figure for reference while answering a specific question.

HOW TO PREPARE FOR THE FAA TEST

It is important to realize that to become a competent technician, you need more than just the academic knowledge required to pass a test. A certified Airframe and Powerplant Mechanics school will give you the practical shop skills that are indispensible to mechanics working in the field.

You will also benefit more from your study if you test yourself as you proceed through the Study Guide. Cover the answers in the right-hand column, read each question, and choose what you consider the best answer. A sliding mask is provided for this purpose. Move the sliding mask down and read the answer and explanation for that question. You may want to mark the questions you miss for further study and review prior to taking the exam.

The sooner you take the exam after you complete your study, the better. This way, the information will be fresh in your mind, and you will be more confident when you actually take the FAA test.

WHO CAN TAKE THE TEST

The Aviation Mechanic General Exam is usually taken in conjunction with either the Aviation Mechanic Airframe or Powerplant exam. When you are ready to take one of these FAA computerized tests, you must present either a graduation certificate or certificate of completion from a certified aviation maintenance technician school, or documentary evidence of practical work experience. For a single rating, you must have at least 18 months of practical experience with the procedures, practices, and equipment generally used in constructing, maintaining, or altering airframes or powerplants. To test for both ratings, you must show at least 30 months of practical experience concurrently performing the duties appropriate to both the airframe and powerplant ratings. Documentary evidence of practical experience must be satisfactory to the administrator.

You also must provide evidence of a permanent mailing address, appropriate identification, and proof of your age. The identification must include a current photograph, your signature, and your residential address, if different from your mailing address. You may present this information in more than one form of identification, such as a driver's license, government identification card, passport, alien residency (green) card, or a military identification card.

GENERAL INFORMATION — FAA COMPUTER TESTS

Detailed information on FAA computer testing is contained in FAA Order 8080.6A, *Conduct of Airmen Knowledge Tests Via The Computer Medium*. This FAA order provides guidance for Flight Standards District Offices (FSDOs) and personnel associated with organizations that are participating in, or are seeking to participate in, the FAA Computer-Assisted Airmen Knowledge Testing Program.

As an applicant, you don't need all of the details contained in FAA Orders, but you will be interested in some of the general information about computer testing facilities. A **computer testing designee (CTD)** is an organization authorized by the FAA to administer FAA airmen knowledge tests via the computer medium. A **computer testing manager (CTM)** is a person selected by the CTD to serve as manager of its national computer testing program. A **Testing Center Supervisor (TCS)** is a person selected by the CTD, with FAA approval, to administer FAA airmen knowledge tests at approved testing centers. The TCS is responsible for the operation of the testing center.

CTDs are selected by the FAA's Flight Standards Service. Those selected may include companies, schools, universities, or other organizations that meet specific requirements. For example, they must clearly demonstrate competence in computer technology, centralized database management, national communications network operation and maintenance, national facilities management, software maintenance and support, and technical training and customer support. They must provide computer-assisted testing, test administration, and data transfer service on a national scale. This means they must maintain a minimum of 20 operational testing centers geographically dispersed throughout the United States. In addition, CTDs must offer operational hours that are convenient to the public. An acceptable plan for test security is also required.

TEST MATERIALS, REFERENCE MATERIALS, AND AIDS

You are allowed to use aids, reference materials, and test materials within specified guidelines, provided the actual test questions or answers are not revealed. All models of aviation-oriented computers, regardless of manufacturer, may be used, including hand-held computers designed expressly for aviation use, and also small electronic calculators that perform arithmetic functions. Simple programmable memories, which allow addition to, subtraction from, or retrieval of one number from the memory, are acceptable. Simple functions such as square root or percent keys are also acceptable.

In addition, you may use any reference materials provided with the test. You will find that these reference materials are the same as those in your Study Guide. They include a printed Computerized Testing Supplement with the applicable figures.

WHAT TO EXPECT ON A COMPUTER TEST

Computer testing centers are required to have an acceptable method for the "on-line" registration of test applicants during normal business hours. They must provide a dual method, for example, keyboard, touch screen, or mouse, for answering questions. Features that must be provided also include an introductory lesson to familiarize you with computer testing procedures, the ability to return to a test question previously answered (for the purpose of review or answer changes), and a suitable display of multiple-choice and other question types on the computer screen in one frame. Other required features include a display of the time remaining for the completion of the test, a "HELP" function which permits you to review test questions and optional responses, and provisions for your test score on an Airman Computer Test Report.

On computer tests, the selection of questions is done for you, and you will answer the questions that appear on the screen. You will be given a specific amount of time to complete the test, which is based on past experience with others who have taken the exam. If you are prepared, you should have plenty of time to complete the test. After you begin the test, the screen will show you the time remaining for completion. When taking the test, keep the following points in mind:

1. Answer each question in accordance with the latest regulations and procedures. If the regulation or procedure has recently changed, you will receive credit for the affected question. However, these questions will normally be deleted or updated on the FAA computerized exams.

2. Read each question carefully before looking at the possible answers. You should clearly understand the problem before attempting to solve it.

3. After formulating an answer, determine which of the alternatives most nearly corresponds with that answer. The answer chosen should completely resolve the problem.

4. From the answers given, it may appear that there is more than one possible answer; however, there is only one answer that is correct and complete. The other answers are either incomplete or are derived from popular misconceptions.

5. Make sure you select an answer for each question. Questions left unanswered will be counted as incorrect.

6. If a certain question is difficult for you, it is best to proceed to other questions. After you answer the less difficult questions, return to those which were unanswered. The computer-aided test format helps you identify unanswered questions, as well as those questions you wish to review.

7. When solving a calculator problem, select the answer nearest your solution. The problem has been checked with various types of calculators; therefore, if you have solved it correctly, your answer will be closer to the correct answer than the other choices.

8. Generally, the test results will be available almost immediately. Your score will be recorded on an Airman Computer Test Report form. [Figure 1]

```
 1
 2
 3
 4
 5
 6                          Federal Aviation Administration
 7                          Airmen Computer Test Report
 8
 9   EXAM TITLE:  Aviation Mechanic Powerplant (AMP)
10
11   NAME:  Jones David John
12
13   ID NUMBER:  123456789              TAKE 1
14
15   DATE: 08/14/—              SCORE:  82              GRADE:  Pass
16
17
18
19
20   -----------------------------------------------------------------
21
22
23   Knowledge area codes in which questions were answered incorrectly.
24   See Appendix 1. A code may represent more than one incorrect
25   response.
26
27   A20  B08  B13  H01  H04  H06  I21  I22  J03  J05  M52  N27
28
29
30
31   EXPIRATION DATE:  08/31/—
32
33
34
35                      DO NOT LOSE THIS REPORT
36
37   -----------------------------------------------------------------
38   Authorized instructor's statement. (If applicable)
39
40   I have given Mr./Ms. _____  additional instruction in
41   each subject area shown to be deficient and consider the applicant competent to
42   pass the test.
43
44   Last _____ Initial _____ Cert. No. _____ Type _____
45   (Print Clearly)
46
47
48   Signature _____
49
50
51
52
53
54                                              CTD's Embossed Seal
```

FIGURE 1. This sample Airman Computer Test Report shows the applicants test results. Take 1 indicates this is the first time the applicant has taken this test. Knowledge area codes for incorrect answers are listed in the center portion of the report, and an additional instruction section is included in the last part.

The Airmen Computer Test Report includes subject matter knowledge codes for incorrect answers. To determine the knowledge area in which a particular question was incorrectly answered, compare the subject matter knowledge codes on this report to Appendix 1, Subject Matter Knowledge Codes.

Computer testing designees must provide a way for applicants, who challenge the validity of test questions, to enter comments into the computer. The test proctor should advise you, if you have complaints about test scores, or specific test questions, to write directly to the appropriate FAA office. In addition to comments, you will be asked to respond to a critique form which may vary at different computer testing centers. The TCS must provide a method for you to respond to critique questions projected on the computer screen. [Figure 2]

1. Did the test administration personnel give you an adequate briefing on testing procedures?

2. Was the "sign-on" accomplished efficiently?

3. Did you have any difficulty reading the computer presentation of test questions?

4. Was the test supplementary material (charts, graphs, tables, etc.) presented in a usable manner?

5. Did you have any difficulty using the "return to previous question for review" procedure?

6. Was the testing room noise level distracting?

7. Did you have adequate work space?

8. Did you have adequate lighting?

9. What is your overall evaluation of the computer testing experience?

   a. Unsatisfactory.

   b. Poor.

   c. Satisfactory.

   d. Highly satisfactory.

   e. Outstanding.

FIGURE 2. Critique forms used at different computer testing centers may vary. This sample form contains typical questions.

RETESTING

As stated in FAR 65.19, an applicant who fails a test may not apply for retesting until 30 days after the date the test was failed. However, in the case of a first failure, the applicant may apply for retesting before the 30 days have expired provided the applicant presents a signed statement from an airman holding the certificate and rating sought by the applicant certifying that the airman has given the applicant additional instruction in each of the subjects failed and that the airman considers the applicant ready for retesting.

WHERE TO TAKE THE FAA TEST

Almost all testing is now administered via computer at FAA-designated test centers. As indicated, these CTDs are located throughout the U.S. You can expect to pay a fee and the cost varies at different locations. The following is a listing of the approved computer testing designees at the time of publication of this Study Guide. You may want to check with your local FSDO for changes.

Aviation Business Services
1-800-947-4228
Outside U.S. (415) 259-8550

Sylvan Prometric
1-800-359-3278
1-800-967-1100
Outside U.S. (410) 880-0880, Extension 8890

RECIPROCATING ENGINES

This chapter covers the theory of reciprocating engine operation. It includes the basic practices and tools used to inspect, repair, overhaul, and service reciprocating engines, as well as presents information on powerplant removal, troubleshooting, and installation. The FAA exam questions that apply to this chapter include:

8001, 8002, 8003, 8004, 8005, 8006, 8007, 8008, 8009, 8010, 8011, 8012, 8013, 8014, 8015, 8016, 8017, 8018, 8019, 8020, 8021, 8022, 8023, 8024, 8025, 8026, 8027, 8028, 8029, 8030, 8031, 8032, 8033, 8034, 8035, 8036, 8037, 8038, 8039, 8040, 8041, 8042, 8043, 8044, 8045, 8046, 8047, 8048, 8049, 8050, 8051, 8052, 8053, 8054, 8055, 8056, 8057, 8058, 8059, 8060, 8061, 8062, 8063, 8064, 8065, 8066, 8067, 8068, 8069, 8070, 8071, 8072, 8073, 8074, 8075, 8076, 8077, 8078, 8079, 8080, 8081, 8082, 8083, 8084, 8085, 8086, 8087, 8088, 8089, 8090, 8091, 8092, 8093, 8094, 8095, 8096, 8097, 8098, 8099, 8100, 8101, 8102, 8103, 8104, 8105, 8106, 8107.

8001.   A01

Which statement is true regarding bearings used in high-powered reciprocating aircraft engines?

A — The outer race of a single-row, self-aligning ball bearing will always have a radius equal to the radius of the balls.
B — There is less rolling friction when ball bearings are used than when roller bearings are employed.
C — Crankshaft bearings are generally of the ball-type due to their ability to withstand extreme loads without overheating.

8002.   A01

Which propeller reduction gear ratio will cause the highest propeller RPM? (Assume the same engine RPM in each case.)

A — 16:7.
B — 20:9.
C — 3:2.

8001. Answer B. AC 65-12A

Both ball bearings and roller bearings are used in aircraft engines. However, since the steel balls in a ball bearing offer less surface contact than the rollers of a roller bearing, ball bearings produce less rolling friction (answer B). Therefore, ball bearings are generally used in high-powered reciprocating engines to keep friction to a minimum. Answer (A) is incorrect because self-aligning ball bearings have two rows of balls. Answer (C) is incorrect because most high-powered aircraft engines utilize roller bearings for the crankshaft main bearings because of their ability to withstand both radial and thrust loads.

8002. Answer C. AC 65-9A

The question identifies a propeller gear reduction ratio, which means the propeller will be turning slower than the engine. Answer (C) indicates a ratio of 3:2 which means the engine would turn three times for each two revolutions of the propeller. For example, if an engine is turning at 1,000 rpm the propeller will rotate at 666.7 rpm.

$$\frac{3}{2} = \frac{1,000}{x}$$

$$3x = 2,000$$

$$x = 666.7$$

If you apply the same engine rpm to answers (A) and (B) the propeller would rotate at 437.5 rpm and 450 rpm respectively. Therefore, the ratio of 3:2 is the smallest gear reduction and will produce the highest propeller RPM for a given engine speed.

8003.   **A01**

Which condition would be the least likely to be caused by failed or failing engine bearings?

A — Excessive oil consumption.
B — High oil temperatures.
C — Low oil temperatures.

8004.   **A01**

What is the principal advantage of using propeller reduction gears?

A — To enable the propeller RPM to be increased without an accompanying increase in engine RPM.
B — To enable the engine RPM to be increased with an accompanying increase in power and allow the propeller to remain at a lower, more efficient RPM.
C — To enable the engine RPM to be increased with an accompanying increase in propeller RPM.

8005.   **A01**

Which of the following will decrease volumetric efficiency in a reciprocating engine?

1. Full throttle operation.
2. Low cylinder head temperatures.
3. Improper valve timing.
4. Sharp bends in the induction system.
5. High carburetor air temperatures.

A — 2, 4, and 5.
B — 1, 2, 3, and 4.
C — 3, 4, and 5.

8006.   **A01**

Which of the following is a characteristic of a thrust bearing used in most radial engines?

A — Tapered roller.
B — Double-row ball.
C — Deep-groove ball.

8003. Answer C. AC 65-12A

If a bearing fails or is in the process of failing, metal to metal contact is occurring. The friction which accompanies this metal to metal contact generates a great deal of heat and can cause high oil temperatures (answer B). The higher the oil temperature, the more oil is consumed (answer A). Since the question asks for the condition that is least likely to be caused by a failed bearing, answer (C) is the best choice.

8004. Answer B. AC 65-12A

The amount of horsepower an engine produces is directly related to the engine's rpm. Therefore, most aircraft engines must run at a speed in excess of 2,000 rpm to develop sufficient power. However, propeller efficiency at these speeds decreases rapidly. Therefore, in order to maintain an acceptable level of propeller efficiency a reduction gear is used. A reduction gear allows an engine to run at the high rpm needed to produce more horsepower while at the same time, allow the propeller to rotate at a lower, more efficient rpm. Answer (A) is wrong because it implies that a reduction gear is used to increase propeller rpm above that of the engine and answer (C) is wrong because it implies that a reduction gear allows propeller rpm and engine rpm to remain the same.

8005. Answer C. AC 65-12A

Volumetric efficiency is a comparison of the volume of a fuel/air charge inducted into all cylinders to the total piston displacement. Factors that reduce volumetric efficiency include part-throttle operation, long, small diameter intake pipes, sharp bends in the induction system, excessive carburetor air temperatures, excessive cylinder head temperatures, incomplete scavenging, and improper valve timing. Of the five choices given in the question only #3, #4, and #5 (answer C) affect volumetric efficiency.

8006. Answer C. AC 65-12A

Special deep-groove ball bearings are used as thrust bearings in most radial engines. This type of bearing generates the least amount of friction of all the types of bearings listed while still being able to withstand both the thrust and radial loads. Although tapered roller bearings (answer A) and double-row ball bearings (answer B) are capable of withstanding both thrust and radial loads, they produce more friction than a deep-groove ball bearing.

8007.   A01
Which bearing is least likely to be a roller or ball bearing?

A — Rocker arm bearing (overhead valve engine).
B — Master rod bearing (radial engine).
C — Crankshaft main bearing (radial engine).

8007. Answer B. AC 65-12A
The question asks for the least likely use of a roller or ball bearing. Answers (A) and (C) are incorrect because roller bearings and ball bearings are designed to withstand radial and thrust loads produced by crankshafts and rocker arms. Master rod bearings on radial engines are generally subjected to radial loads only and, therefore, plain bearings are used. Therefore, answer (B) is correct.

8008.   A01
The operating temperature valve clearance of a radial engine as compared to cold valve clearance is

A — greater.
B — less.
C — the same.

8008. Answer A. AC 65-12A
As a radial engine warms up, the aluminum alloy cylinder heads expand causing the rocker arm in the head to move away from the crankcase. At the same time, the pushrod also expands but at a lesser rate than the cylinder head. The difference in expansion amounts between the cylinder head and pushrod effectively increases the space between the valve stem and rocker arm (valve clearance). Therefore, answer (A) is correct.

8009.   A01
A nine-cylinder engine with a bore of 5.5 inches and a stroke of 6 inches will have a total piston displacement of

A — 740 cubic inches.
B — 1,425 cubic inches.
C — 1,283 cubic inches.

8009. Answer C. AC 65-12A
The total piston displacement of an engine is equal to the displacement, or volume of one cylinder multiplied by the total number of cylinders. The volume of a cylinder is calculated using the formula $V = pi\ r^2\ h$, where (V) is the volume, (r) is the radius of the cylinder, and (h) is the height, or stroke of the piston. The displacement of each cylinder is 142.55 cubic inches ($3.1416 \times 2.75^2 \times 6 = 142.55$). To determine the displacement of the entire engine, multiply the displacement of each cylinder by the total number of cylinders. The total engine displacement is 1,282.95 cubic inches ($142.55 \times 9 = 1,282.95$). Answer (C) is the closest.

8010.   A01
The five events of a four-stroke cycle engine in the order of their occurrence are

A — intake, ignition, compression, power, exhaust.
B — intake, power, compression, ignition, exhaust.
C — intake, compression, ignition, power, exhaust.

8010. Answer C. AC 65-12A
The four-stroke cycle begins when the piston starts moving down in the cylinder on the intake stroke. When the piston reaches bottom center it reverses direction and starts moving up on the compression stroke. Near the top of the compression stroke, the spark plug fires causing ignition of the fuel/air mixture. As soon as the fuel/air mixture begins to burn, the piston is forced down in the power stroke. As the piston approaches bottom center, the exhaust valve opens and the piston reverses direction to begin the exhaust stroke. Therefore, the five events of a four stroke engine are intake, compression, ignition, power, and exhaust. Answers (A) and (B) are wrong because they do not list the five events in the proper sequence.

8011.   A02

The primary concern in establishing the firing order for an opposed engine is to

A — provide for balance and eliminate vibration to the greatest extent possible.
B — keep power impulses on adjacent cylinders as far apart as possible in order to obtain the greatest mechanical efficiency.
C — keep the power impulses on adjacent cylinders as close as possible in order to obtain the greatest mechanical efficiency.

8012.   A02

If fuel/air ratio is proper and ignition timing is correct, the combustion process should be completed

A — 20 to 30° before top center at the end of the compression stroke.
B — when the exhaust valve opens at the end of the power stroke.
C — just after top center at the beginning of the power stroke.

8013.   A02

Grinding the valves of a reciprocating engine to a feather edge is likely to result in

A — normal operation and long life.
B — excessive valve clearance.
C — preignition and burned valves.

8014.   A02

Which statement is correct regarding engine crankshafts?

A — Moveable counterweights serve to reduce the dynamic vibrations in an aircraft reciprocating engine.
B — Moveable counterweights serve to reduce the torsional vibrations in an aircraft reciprocating engine.
C — Moveable counterweights are designed to resonate at the natural frequency of the crankshaft.

8011. Answer A. AC 65-12A

The firing order within an engine is designed to provide for balance and to eliminate vibration to the greatest extent possible. Answers (B) and (C) are incorrect because mechanical efficiency is obtained by having the power impulses evenly divided.

8012. Answer C. AC 65-12A

Combustion is the third event in the cycle of a four-stroke engine. The combustion process begins as the piston reaches the top of the compression stroke and the fuel/air charge is ignited by means of an electric spark. The time of ignition varies from 20 to 35 degrees before top dead center to ensure complete combustion by the time the piston is slightly past the top dead center position. Answer (A) is incorrect because it describes the beginning of the combustion process and answer (B) is incorrect because it describes the start of the exhaust stroke.

8013. Answer C. AC 65-12A

A thin edge on a poppet valve is called a feather edge. Valves with a feather edge are likely to overheat and burn away in a short period of time. Both of these conditions can lead to preignition. Answer (A) is incorrect because normal operation and long life are not characteristics of valves with a feather edge. Answer (B) is wrong because the type of edge on a valve does not affect valve clearance.

8014. Answer A. AC 65-12A

Each time a cylinder on an engine fires, a pulse of energy is transferred to the crankshaft, causing the crankshaft to flex and vibrate. When the engine is running, the crankshaft receives hundreds of these pulses each minute and vibrates constantly. To help minimize these vibrations, moveable counterweights, sometimes called dynamic dampers, are installed on a crankshaft. Answer (B) is incorrect because severe torsional vibration typically occurs only when an engine is equipped with a propeller reduction gear system and is reduced by the use of a quill shaft. Answer (C) is wrong because the moveable counterweights resonate at the frequency of the power impulses, not at the crankshaft's natural frequency.

8015.   A02
On which strokes are both valves on a four-stroke cycle reciprocating engine open?

A — Power and exhaust.
B — Intake and compression.
C — Exhaust and intake.

8015. Answer C. AC 65-12A
For a reciprocating engine to operate properly, each valve must open at the proper time, stay open for a specific length of time, and close at the proper time. In a typical reciprocating engine, the intake valve opens just before the piston reaches top dead center on the exhaust stroke and remains open into the intake stroke. On the other hand, the exhaust valve is open throughout the exhaust stroke and remains open after top dead center when the piston begins the intake stroke. Therefore, at the end of the exhaust stroke and the beginning of the intake stroke both valves are open at the same time.

8016.   A02
Master rod bearings are generally what type?

A — Plain.
B — Roller.
C — Ball.

8016. Answer A. AC 65-12A
The master rod in a radial engine is subjected to radial loads only and, therefore, plain bearings are typically used as master rod bearings.

8017.   A02
The actual power delivered to the propeller of an aircraft engine is called

A — friction horsepower.
B — brake horsepower.
C — indicated horsepower.

8017. Answer B. AC 65-12A
Brake horsepower is the horsepower that is delivered to the propeller shaft. One way to determine an engine's brake horsepower is to subtract an engine's friction horsepower from its indicated horsepower. Answer (A) is wrong because friction horsepower represents the amount of horsepower required to overcome internal engine friction. Answer (C) is incorrect because indicated horsepower is the power developed in the combustion chambers without reference to friction losses.

8018.   A02
Cam-ground pistons are installed in some aircraft engines to

A — provide a better fit at operating temperatures.
B — act as a compensating feature so that a compensated magneto is not required.
C — equalize the wear on all pistons.

8018. Answer A. AC 65-12A
A cam-ground piston is constructed with a slightly oval cross-section. In other words, the piston's diameter perpendicular to the piston pin is slightly larger than the diameter parallel to the piston pin. This oval shape holds the piston square in the cylinder when an engine is cold and allows the greater mass of the piston pin bosses to expand more freely at operating temperatures. Once expanded, cam-ground pistons provide a better fit within the cylinder. Answer (B) is wrong because a compensated magneto has nothing to do with piston design and answer (C) is incorrect because, although a cam-ground piston wears more evenly than a conventional piston, individual piston wear on all pistons within an engine is dependent on several other factors.

8019.   A02

Using the following information, determine how many degrees the crankshaft will rotate with both the intake and exhaust valves seated.

Intake opens 15° BTDC.
Exhaust opens 70° BBDC.
Intake closes 45° ABDC.
Exhaust closes 10° ATDC.

A — 290°.
B — 245°.
C — 25°.

8020.   A02

Some aircraft engine manufacturers equip their product with choked or taper-ground cylinders in order to

A — provide a straight cylinder bore at operating temperatures.
B — flex the rings slightly during operation and reduce the possibility of the rings sticking in the grooves.
C — increase the compression pressure for starting purposes.

8021.   A02

An aircraft reciprocating engine using hydraulic valve lifters is observed to have no clearance in its valve-operating mechanism after the minimum inlet oil and cylinder head temperatures for takeoff have been reached. When can this condition be expected?

A — During normal operation.
B — When the lifters become deflated.
C — As a result of carbon and sludge becoming trapped in the lifter and restricting its motion.

8022.   A02

What tool is generally used to measure the crankshaft rotation in degrees?

A — Dial indicator.
B — Timing disk.
C — Prop protractor.

8019. Answer B. AC 65-12A

One complete revolution of a crankshaft and piston takes 360 degrees, with top dead center (TDC) being 0 degrees and bottom dead center (BDC) 180 degrees. The only time both valves are closed in a four-stroke engine is during a portion of the compression and combustion strokes. This question indicates that the intake valve closes 45 degrees after bottom dead center, or 135 degrees before top dead center (180 - 45 = 135). The exhaust valve, on the other hand, opens 70 degrees before bottom dead center, or 110 degrees after top dead center (180 - 70 = 110). Therefore the number of degrees both valves are seated is 245 degrees (135 + 110 = 245).

8020. Answer A. ITP-P2

Most cylinders have a certain degree of choke, or taper. This means that the cylinder barrel is slightly narrower at the cylinder head than at the cylinder skirt. A choked cylinder allows for cylinder expansion resulting from the higher operating temperatures near the head. Once a choked cylinder reaches operating temperature, the choked area expands to match the bore at the skirt, and the entire bore becomes straight. Therefore, answer (A) is correct.

8021. Answer A. AC 65-12A

In a zero-lash or zero-clearance hydraulic valve lifter, oil pressure forces the lifter outward until all clearance between the rocker arm and the valve stem is removed. This condition in an engine is normal. Answers (B) and (C) are incorrect because when oil pressure is removed or if sludge restricts hydraulic lifter movement, valve clearance increases to a value greater than zero.

8022. Answer B. AC 65-12A

The timing disk is a more accurate crankshaft positioning device than timing reference marks. When setting up the ignition timing on an engine, a timing disk should be attached to the engine to measure the crankshaft rotation in degrees. Answer (A) is wrong because a dial indicator is used to measure an out of round condition on crankshafts or piston pins. Answer (C) is wrong because a prop protractor is used to measure propeller blade angles and degree of control surface deflection.

8023.   A02
If an engine with a stroke of 6 inches is operated at 2,000 RPM, the piston movement within the cylinder will be

A — at maximum velocity around TDC.
B — constant during the entire 360° of crankshaft travel.
C — at maximum velocity 90° after TDC.

8023. Answer C. AC 65-12A
As a piston leaves top dead center (TDC) and bottom dead center (BDC), it accelerates and attains its maximum speed at 90 degrees after TDC and 90 degrees after BDC. Answers (A) and (B) are incorrect because piston speed must slow to allow for a change in the direction of movement at TDC and BDC.

8024.   A02
If the intake valve is opened too early in the cycle of operation of a four-stroke cycle engine, it may result in

A — improper scavenging of exhaust gases.
B — engine kickback.
C — backfiring into the induction system.

8024. Answer C. AC 65-12A
The distance an intake valve may be opened before TDC is limited by several factors. For example, if the intake valve opens too early hot gases remaining in the cylinder may flash back into the intake pipe and induction system causing a backfire. Answer (A) is incorrect because exhaust gas scavenging is accomplished through the exhaust valve. Answer (B) is incorrect because engine kickback is a function of faulty ignition timing rather than valve timing.

8025.   A02
Some cylinder barrels are hardened by

A — nitriding.
B — shot peening.
C — tempering.

8025. Answer A. AC 65-12A
The cylinder barrel of a reciprocating engine is made of a steel alloy forging with its inner surface hardened to resist wear. One method used to harden cylinders is nitriding. In the nitriding process, the cylinder is heated and exposed to ammonia or cyanide gas. Nitrogen from the gas is absorbed by the steel causing iron nitrides to form on the steel's surface. Both answers (B) and (C) are incorrect because shot peening and tempering are methods used to relieve stresses within metals and not methods of hardening.

8026.   A02
Which statement is correct regarding a four-stroke cycle aircraft engine?

A — The intake valve closes on the compression stroke.
B — The exhaust valve opens on the exhaust stroke.
C — The intake valve closes on the intake stroke.

8026. Answer A. AC 65-12A
Depending upon the specific engine, an intake valve is timed to open prior to the piston reaching top dead center on the exhaust stroke and to close about 50 to 75 degrees past bottom dead center on the compression stroke (answer A). This allows the momentum of the incoming gases to charge the cylinder more completely. The exhaust valve, on the other hand, typically opens around 70 degrees before bottom dead center on the power stroke and closes at approximately 15 degrees after top dead center on the intake stroke.

8027.   A02
On which part of the cylinder walls of a normally operating engine will the greatest amount of wear occur?

A — Near the center of the cylinder where piston velocity is greatest.
B — Near the top of the cylinder.
C — Wear is normally evenly distributed.

8027. Answer B. AC 65-12A
At the top of a stroke, a piston is subjected to extreme heat, pressure, and a more erosive environment than at the bottom of a stroke. These factors tend to cause greater piston movement at the top of a cylinder. Therefore, cylinder walls tend to wear more at the top than at the bottom (answer B).

8028.   **A02**

During overhaul, reciprocating engine exhaust valves are checked for stretch

A — with a suitable inside spring caliper.
B — with a contour or radius gauge.
C — by placing the valve on a surface plate and measuring its length with a vernier height gauge.

8028. Answer B. AC 65-12A

Intake and exhaust valves can be checked for stretch by one of two methods. One involves checking the diameter of the valve stem near the neck of the valve with a micrometer. If the diameter is smaller than normal, the valve has been stretched. The second method involves checking the valve with a radius or contour gauge. The contour gauge is designed to fit along the underside of the valve head. If the contour of the gauge and that of the valve do not match, it indicates that the valve has been stretched. Answer (A) is wrong because an inside spring caliper is used to measure inside dimensions and answer (C) is wrong because a vernier height gauge is not meant to be used for measuring valve clearance.

8029.   **A02**

When is the fuel/air mixture ignited in a conventional reciprocating engine?

A — When the piston has reached top dead center of the intake stroke.
B — Shortly before the piston reaches the top of the compression stroke.
C — When the piston reaches top dead center on the compression stroke.

8029. Answer B. AC 65-12A

In a reciprocating engine, the fuel/air charge is fired by means of an electric spark shortly before the piston reaches top dead center on the compression stroke. The time of ignition varies from 20 degrees to 35 degrees before top dead center, depending upon the engine requirements. By igniting the fuel/air charge before the piston reaches top dead center, complete combustion is ensured by the time the piston is slightly past top dead center and maximum power is delivered to the crankshaft.

8030.   **A02**

Ignition occurs at 28° BTDC on a certain four-stroke cycle engine, and the intake valve opens at 15° BTDC. How many degrees of crankshaft travel after ignition does the intake valve open? (Consider one cylinder only.)

A — 707°.
B — 373°.
C — 347°.

8030. Answer B. AC 65-12A

Ignition occurs at 28 degrees before top dead center. Therefore, the piston will travel 28 degrees to complete the stroke. As the piston moves from top to bottom dead center on the power stroke, the crankshaft turns another 180 degrees. According to the question, the intake valve opens 15 degrees before top dead center of the exhaust stroke, or 165 degrees after bottom dead center. Therefore, total crankshaft travel is 375 degrees (28 + 180 + 165 = 373).

8031.   **A02**

What is the purpose of the safety circlet installed on some valve stems?

A — To hold the valve guide in position.
B — To hold the valve spring retaining washer in position.
C — To prevent valves from falling into the combustion chamber.

8031. Answer C. AC 65-12A

The stems of some valves have a narrow groove cut in them just below the lock ring groove that allows for the installation of safety circlets or spring rings. The circlets are designed to prevent the valves from falling into the combustion chamber should the valve tip break during engine operation. Answer (A) is incorrect because valve guides are held in position by a shrink fit in the cylinder head and answer (B) is wrong because valve spring retaining washers are held in position by split stem keys or keepers.

8032.   **A02**

Valve overlap is defined as the number of degrees of crankshaft travel

A — during which both valves are off their seats.
B — between the closing of the intake valve and the opening of the exhaust valve.
C — during which both valves are on their seats.

8033.   **A02**

The operating valve clearance of an engine using hydraulic lifters should not exceed

A — 0.15 inch.
B — 0.00 inch.
C — 0.25 inch.

8034.   **A02**

If the exhaust valve of a four-stroke cycle engine is closed and the intake valve is just closing, the piston is on the

A — intake stroke.
B — power stroke.
C — compression stroke.

8035.   **A02**

How many of the following are factors in establishing the maximum compression ratio limitations of an aircraft engine?

1. Detonation characteristics of the fuel used.
2. Design limitations of the engine.
3. Degree of supercharging.
4. Spark plug reach.

A — Four.
B — Two.
C — Three.

8036.   **A02**

Full-floating piston pins are those which allow motion between the pin and

A — the piston.
B — both the piston and the large end of the connecting rod.
C — both the piston and the small end of the connecting rod.

8032. Answer A. AC 65-12A

Valve overlap represents the degree of crankshaft travel in which both the intake valve and exhaust valve are open (off their seat). On most reciprocating engines, the intake valve opens before top dead center on the exhaust stroke, while the exhaust valve closes after the piston has passed TDC and started the intake stroke. This results in a valve overlap of anywhere from 40 to 75 degrees. Answers (B) and (C) are wrong because both valves are not open in either example.

8033. Answer B. AC 65-12A

Most modern aircraft reciprocating engines incorporate hydraulic lifters which automatically keep the valve clearance at zero. This eliminates the necessity for any valve clearance adjustment mechanism. With this type of system, the maximum and minimum clearance at any time should be 0.00 inches. Answers (A) and (C) are wrong because they both indicate measurements in excess of 0.00 inches.

8034. Answer C. AC 65-12A

The intake valve of a reciprocating engine is timed to close about 50 to 75 degrees past bottom dead center on the compression stroke. After the intake valve closes, the continued upward travel of the piston compresses the fuel/air mixture to obtain the desired burning and expansion characteristics. On the intake stroke (answer A), the exhaust valve is just closing, while the intake valve is open and on the power stroke (answer B) both valves are closed.

8035. Answer C. AC 65-12A

An engine's compression ratio is the controlling factor in determining the amount of horsepower an engine develops. Some of the factors that must be considered when establishing a maximum compression ratio include the detonation characteristics of the fuel used, the engine's design limitations, and the degree of supercharging. Spark plug reach does not limit an engine's compression ratio. Based on this, three of the four factors listed (answer C) are valid limitations.

8036. Answer C. AC 65-12A

A full-floating piston pin gets its name from the fact that the pin is free to rotate in both the piston and in the small end of the connecting rod. Answer (A) is wrong because a full-floating piston pin is free to rotate in more than just the piston and answer (B) is incorrect because the large end of a connecting rod does not utilize a piston pin.

8037.   A02
The primary purpose in setting proper valve timing and overlap is to

A — permit the best possible charge of fuel/air mixture into the cylinders.
B — gain more thorough exhaust gas scavenging.
C — obtain the best volumetric efficiency and lower cylinder operating temperatures.

8038.   A02
If the hot clearance is used to set the valves when the engine is cold, what will occur during operation of the engine?

A — The valves will open early and close early.
B — The valves will open late and close early.
C — The valves will open early and close late.

8039.   A02
The purpose of two or more valve springs in aircraft engines is to

A — equalize side pressure on the valve stems.
B — eliminate valve spring surge.
C — equalize valve face loading.

8040.   A02
During overhaul, the disassembled parts of an engine are usually degreased with some form of mineral spirits solvent rather than water-mixed degreasers primarily because

A — solvent degreasers are much more effective.
B — water-mixed degreaser residues may cause engine oil contamination in the overhauled engine.
C — water-mixed degreasers cause corrosion.

8041.   A02
Why does the smoothness of operation of an engine increase with a greater number of cylinders?

A — The power impulses are spaced closer together.
B — The power impulses are spaced farther apart.
C — The engine has larger counterbalance weights.

8037. Answer C. AC 65-12A
Reciprocating engines are timed so that both the intake and exhaust valves are open near the end of the exhaust stroke and into the beginning of the intake stroke. This valve overlap allows a larger quantity of the fuel/air charge to be drawn into the cylinder which, in return, increases volumetric efficiency. Furthermore, overlap helps to expel the exhaust gases from the previous power stroke and lower operating temperatures.

8038. Answer B. AC 65-12A
When an engine is hot, the clearance between the rocker arm and the valve stem is greater than when the engine is cold. Therefore, if the valves are set to hot clearances when the engine is cold, the overall valve clearance will be excessive and the valves will open late and close early. Both answers (A) and (C) are wrong because the valves will open late, not early as indicated.

8039. Answer B. AC 65-12A
Each valve on a reciprocating engine is closed by two or three helical-coiled springs. If only a single spring were used to close a valve, the spring would vibrate or surge at certain speeds. However, with multiple springs, each spring vibrates at a different engine speed resulting in rapid dampening of all spring surge vibrations. Neither answer (A) nor (C) is correct because the use of a single spring does not produce uneven side pressures on a valve stem or unequal valve face loading.

8040. Answer B. AC 65-12A
Water-mixed degreasing compounds usually contain some form of alkali. If allowed to remain in the pores of metal engine parts when the engine is returned to service, the alkali will contaminate the oil and cause oil foaming. Answer (A) is incorrect because some water-mixed degreasers are just as effective as solvent degreasers. Answer (C) is wrong because, although water-mixed degreasers can cause corrosion in aluminum and magnesium parts, it is not an absolute.

8041. Answer A. AC 65-12A
The more cylinders an engine has, the closer together the power impulses occur and the smoother the engine operates. Answer (B) is incorrect because the power pulses are spaced closer together not further apart and answer (C) is incorrect because the number of cylinders does not dictate the size of the counterbalance weights.

8042.   A02

Compression ratio is the ratio between the

A — piston travel on the compression stroke and on the intake stroke.
B — combustion chamber pressure on the combustion stroke and on the exhaust stroke.
C — cylinder volume with piston at bottom dead center and at top dead center.

8042. Answer C. AC 65-12A

The compression ratio of an engine is a comparison of the volume of a cylinder when the piston is at the bottom of a stroke to the volume of the same cylinder when the piston is at the top of a stroke. Answer (A) is wrong because the amount of piston travel is identical on every stroke and answer (B) is incorrect because compression ratio is a ratio of volumes, not pressures.

8043.   A02

If the crankshaft runout readings on the dial indicator are plus .002 inch and minus .003 inch, the runout is

A — .005 inch.
B — plus .001 inch.
C — minus .001 inch.

8043. Answer A. AC 65-12A

The total indicator reading for runout on a crankshaft is the sum of the plus (+) and minus (-) readings. In this case, the runout is .005 in. (.002 + .003 = .005).

8044.   A02

(1) Cast iron piston rings may be used in chrome-plated cylinders.
(2) Chrome-plated rings may be used in plain steel cylinders.

Regarding the above statements,

A — only No.1 is true.
B — neither No.1 nor No.2 is true.
C — both No.1 and No.2 are true.

8044. Answer C. AC 65-12A

Both statements (1) and (2) are true. As a general rule, chrome rings should never be used in a chrome cylinder. However, it is extremely important that only approved piston ring and cylinder combinations be used. If approved combinations are not used, excessive cylinder and/or piston ring wear could result.

8045.   A02

How is proper end-gap clearance on new piston rings assured during the overhaul of an engine?

A — By accurately measuring and matching the outside diameter of the rings with the inside diameter of the cylinders.
B — By using rings specified by the engine manufacturer.
C — By placing the rings in the cylinder and measuring the end-gap with a feeler gauge.

8045. Answer C. AC 65-12A

The end gap clearance of piston rings is checked by placing a piston ring in the cylinder and inserting a thickness, or feeler gauge, between the two ring ends to determine the amount of clearance. Answer (A) is wrong because a ring must be compressed by inserting it into a cylinder before end gap can be properly checked. Answer (B) is incorrect because, although new piston rings specified by a manufacturer should have the correct end-gap clearance, the only way to ensure the correct clearance is to measure it.

8046.   A02

The volume of a cylinder equals 70 cubic inches when the piston is at bottom center. When the piston is at the top of the cylinder, the volume equals 10 cubic inches. What is the compression ratio?

A — 1:7.
B — 7:10.
C — 7:1.

8046. Answer C. AC 65-12A

An engine's compression ratio is a comparison of the volume of a cylinder when the piston is at the bottom of a stroke to the volume of the same cylinder when the piston is at the top of the stroke. In this question, the ratio is 70:10 which reduces to 7:1.

8047.   A02
When cleaning aluminum and magnesium engine parts, it is inadvisable to soak them in solutions containing soap because

A — some of the soap will become impregnated in the surface of the material and subsequently cause engine oil contamination and foaming.
B — the soap can chemically alter the metals causing them to become more susceptible to corrosion.
C — the parts can be destroyed by dissimilar metal electrolytic action if they are placed together in the solution for more than a few minutes.

8048.   A03
What is the purpose of a power check on a reciprocating engine?

A — To check magneto drop.
B — To determine satisfactory performance.
C — To determine if the fuel/air mixture is adequate.

8049.   A03
What will be the likely result if the piston ring gaps happen to be aligned when performing a differential-pressure compression check on a cylinder?

A — Little or no effect.
B — The rings will not be seated.
C — A worn or defective ring(s) indication.

8050.   A03
Which of the following will be caused by excessive valve clearance of a cylinder on a reciprocating aircraft engine?

A — Reduced valve overlap period.
B — Intake and exhaust valves will open early and close late.
C — A power increase by shortening the exhaust event.

8051.   A03
The floating control thermostat, used on some reciprocating engine installations, helps regulate oil temperature by

A — controlling oil flow through the oil cooler.
B — recirculating hot oil back through the sump.
C — controlling air flow through the oil cooler.

8047. Answer A. AC 65-12A
Water-mixed degreasing compounds usually contain alkali or soap which, if allowed to remain in the pores of the metal, will react with hot oil and cause foaming. Answer (B) is incorrect because soap does not chemically alter aluminum and magnesium. Answer (C) is wrong because soap solutions do not cause dissimilar metal electrolytic action which can destroy engine parts in a matter of minutes. Water-mixed degreasing solutions containing soap are potentially corrosive to aluminum and magnesium engine parts only if the parts are not rinsed thoroughly after cleaning.

8048. Answer B. AC 65-12A
The basic principle behind doing a power check is to measure the performance of an engine against an established standard and determine if the engine is performing satisfactorily. Answer (A) is incorrect because a magneto check is used to check for the appropriate magneto drop and answer (C) is wrong because the fuel/air mixture is checked during the cruise mixture check.

8049. Answer C. AC 65-12A
If all the ring gaps happen to be aligned when performing a differential pressure compression check they will allow air to escape from the cylinder and give the same indication as if the rings were defective or worn. To remedy this problem, run the engine for a period of time so the ring gaps have a chance to shift. Answer (A) is incorrect because if the ring gaps are aligned a drop of 10 to 20 psi can result during a compression check. Answer (B) is incorrect because proper ring seating is a function of a proper "break in" schedule and is not affected by ring gap location.

8050. Answer A. AC 65-12A
When valve clearance is excessive, the valves will not open as wide or remain open as long as they should. Therefore, both the intake and exhaust valves will open late and close early resulting in a reduced valve overlap period. Answer (B) is incorrect because the valves will open late and close early, not open early and close late. Furthermore, excessive valve clearances decrease engine power output due to the reduced volumetric efficiency caused by the reduced overlap period.

8051. Answer C. AC 65-12A
One of the most widely used automatic oil temperature control devices is the floating control thermostat. This unit provides both manual and automatic control of the amount of air that passes through the oil cooler by controlling the oil cooler air-exit door. Both answers (A) and (B) are wrong because a floating control thermostat does not control oil flow through the oil cooler or recirculate hot oil back through the sump.

8052.   A03

Which of the following would indicate a general weak-engine condition when operated with a fixed-pitch propeller or test club?

A — Lower than normal static RPM, full throttle operation.
B — Manifold pressure lower at idle RPM than at static RPM.
C — Lower than normal manifold pressure for any given RPM.

8053.   A03

What is required by FAR Part 43 appendix D when performing an annual/100-hour inspection on a reciprocating engine aircraft?

A — Magneto timing check.
B — Cylinder compression check.
C — Valve clearance check.

8054.   A03

After spark plugs from an opposed engine have been serviced, in what position should they be reinstalled?

A — Next in firing order to the one from which they were removed.
B — Swapped bottom to top.
C — Next in firing order to the one from which they were removed and swapped bottom to top.

8055.   A03

As the pressure is applied during a reciprocating engine compression check using a differential pressure tester, what would a movement of the propeller in the direction of engine rotation indicate?

A — The piston was on compression stroke.
B — The piston was on exhaust stroke.
C — The piston was positioned past top dead center.

8056.   A03

Excessive valve clearance results in the valves opening

A — late and closing early.
B — early and closing late.
C — late and closing late.

8052. Answer A. AC 65-12A

When performing a power check on a reciprocating engine, it should be noted that with a constant air density, a given propeller and blade angle will always turn at the same rpm for a given horsepower. Therefore, if an engine is producing a lower than normal rpm at a full throttle setting, the engine may be weak. Answers (B) and (C) are incorrect because a low manifold pressure is often the result of early ignition timing and not necessarily an indication of a weak engine.

8053. Answer B. Part 43, Appendix D

According to FAR 43, Appendix D, a cylinder compression check is required when performing an annual/100-hour inspection on a reciprocating engine aircraft. Although a magneto timing check (answer A) and a valve clearance check (answer C) on nonhydraulic lifters are valuable checks that should be done periodically, they are not required on a 100-hour inspection.

8054. Answer C. ITP-P2

When a spark occurs between the electrodes of a spark plug, metal is taken from one electrode and deposited onto another. Therefore, when a spark plug fires positively, the ground electrode wears more than the center electrode and when a spark plug fires negatively, the center electrode wears more than the ground electrode. Furthermore, lead and other impurities produced during the combustion process tend to precipitate to the lower spark plugs, causing them to wear. To help equalize spark plug wear, each time spark plugs are removed they should be replaced in the cylinder next in the firing order to the one from which they were removed and switched from top to bottom.

8055. Answer C. AC 65-12A

When a differential compression test is being performed on an aircraft engine, the piston should be at top dead center when the air pressure is introduced into the cylinder. If the piston is past top dead center, the air pressure will force the piston to the bottom of the cylinder causing the propeller to rotate in the normal direction of rotation. Both answers (A) and (B) are incorrect because if the piston was on the compression stroke the piston would move counter to engine rotation and if the piston were on the exhaust stroke the exhaust valve would be open and no pressure could be retained.

8056. Answer A. AC 65-12A

Excessive valve clearance describes a condition where there is too much clearance between a rocker arm and the end of a valve stem. The excessive clearance results in the valve opening late due to the time required for the rocker arm to contact the valve stem. Furthermore, the valve will close early due to the decreased dwell time.

8057.   **A03**

During routine inspection of a reciprocating engine, a deposit of small, bright, metallic particles which do not cling to the magnetic drain plug is discovered in the oil sump and on the surface of the oil filter. This condition

A — may be a result of abnormal plain type bearing wear and is cause for further investigation.
B — is probably a result of ring and cylinder wall wear and is cause for engine removal and/or overhaul.
C — is normal in engines utilizing plain type bearings and aluminum pistons and is not cause for alarm.

8058.   **A03**

A characteristic of dyna-focal engine mounts as applied to aircraft reciprocating engines is that the

A — shock mounts eliminate the torsional flexing of the powerplant.
B — engine attaches to the shock mounts at the engine's center of gravity.
C — shock mounts point toward the engine's center of gravity.

8059.   **A03**

If metallic particles are found in the oil filter during an inspection,

A — it is an indication of normal engine wear unless the particles are nonferrous.
B — the cause should be identified and corrected before the aircraft is released for flight.
C — it is an indication of normal engine wear unless the deposit exceeds a specified amount.

8060.   **A03**

If the oil pressure gauge fluctuates over a wide range from zero to normal operating pressure, the most likely cause is

A — low oil supply.
B — broken or weak pressure relief valve spring.
C — air lock in the scavenge pump intake.

8057. Answer A. AC 65-12A

Plain bearings used in aircraft engines are usually made of nonferrous metals, such as silver, bronze, aluminum, and various alloys of copper, tin, or lead. If this type of material is found in the oil sump of an engine and on the surface of the oil filter, it is an indication that the bearings may be experiencing abnormal wear. Answer (B) is incorrect because rings and cylinder walls are made of ferrous metals that would cling to a magnetic drain plug, and answer (C) is wrong because the type of wear described is not normal.

8058. Answer C. AC 65-12A

One characteristic of dyna-focal engine mounts is that the shock mounts point toward the engine's center of gravity. This design feature helps prevent vibration from being transmitted to the airframe. The shock mounts consist of a piece of rubber inside a round metal mount. The rubber within the mount helps absorb vibration and allows some torsional flexing. Therefore, answer (A) is incorrect. Answer (B) is wrong because an engine's center of gravity is inside the engine and you cannot attach an engine mount inside the engine.

8059. Answer B. AC 65-12A

Metal particles on engine oil screens or magnetic sump plugs are generally an indication of partial internal engine failure. However, due to the construction of aircraft oil systems, it is possible that metal particles could have collected in the oil system sludge at the time of a previous engine failure. At any rate, the cause or source of the particles should be determined before the engine is returned to service. Answers (A) and (C) are incorrect because you cannot just assume the discovery of metal particles is normal. The discovery of metallic particles may indicate the beginning of a serious problem.

8060. Answer A. AC 65-12A

The most likely cause of oil pressure fluctuating between zero and normal oil pressure is a low oil supply. If you have an engine with a low oil supply, the oil pressure will be normal as long as the oil is being picked up by the pump. However, momentary losses of oil pick-up will cause the oil pressure to drop to zero. Answer (B) is incorrect because a weak or broken pressure relief valve spring would result in low or possibly no oil pressure. Answer (C) is wrong because a scavenge pump used in a dry-sump system pumps oil from the engine sump back to the tank and has nothing to do with the oil pressure within the system.

8061.   A03

What special procedure must be followed when adjusting the valves of an engine equipped with a floating cam ring?

A — Adjust valves when the engine is hot.
B — Adjust all exhaust valves before intake valves.
C — Eliminate cam bearing clearance when making valve adjustment.

8062.   A03

What is most likely to occur if an aircraft reciprocating engine is operated with excessive valve clearances?

A — The valves will remain closed for longer periods than specified by the engine manufacturer.
B — The valves could be unseated, which could make the engine difficult to start.
C — The further decrease in valve clearance that occurs as engine temperatures increase will cause damage to the valve-operating mechanism.

8063.   A03

Excessive valve clearances will cause the duration of valve opening to

A — increase for both intake and exhaust valves.
B — decrease for both intake and exhaust valves.
C — decrease for intake valves and increase for exhaust valves.

8064.   A03

What does valve overlap promote?

A — Lower intake manifold pressure and temperatures.
B — A backflow of gases across the cylinder.
C — Better scavenging and cooling characteristics.

8065.   A03

At what speed must a crankshaft turn if each cylinder of a four-stroke cycle engine is to be fired 200 times a minute?

A — 800 RPM.
B — 1,600 RPM.
C — 400 RPM.

8061. Answer C. AC 65-12A

When adjusting the valves on a radial engine with a floating cam ring, the clearance between the cam ring and cam bearing must be eliminated so the cam is in a definite position prior to adjusting the valve clearance. To do this, specific valves must be depressed and released simultaneously to remove the spring tension from the side positions on the cam. This permits the cam to slide away from the valves you are adjusting. Answer (A) is wrong because valves are rarely adjusted when hot and answer (B) is incorrect because valves can be adjusted in almost any order.

8062. Answer A. AC 65-12A

When the valve clearance on a reciprocating engine is excessive, the push rods open the valves late and close them early. As a result, the valves remain closed for longer periods then specified by the manufacturer. Answer (B) is wrong because valves would be unseated if there was insufficient valve clearance. Answer (C) is incorrect because valve clearance does not decrease as an engine's temperature increases.

8063. Answer B. AC 65-12A

When there is excessive clearance between the valve stem and rocker arm (valve clearance), the valves will not open as wide or remain open as long during engine operation (answer B). This reduces the overlap period and the cylinder's volumetric efficiency.

8064. Answer C. AC 65-12A

Valve overlap represents the number of degrees that both the exhaust and intake valves are open. Two benefits of valve overlap are improved scavenging and cooling characteristics and increased volumetric efficiency. Answers (A) and (B) are wrong because valve overlap does not lower manifold pressure or create a backflow of gases across a cylinder.

8065. Answer C. AC 65-12A

In a four-stroke engine, each cylinder fires once every two crankshaft revolutions. Therefore, in order for a cylinder to fire 200 times a minute, the crankshaft must rotate at a speed of 400 rpm ($200 \times 2 = 400$).

8066.   A03

Engine crankshaft runout is usually checked

1. during engine overhaul.
2. during annual inspection.
3. after a "prop strike" or sudden engine stoppage.
4. during 100-hour inspection.

A — 1, 3, and 4.
B — 1 and 3.
C — 1, 2 and 3.

8067.   A03

Before attempting to start a radial engine that has been shut down for more than 30 minutes,

A — turn the propeller by hand three or four revolutions in the opposite direction of normal rotation to check for liquid lock.
B — turn the ignition switch on before energizing the starter.
C — turn the propeller by hand three to four revolutions in the normal direction of rotation to check for liquid lock.

8068.   A03

An engine misses in both the right and left positions of the magneto switch. The quickest method for locating the trouble is to

A — check for one or more cold cylinders.
B — perform a compression check.
C — check each spark plug.

8069.   A03

A hissing sound from the exhaust stacks when the propeller is being pulled through manually indicates

A — a cracked exhaust stack.
B — exhaust valve blow-by.
C — worn piston rings.

8066. Answer B. AC 65-12A

Engine crankshaft runout is typically checked when the crankshaft is separated from the engine. Therefore, crankshaft runout is usually checked during an engine overhaul. Furthermore, manufacturers generally require runout checks after sudden stoppage or a sudden reduction in speed, such as a prop strike. Answers (A) and (C) are wrong because an engine is not disassembled down to the crankshaft during either an annual or 100-hour inspection.

8067. Answer C. AC 65-12A

Whenever a radial engine remains shut down for more than 30 minutes, oil and fuel may drain into the combustion chambers of the lower cylinders or accumulate in the lower intake pipes. These fluids can cause a liquid lock, or hydraulic lock, which can damage the engine if a start is attempted. To check for a liquid lock, the propeller should be turned by hand in the normal direction of rotation a minimum of two complete revolutions. Never attempt to clear a liquid lock by pulling the propeller through in the direction opposite the normal rotation (answer A), since this tends to inject the liquid into the intake pipe, increasing the possibility of a lock during a subsequent start. Answer (B) is incorrect because turning the ignition switch on will not help identify a liquid lock.

8068. Answer A. AC 65-12A

The cold cylinder check determines the operating characteristics of each cylinder of an air-cooled engine. The tendency for any cylinder or cylinders to be cold or to be only slightly warm after the engine was running indicates either a lack of combustion or incomplete combustion. If an engine misses in both the right and left positions of the magneto switch, combustion is not taking place in one or more cylinders. Any time there is a lack of combustion or incomplete combustion, the cylinder(s) affected will feel cooler than the cylinder(s) where complete combustion is occurring. Answer (B) is incorrect because conducting a compression check will not identify the cause of a misfire and answer (C) is wrong because checking each spark plug is not the quickest way to locate a misfiring cylinder.

8069. Answer B. AC 65-12A

Exhaust valve blow-by occurs when the exhaust valve does not seat properly, allowing a portion of the fuel/air charge to escape before combustion takes place. Exhaust valve blow-by is identified by a hissing or whistling sound coming from the exhaust stacks. Answer (A) is incorrect because you could never get enough air to pass through the exhaust stack to produce a hissing sound in a cracked exhaust. Answer (C) is wrong because worn piston rings produce more of a grinding sound than a hissing sound.

8070.   **A03**

If the oil pressure of a cold engine is higher than at normal operating temperatures, the

A — oil system relief valve should be readjusted.
B — engine's lubrication system is probably operating normally.
C — oil dilution system should be turned on immediately.

8071.   **A03**

If an engine operates with a low oil pressure and a high oil temperature, the problem may be caused by a

A — leaking oil dilution valve.
B — sheared oil pump shaft.
C — clogged oil cooler annular jacket.

8072.   **A03**

Which fuel/air mixture will result in the highest engine temperature (all other factors remaining constant)?

A — A mixture leaner than a rich best-power mixture of .085.
B — A mixture richer than a full-rich mixture of .087.
C — A mixture leaner than a manual lean mixture of .060.

8073.   **A03**

If an engine cylinder is to be removed, at what position in the cylinder should the piston be?

A — Bottom dead center.
B — Top dead center.
C — Halfway between top and bottom dead center.

8074.   **A03**

The horsepower developed in the cylinders of a reciprocating engine is known as the

A — shaft horsepower.
B — indicated horsepower.
C — brake horsepower.

8075.   **A03**

Engine operating flexibility is the ability of the engine to

A — deliver maximum horsepower at a specific altitude.
B — meet exacting requirements of efficiency and low weight per horsepower ratio.
C — run smoothly and give the desired performance at all speeds.

8070. Answer B. AC 65-12A

On engines that are equipped with a compensated oil pressure relief valve, a higher oil pressure is maintained when the oil is cold. This helps ensure adequate lubrication when the oil is partially congealed. However, as the oil heats up, the relief valve automatically lowers the system pressure to the normal operating range.

8071. Answer A. AC 65-12A

Some lubrication systems provide a means of diluting oil with fuel. When oil is diluted, less power is needed for starting and starting is accomplished more rapidly. However, if an oil dilution valve leaks (answer A), the oil will become excessively thin and cause a reduction in oil pressure. Furthermore, because fuel thinned-oil cannot transfer heat as readily as normal oil, an engine operated with diluted oil will have higher oil temperatures.

8072. Answer C. AC 65-12A

The fuel/air mixture which will result in the highest engine temperature varies according to the engine's power setting. For example, at high power settings, lean mixtures produce the highest temperature. Therefore, a mixture leaner than a manual lean mixture of .060 will produce very high temperatures at high power settings. Although a mixture leaner than a rich best-power mixture of .085 (answer A) will produce an elevated temperature, it will not produce the highest of the choices listed. Answer (B) is wrong because any time you have a mixture richer than full-rich, cool temperatures result.

8073. Answer B. AC 65-12A

Before removing a cylinder from an engine, the piston should be at top dead center on the compression stroke (answer B). Having the piston in this position helps prevent damage to the cylinder, piston, and valves and helps relieve pressure on both the intake and exhaust rocker arms.

8074. Answer B. AC 65-12A

The horsepower developed in the combustion chambers without considering friction is referred to as indicated horsepower. Answer (A) is incorrect because shaft horsepower represents the horsepower available at a rotating shaft and answer (C) is incorrect because brake horsepower represents the amount of horsepower delivered to the propeller.

8075. Answer C. AC 65-12A

Operating flexibility is defined as the ability of an engine to run smoothly and give desired performance at all engine speeds. Both answers (A) and (B) are wrong because delivering maximum horsepower at a specific altitude and meeting requirements of efficiency and weight to horsepower ratio are not part of operating flexibility.

8076. **A03**

Standard aircraft cylinder oversizes usually range from 0.010 inch to 0.030 inch. Oversize on automobile engine cylinders may range up to 0.100 inch. This is because aircraft engine cylinders

A — have more limited cooling capacity.
B — have relatively thin walls and may be nitrided.
C — operate at high temperatures.

8077. **A03**

If the ignition switch is moved from BOTH to either LEFT or RIGHT during an engine ground check, normal operation is usually indicated by a

A — large drop in RPM.
B — momentary interruption of both ignition systems.
C — slight drop in RPM.

8078. **A03**

During ground check an engine is found to be rough-running, the magneto drop is normal, and the manifold pressure is higher than normal for any given RPM. The trouble may be caused by

A — several spark plugs fouled on different cylinders.
B — a leak in the intake manifold.
C — a dead cylinder.

8079. **A03**

What is the best indication of worn valve guides?

A — High oil consumption.
B — Low compression.
C — Low oil pressure.

8080. **A03**

By use of a differential pressure compression tester, it is determined that the No.3 cylinder of a nine-cylinder radial engine will not hold pressure after the crankshaft has been rotated 260° from top dead center compression stroke No.1 cylinder. How can this indication usually be interpreted?

A — A normal indication.
B — Exhaust valve blow-by.
C — A damaged exhaust valve or insufficient exhaust valve clearance.

8076. Answer B. AC 65-12A

Generally, standard aircraft cylinder oversizes are 0.010 inch, 0.015 inch, 0.020 inch, or 0.030 inch. The reason aircraft cylinders cannot be oversized as much as automobile cylinders is because aircraft cylinders have relatively thin walls and may have a nitrided surface. Both answers (A) and (C) are incorrect because aircraft cylinders do not have a more limited cooling capacity nor do they operate at excessively high temperatures.

8077. Answer C. AC 65-12A

A magneto check is conducted with the propeller in the high rpm position at a speed between approximately 1,000 and 1,700 rpm. During this check, the ignition switch is moved from the BOTH to the RIGHT position, and then the BOTH to the LEFT position. While switching from BOTH to a single magneto position, a slight but noticeable drop in rpm should occur. If a large rpm drop occurs (answer A), or if there is a momentary interruption of both ignition systems (answer B), the ignition system is not operating properly.

8078. Answer C. AC 65-12A

The most likely cause of a rough running engine which has normal magneto drop and high manifold pressure is a dead cylinder (answer C). Answer (A) is incorrect because if several spark plugs were fouled on different cylinders the magneto drop would not be normal. Answer (B) is wrong because, although a leak in an intake manifold could cause a rough running engine, manifold pressure would not necessarily be higher than normal at all rpm settings.

8079. Answer A. AC 65-12A

If the valve guides of an engine are worn, there will be excessive clearance between the valve guide and the valve stem. The excessive clearance allows oil to seep by the valve stems and enter the intake and exhaust ports, causing high oil consumption. Answer (B) is wrong because, as long as the valves are seating properly, worn valve guides will not affect cylinder compression. Answer (C) is incorrect because the oil that seeps by the valve stems is not under pressure and, therefore, cannot in itself cause a low oil pressure reading.

8080. Answer A. AC 65-12A

When the piston in cylinder number one is rotated 260 degrees past top dead center on the compression stroke, cylinder number three will be 180 degrees past top dead center between the end of the compression stroke and the beginning of the exhaust stroke. When the number three piston is in this position, the exhaust valve is open and the cylinder would not be able to hold pressure. Both answers (B) and (C) are incorrect because, with the piston in the position indicated, the listed conditions are not possible.

8081.   A03
When does valve overlap occur in the operation of an aircraft reciprocating engine?

A — At the end of the exhaust stroke and the beginning of the intake stroke.
B — At the end of the power stroke and the beginning of the exhaust stroke.
C — At the end of the compression stroke and the beginning of the power stroke.

8081. Answer A. AC 65-12A
Valve overlap identifies the period when both the intake and exhaust valves are open in a cylinder. The only time valve overlap occurs is at the end of the exhaust stroke and the beginning of the intake stroke. Answers (B) and (C) are incorrect because both valves are not open simultaneously during the cycles indicated.

8082.   A03
What is an advantage of using metallic-sodium filled exhaust valves in aircraft reciprocating engines?

A — Increased strength and resistance to cracking.
B — Reduced valve operating temperatures.
C — Greater resistance to deterioration at high valve temperatures.

8082. Answer B. AC 65-12A
Metallic-sodium is used in some valves because it is an excellent heat conductor. In a metallic-sodium filled valve, the sodium melts at approximately 208°F. When this happens, the reciprocating motion of the valve circulates the liquid sodium enabling it to carry away excess heat, thereby reducing valve operating temperatures. Answer (A) is incorrect because filling a valve with metallic sodium does not increase its strength and answer (C) is wrong because metallic sodium valves do not have a greater resistance to deterioration at high temperature.

8083.   A03
Valve clearance changes on opposed-type engines using hydraulic lifters are accomplished by

A — rocker arm adjustment.
B — rocker arm replacement.
C — push rod replacement.

8083. Answer C. AC 65-12A
The only way to adjust the valve clearance on an engine using hydraulic lifters is to insert a different sized push rod. Both answers (A) and (B) are wrong because adjusting or replacing the rocker arms in an engine with hydraulic lifters will not change valve clearances.

8084.   A03
What is likely to occur if a reciprocating engine is operated at high power settings before it is properly warmed up?

A — Oil starvation of bearings and other parts.
B — Excessive thinning of the engine oil.
C — Accelerated oil breakdown and oxidation.

8084. Answer A. AC 65-12A
The viscosity of oil is affected by temperature and it is not uncommon for some grades of oil to become extremely stiff in cold weather. As you know, stiff oil does not circulate well within an engine and, therefore, if a reciprocating engine is operated at high power settings before it is properly warmed up, oil starvation to some parts is likely to occur. Answers (B) and (C) are incorrect because neither excessive thinning nor accelerated oil breakdown will occur under the conditions indicated.

8085.   A04
An increase in manifold pressure with a constant RPM will cause the bearing load in an engine to

A — decrease.
B — remain relatively constant.
C — increase.

8085. Answer C. AC 65-12A
Manifold pressure represents the absolute pressure of the fuel/air mixture prior to entering the cylinders. Therefore, an increase in manifold pressure (answer C) for a given rpm represents a higher pressure fuel/air mixture entering the cylinders. This higher pressure produces a corresponding increase in brake mean effective pressure and power output. Any time the brake mean effective pressure or power output is increased, additional force is transmitted through the pistons to the crankshaft and bearing load increases.

8086.   A04
Direct mechanical push-pull carburetor heat control linkages should normally be adjusted so that the stop located on the diverter valve will be contacted

A — before the stop at the control lever is reached in both HOT and COLD positions.
B — before the stop at the control lever is reached in the HOT position and after the stop at the control lever is reached in the COLD position.
C — after the stop at the control lever is reached in both HOT and COLD positions.

8087.   A04
Reduced air density at high altitude has a decided effect on carburetion, resulting in a reduction of engine power by

A — excessively enriching the air/fuel mixture.
B — excessively leaning the air/fuel mixture.
C — reducing fuel vaporization.

8088.   A04
Increased water vapor (higher relative humidity) in the incoming air to a reciprocating engine will normally result in which of the following?

A — Decreased engine power at a constant RPM and manifold pressure.
B — Increased power output due to increased volumetric efficiency.
C — A leaning effect on engines which use non-automatic carburetors.

8089.   A04
(1) Preignition is caused by improper ignition timing.
(2) Detonation occurs when an area of the combustion chamber becomes incandescent and ignites the fuel/air mixture in advance of normal timed ignition.

Regarding the above statements,

A — only No.1 is true.
B — both No.1 and No.2 are true.
C — neither No.1 nor No.2 is true.

8090.   A04
Which of the following engine servicing operations generally requires engine pre-oiling prior to starting the engine?

A — Engine oil and filter change.
B — Engine installation.
C — Replacement of oil lines.

8086. Answer A. AC 65-12A
When rigging any carburetor control linkage, the component being moved must contact its stop prior to the stop in the cockpit is reached. This ensures full control travel. Answers (B) and (C) are incorrect because they both indicate conditions where the cabin control reaches its stop prior to the component reaching its stop.

8087. Answer A. AC 65-12A
A combustion engine relies on a specific air/fuel mixture to produce a given amount of power. Any deviation from this mixture affects power output. As an aircraft climbs, air density decreases thereby decreasing the amount of air in the fuel/air mixture. This results in an excessively rich air/fuel mixture which causes a reduction in engine power.

8088. Answer A. AC 65-9A
When an engine takes in air with a high water vapor content, there is less oxygen available for combustion. Any time there is less oxygen available for combustion there is a corresponding decrease in engine power for any given rpm and manifold pressure. Answer (B) is incorrect because both power output and volumetric efficiency decrease and answer (C) is wrong because humid air typically produces an enriching effect on piston engines.

8089. Answer C. AC 65-12A
Both statements are false. Preignition occurs when the fuel/air mixture is ignited prior to the spark plugs firing and has nothing to do with how an ignition system is timed. Detonation, on the other hand, is the uncontrolled burning of the fuel/air mixture. Typical causes of detonation include use of the improper fuel grade and engine overheating.

8090. Answer B. AC 65-12A
After an engine is installed it should be pre-oiled prior to starting. Pre-oiling helps prevent excessive wear or failure of the engine bearings. Both answers (A) and (C) are incorrect because neither operation depletes the supply of residual oil within an engine.

8091.   A04

During the inspection of an engine control system in which push-pull control rods are used, the threaded rod ends should

A — not be adjusted in length for rigging purposes because the rod ends have been properly positioned and staked during manufacture.

B — be checked for thread engagement of at least two threads but not more than four threads.

C — be checked for the amount of thread engagement by means of the inspection holes.

8092.   A04

Which of the following conditions would most likely lead to detonation?

A — Late ignition timing.

B — Use of fuel with too high an octane rating.

C — Use of fuel with too low an octane rating.

8093.   A04

An unsupercharged engine, operated at full throttle at sea level, to 10,000 feet, provided the RPM is unchanged will

A — lose power due to the reduced volume of air drawn into the cylinders.

B — produce constant power due to the same volume of air drawn into the cylinders.

C — lose power due to the reduced density of the air drawn into the cylinders.

8094.   A04

Which of the following would most likely cause a reciprocating engine to backfire through the induction system at low RPM operation?

A — Idle mixture too rich.

B — Clogged derichment valve.

C — Lean mixture.

8095.   A04

How may it be determined that a reciprocating engine with a dry sump is preoiled sufficiently?

A — The engine oil pressure gauge will indicate normal oil pressure.

B — Oil will flow from the engine return line or indicator port.

C — When the quantity of oil specified by the manufacturer has been pumped into the engine.

8091. Answer C. AC 65-12A

After a push/pull control rod has been adjusted you should check the number of threads engaging the rod end. To check for the proper amount of engagement, an inspection hole is typically provided in which a piece of safety wire is inserted. If the safety wire can pass through the hole, there is insufficient thread engagement. Answer (A) is incorrect because push-pull rods must be adjusted from time to time. Answer (B) is wrong because the minimum number of threads engaged is typically greater than two threads and there is no maximum thread engagement requirement for rod ends.

8092. Answer C. AC 65-12A

Detonation is the uncontrolled burning of the fuel/air mixture. Typical causes of detonation include use of fuel with too low an octane rating, high manifold pressure, high intake air pressure, and engine overheating. Both answers (A) and (B) are incorrect because neither late ignition timing nor the use of a higher fuel grade will cause detonation.

8093. Answer C. AC 65-12A

As a rule, an unsupercharged reciprocating engine operated at altitude produces less power than it does at sea level. This is because, at higher altitudes, less dense air is drawn into the cylinders resulting in a less potent fuel/air charge. Answer (A) is incorrect because the volume of air drawn into the cylinders remains constant regardless of altitude, and answer (B) is wrong because engine power decreases with increases in altitude.

8094. Answer C. AC 65-12A

An extremely lean mixture will either not burn at all or burn so slowly that combustion continues until the intake valve opens near the end of the exhaust stroke. When this happens, the flame in the cylinder ignites the contents in the intake manifold causing an explosion, or backfire within the induction manifold. Answer (A) is wrong because an excessively rich mixture causes flooding and spark plug fouling, not backfiring. Answer (B) is incorrect because there is no such thing as a derichment valve.

8095. Answer B. AC 65-12A

When an engine is being pre-oiled, a line from the inlet side of the engine-driven oil pump must be disconnected to permit the pre-oiler tank to be connected. Then, a line near the nose of the engine is disconnected to allow oil to flow out. Once oil flows out of the engine pre-oiling is complete. Answer (A) is incorrect because the oil pressure gauge will not indicate an oil pressure when pre-oiling, and answer (C) is wrong because manufacturers do not specify the specific oil quantity used to pre-oil.

8096.   A04

What is the basic operational sequence for reducing the power output of an engine equipped with a constant-speed propeller?

A — Reduce the RPM, then the manifold pressure.
B — Reduce the manifold pressure, then retard the throttle to obtain the correct RPM.
C — Reduce the manifold pressure, then the RPM.

8097.   A04

Which statement pertaining to fuel/air ratios is true?

A — The mixture ratio which gives the best power is richer than the mixture ratio which gives maximum economy.
B — A rich mixture is faster burning than a normal mixture.
C — The mixture ratio which gives maximum economy may also be designated as best power mixture.

8098.   A04

Backfiring through the carburetor generally results from the use of

A — an excessively lean mixture.
B — excessively atomized fuel.
C — an excessively rich mixture.

8099.   A04

Which of these conditions will cause an engine to have an increased tendency to detonate?

1. High manifold pressure.
2. High intake air temperature.
3. Engine overheated.
4. Late ignition timing.

A — 1, 4.
B — 1, 2, 3.
C — 1, 2, 3, 4.

8100.   A04

When will small induction system air leaks have the most noticeable effect on engine operation?

A — At high RPM.
B — At maximum continuous and takeoff power settings.
C — At low RPM.

8096. Answer C. AC 65-12A

When reducing power on an engine equipped with a constant speed propeller, care should be taken to never let the manifold pressure get too high for a given rpm. To do this, the throttle should be pulled back to reduce the manifold pressure first followed by a slow reduction in rpm. Answer (A) is wrong because manifold pressure is reduced first followed by rpm, and answer (B) is wrong because the propeller control is used to reduce rpm, not the throttle.

8097. Answer A. AC 65-12A

For a given rpm, the fuel/air mixture that results in best power is always richer than the mixture used for best economy. One way to remember this is to associate best power with using more fuel and best economy with using less fuel. With this in mind there is no way the mixture used for maximum economy can also be used for best power (answer C). Answer (B) is incorrect because a rich mixture burns slower than a normal mixture.

8098. Answer A. AC 65-12A

An extremely lean mixture will either not burn at all or burn so slowly that combustion continues until the intake valve opens near the end of the exhaust stroke. When this happens, the flame in the cylinder ignites the contents in the intake manifold causing an explosion known as a backfire. Answer (B) is wrong because excessively atomized fuel typically burns completely and rapidly making a backfire impractical, and answer (C) is incorrect because an excessively rich mixture causes flooding and spark plug fouling, not backfiring.

8099. Answer B. AC 65-12A

Detonation is the uncontrolled burning of the fuel/air mixture. Typical causes of detonation include use of fuel with too low an octane rating, high manifold pressure, high intake air pressure, and engine overheating. Of the conditions provided, only numbers 1, 2, and 3 (answer B) are correct.

8100. Answer C. AC 65-12A

A small induction system air leak will have the most noticeable effect on engine operation at idle. The reason for this is that at low engine speeds the volume of air entering the induction system is small. Therefore, the additional air coming in through a crack will lean the fuel/air mixture appreciably. Both answers (A) and (B) are incorrect because a small induction leak typically is not noticeable at high power settings.

8101. A04

To reduce the power output of an engine equipped with a constant-speed propeller and operating near maximum BMEP, the

A — manifold pressure is reduced with the throttle control before the RPM is reduced with the propeller control.
B — manifold pressure is reduced with the propeller control before the RPM is reduced with the throttle control.
C — RPM is reduced with the propeller control before the manifold pressure is reduced with the throttle control.

8102. A04

One of the best indicators of reciprocating engine combustion chamber problems is

A — excessive engine vibration.
B — starting difficulties.
C — spark plug condition.

8103. A04

What could cause excessive pressure buildup in the crankcase of a reciprocating engine?

A — Plugged crankcase breather.
B — Improper warmup operation.
C — An excessive quantity of oil.

8104. A04

Excessive valve clearance in a piston engine

A — increases valve overlap.
B — increases valve opening time.
C — decreases valve overlap.

8101. Answer A. AC 65-12A

When reducing power on an engine equipped with a constant speed propeller, care should be taken to never let the manifold pressure get too high for a given rpm. To do this, the throttle should be pulled back to reduce the manifold pressure first followed by a slow reduction in rpm. Answer (B) is wrong because manifold pressure is reduced using the throttle not the propeller control and the rpm is reduced with the propeller control instead of the throttle. Answer (C) is wrong because manifold pressure is reduced prior to reducing rpm.

8102. Answer C. AC 65-12A

One way of determining combustion chamber problems is by examining the condition of the spark plugs. For example, normal operation is indicated by a spark plug having a relatively small amount of light brown or tan deposit on the nose of the center electrode insulator. However, if heavy oily deposits are found on the spark plugs, it is a good indication that the rings or valve seals are worn and allowing oil to seep into the cylinder. Answer (A) is incorrect because excessive engine vibration is normally caused by a malfunctioning ignition system or propeller imbalance, not spark plugs. Answer (B) is incorrect because most starting difficulties are from mismanagement of the fuel system or from incorrect ignition timing.

8103. Answer A. AC 65-12A

All piston rings let some combustion chamber pressure into the engine crankcase. This pressure is vented to the atmosphere through a crankcase breather. Therefore, if a crankcase breather becomes plugged, pressure will build up inside the crankcase. Answer (B) is incorrect because as long as the breather tube is open an improper warmup will not cause excessive pressure and answer (C) is wrong because any excessive oil typically drains out through the breather tube.

8104. Answer C. AC 65-12A

Valve overlap represents the time when both the intake and exhaust valves are open simultaneously. When there is too much valve clearance, the valves do not open as wide or remain open as long as they should. If the valves are not open as long, the amount of overlap decreases.

8105.   A04
To what altitude will a turbo charged engine maintain sea level pressure?

A — Critical altitude.
B — Service ceiling.
C — Pressure altitude.

8105. Answer A. AC 65-12A
A reciprocating engine's critical altitude is that altitude at which the engine can maintain sea level power. Any increase above an engine's critical altitude results in a decrease in available horsepower. The critical altitude of a typical turbocharged engine is generally between 8,000 and 16,000 feet MSL. An aircraft's service ceiling (answer B) represents the altitude at which an aircraft is able to maintain a maximum climb rate of 100 feet per minute. Answer (C), pressure altitude, represents the altitude read off the altimeter with 29.92 set in the barometric window.

8106.   A04
If air is heard coming from the crankcase breather or oil filler during a differential compression check, what is this an indication of?

A — Exhaust valve leakage.
B — Intake valve leakage.
C — Piston ring leakage.

8106. Answer C. AC 65-12A
Excessive leakage past the piston rings can be detected by the sound of escaping air at the engine breather tube or oil filler cap. Leakage at the exhaust valve (answer A) is detected by listening for air at the exhaust outlet, and intake valve leakage (answer B) is detected at the air intake.

8107.   A04
One cause of afterfiring in an aircraft engine is

A — sticking intake valves.
B — an excessively lean mixture.
C — an excessively rich mixture.

8107. Answer C. AC 65-12A
Afterfiring refers to a condition when unburned fuel from an excessively rich fuel/air mixture combines with air in the exhaust stacks and ignites, or fires, in the exhaust system. Sticking intake valves (answer A) cause timing conflicts that can lead to flash back in the intake pipe and high engine temperatures, whereas an excessively lean mixture (answer B) causes backfiring.

CHAPTER 2

TURBINE ENGINES

Chapter 2 looks at the theory of turbine engine operation as well as the methods commonly employed in turbine engine maintenance and repair. In addition, this chapter examines basic turbine engine overhaul, removal, troubleshooting, and installation techniques. The FAA exam questions that pertain to this material include:

8108, 8109, 8110, 8111, 8112, 8113, 8114, 8115, 8116, 8117, 8118, 8119, 8120, 8121, 8122, 8123, 8124, 8125, 8126, 8127, 8128, 8129, 8130, 8131, 8132, 8133, 8134, 8135, 8136, 8137, 8138, 8139, 8140, 8141, 8142, 8143, 8144, 8145, 8146, 8147, 8148, 8149, 8150, 8151, 8152, 8153, 8154, 8155, 8156, 8157, 8158, 8159, 8160, 8161, 8162, 8163, 8164, 8165, 8166, 8167, 8168, 8169, 8170, 8171, 8172, 8173, 8174, 8175, 8176, 8177, 8178, 8179, 8180, 8181, 8182, 8183, 8184, 8185, 8186, 8187, 8188, 8189, 8190, 8191, 8192, 8193, 8194, 8195, 8196, 8197, 8198, 8199, 8200, 8201, 8202, 8203, 8204, 8205, 8206, 8207, 8208, 8209, 8210, 8211, 8212, 8213, 8214, 8215, 8216, 8217, 8218, 8219, 8220, 8221, 8222, 8223, 8224, 8225, 8226, 8227.

8108.   B01

At what point in an axial-flow turbojet engine will the highest gas pressures occur?

A — At the turbine entrance.
B — Within the burner section.
C — At the compressor outlet.

8108. Answer C. AC 65-12A

As air enters the compressor section of a turbine engine, it is compressed. The air then leaves the compressor at its highest pressure and lowest volume. From here, the air passes through a diffuser which causes a slight decrease in pressure. After leaving the diffuser, the air enters the burner section (answer B) where the heat from burning fuel causes the air to expand while remaining at a fairly constant pressure. The expanding gases move rearward into the turbine section (answer A) providing a force to drive the turbine wheels.

8109.   B01

One function of the nozzle diaphragm in a turbine engine is.

A — Decrease the velocity of exhaust gases.
B — Center the fuel spray in the combustion chamber.
C — Direct the flow of gases to strike the turbine buckets at a desired angle.

8109. Answer C. AC 65-12A

When high energy gases leave the combustion section of a turbine engine, they enter the turbine section. The turbine section is made up of stationary and rotating airfoils, or vanes. The stationary vanes, sometimes called a nozzle diaphragm, direct the high energy gases leaving the combustor into the rotating turbine blades. The nozzle diaphragm also increases the velocity of the gases. Answer (A) is incorrect because the nozzle diaphragm actually increases the velocity of the gases and answer (B) is wrong because the nozzle diaphragm directs the flow of air, not fuel.

8110.   B01

What is the profile of a turbine engine compressor blade?

A — The leading edge of the blade.
B — A cutout that reduces blade tip thickness.
C — The curvature of the blade root.

8110. Answer B. AC 65-12A

When looking at the profile of a compressor blade you will see that the tip of each blade is cut out to reduce tip thickness. This shape allows the blade to wear rather than break if the blade tip should come in contact with the case.

8111.   **B01**

The fan rotational speed of a dual axial compressor forward fan engine is the same as the

A — low-pressure compressor.
B — forward turbine wheel.
C — high-pressure compressor.

8112.   **B01**

The abbreviation "P" with subscript t7 used in turbine engine terminology means

A — the total inlet pressure.
B — pressure and temperature at station No.7.
C — the total pressure at station No.7.

8113.   **B01**

The blending of blades and vanes in a turbine engine

A — is usually accomplished only at engine overhaul.
B — should be performed parallel to the length of the blade using smooth contours to minimize stress points.
C — may sometimes be accomplished with the engine installed, ordinarily using power tools.

8114.   **B01**

What turbine engine section provides for proper mixing of the fuel and air?

A — Combustion section.
B — Compressor section.
C — Diffuser section.

8115.   **B01**

In a gas turbine engine, combustion occurs at a constant

A — volume.
B — pressure.
C — density.

8111. Answer A. AC 65-12A

On a dual axial or dual spool turbofan engine, the forward fan is typically bolted to the first compressor making the fan part of the low-pressure compressor. On some turbofan engines, the fan is mounted aft of the turbine wheel but never forward of it (answer B). Answer (C) is wrong because the fan is never mounted to the high-pressure compressor in a dual axial-flow compressor.

8112. Answer C. AC 65-12A

The abbreviation P stands for pressure, and subscript t_7 indicates a total at station 7 which is immediately aft of the last turbine stage. Therefore, Pt_7 is the total pressure aft of the turbine. Answer (A) is incorrect because total inlet pressure is typically not measured and answer (B) is wrong because Pt_7 does not indicate temperature.

8113. Answer B. AC 65-12A

Minor damage to turbine engine blades and vanes can usually be repaired if the damage can be removed without exceeding the allowable limits established by the manufacturer. However, all repairs must be well blended so that the blade's surface is smooth. Blending is almost always done by hand using crocus cloth, fine files, and stones. Furthermore, whenever possible, blending is performed parallel to the length of the blade to minimize stress points. Cracks are normally not allowed, in any area. Answer (A) is incorrect because blending should be done any time blade damage exists and answer (C) is wrong because power tools are seldom used.

8114. Answer A. AC 65-12A

The combustion section of a turbine engine is where the fuel and air are mixed and then burned. The compressor section (answer B) compresses the inlet air and the diffuser section (answer C) directs the compressed air to the burner cans.

8115. Answer B. AC 65-12A

During the combustion process in a turbine engine, burning fuel provides heat to expand the compressed air coming from the compressor. Throughout this process the pressure remains relatively constant. Both answers (A) and (C) are wrong because, during combustion, air volume increases while air density decreases.

8116. **B01**

Which statement is true regarding jet engines?

A — At the lower engine speeds, thrust increases rapidly with small increases in RPM.

B — At the higher engine speeds, thrust increases rapidly with small increases in RPM.

C — The thrust delivered per pound of air consumed is less at high altitude than at low altitude.

8117. **B01**

Some high-volume turboprop and turbojet engines are equipped with two-spool or split compressors. When these engines are operated at high altitudes, the

A — low-pressure rotor will increase in speed as the compressor load decreases in the lower density air.

B — throttle must be retarded to prevent overspeeding of the high-pressure rotor due to the lower density air.

C — low-pressure rotor will decrease in speed as the compressor load decreases in the lower density air.

8118. **B01**

Turbine nozzle diaphragms located on the upstream side of each turbine wheel are used in the gas turbine engine to

A — decrease the velocity of the heated gases flowing past this point.

B — direct the flow of gases parallel to the vertical line of the turbine blades.

C — increase the velocity of the heated gases flowing past this point.

8119. **B01**

Where is the highest gas pressure in a turbojet engine?

A — At the outlet of the tailpipe section.

B — At the entrance of the turbine section.

C — In the entrance of the burner section.

8120. **B01**

An exhaust cone placed aft of the turbine in a jet engine will cause the pressure in the first part of the exhaust duct to

A — increase and the velocity to decrease.

B — increase and the velocity to increase.

C — decrease and the velocity to increase.

8116. Answer B. DSA-25

In a typical turbine engine, a small increase in rpm produces a relatively proportional increase in thrust when operating at low engine speeds. However, at high engine speeds a small increase in rpm produces a large increase in thrust. Answer (C) is incorrect because the amount of thrust delivered per pound of air consumed remains relatively constant regardless of altitude.

8117. Answer A. AC 65-12A

A two-spool or dual spool turbine engine is one in which there are two independently rotating units. The front compressor is called the low-pressure compressor, and the rear compressor is called the high-pressure compressor. This type of engine has more operating flexibility than a single spool engine because the two compressors are free to find their own optimum rpm. This allows the low pressure compressor to increase in rpm at altitude because of the reduction in drag caused by the decrease in air density. Answer (B) is incorrect because the high-pressure compressor does not increase in speed with decreases in air density and answer (C) is wrong because the low-pressure compressor increases in speed.

8118. Answer C. AC 65-12A

When high energy gases leave the combustion section of a turbine engine, they enter the turbine section. The turbine section is made up of stationary and rotating airfoils, or vanes. The stationary vanes are grouped together to form a nozzle which increases the velocity of the gases and directs the high energy gases leaving the combustor into the turbine's rotating blades. Answer (A) is incorrect because a nozzle diaphragm increases the velocity of the heated gases and answer (B) is incorrect because the flow of gases is not parallel to the turbine buckets.

8119. Answer C. AC 65-12A

The gas pressure in a turbine engine reaches its highest value as compressed air leaves the compressor and enters the burner. Once in the burner section, the air expands due to the heat produced by the burning fuel. From here, the gases pass through a nozzle diaphragm where they are accelerated prior to entering the turbine blades. This increase in gas speed results in a corresponding decrease in gas pressure in both the turbine section (answer B) and tailpipe section (answer A).

8120. Answer A. AC 65-12A

A jet engine exhaust cone collects the exhaust gases discharged from the turbine buckets and gradually converts them into a steady stream. In doing this, the divergent shape of the exhaust cone causes the velocity to decrease and the pressure to increase.

8121.   B01
What is the function of the stator vane assembly at the discharge end of a typical axial-flow compressor?

A — To straighten airflow to eliminate turbulence.
B — To direct the flow of gases into the combustion chambers.
C — To increase air swirling motion into the combustion chambers.

8122.   B01
The turbine section of a jet engine

A — increases air velocity to generate thrust forces.
B — utilizes heat energy to expand and accelerate the incoming gas flow.
C — drives the compressor section.

8123.   B01
When starting a turbine engine,

A — a hot start is indicated if the exhaust gas temperature exceeds specified limits.
B — an excessively lean mixture is likely to cause a hot start.
C — release the starter switch as soon as indication of light-off occurs.

8124.   B01
In the dual axial-flow or twin spool compressor system, the first stage turbine drives the

A — N1 and N2 compressors.
B — N2 compressor.
C — N1 compressor.

8125.   B01
During inspection, turbine engine components exposed to high temperatures may only be marked with such materials as allowed by the manufacturer. These materials generally include

1. layout dye.
2. commercial felt tip marker.
3. wax or grease pencil.
4. chalk.
5. graphite lead pencil.

A — 1, 2, and 4.
B — 1, 3, and 4.
C — 2, 4, and 5.

8121. Answer A. AC 65-12A
As air passes through the compressor section of a typical axial-flow compressor, it becomes extremely turbulent. To help prevent turbulent air from flowing into the combustion section, the air passes through a stator vane which straightens airflow and eliminates turbulence.

8122. Answer C. AC 65-12A
In all turbine engines the turbine transforms a portion of the kinetic energy of the exhaust gases into mechanical energy to drive the compressor section. Answer (A) is wrong because air velocity decreases in the turbine section. Answer (B) is wrong because the expanding and accelerating of gases takes place in the combustion section.

8123. Answer A. AC 65-9A
One of the critical factors to observe when starting a turbine engine is the exhaust gas temperature. A hot start is characterized by the exhaust gas temperature exceeding the specified limits during an attempted start and can cause substantial damage to the combustion and turbine sections. The most likely cause of a hot start is an excessively rich mixture. Answer (C) is wrong because the starter switch should not be released until the start cycle is self-sustaining.

8124. Answer B. AC 65-12A
In a twin spool axial-flow compressor system the first compressor (N_1) is driven by the second stage turbine while the second compressor (N_2) is driven by the first stage turbine.

8125. Answer A. AC 65-12A
Certain materials may be used to mark combustion and turbine components during disassembly and assembly. For example, layout dye, chalk, and some commercial felt-tip markers are considered acceptable for use in marking parts that are directly exposed to an engine's gas path such as turbine blades and disks, turbine vanes, and combustion chamber liners. Answer (B) is incorrect because, if used, wax and grease pencils cause hot spots to form, and answer (C) is wrong because graphite lead pencils can lead to dissimilar metal corrosion.

8126.   B01

When starting a turbine engine, a hung start is indicated if the engine

A — exhaust gas temperature exceeds specified limits.
B — fails to reach idle RPM.
C — RPM exceeds specified operating speed.

8127.   B01

What are the two basic elements of the turbine section in a turbine engine?

A — Impeller and diffuser.
B — Hot and cold.
C — Stator and rotor.

8128.   B01

The function of the exhaust cone assembly of a turbine engine is to

A — collect the exhaust gases and act as a noise suppressor.
B — swirl and collect the exhaust gases into a single exhaust jet.
C — straighten and collect the exhaust gases into a solid exhaust jet.

8129.   B01

What are the two functional elements in a centrifugal compressor?

A — Turbine and compressor.
B — Bucket and expander.
C — Impeller and diffuser.

8130.   B01

What must be done after the fuel control unit has been replaced on an aircraft gas turbine engine?

A — Perform a full power engine run to check fuel flow.
B — Recalibrate the fuel nozzles.
C — Retrim the engine.

8131.   B01

If, during inspection at engine overhaul, ball or roller bearings are found to have magnetism but otherwise have no defects, they

A — cannot be used again.
B — are in an acceptable service condition.
C — must be degaussed before use.

8126. Answer B. AC 65-9A

A hung start occurs if a turbine engine starts normally but the rpm remains at some low value rather than increasing to the normal idle rpm. Hung starts are generally a result of shutting off the starter too soon, or by insufficient starter power. In contrast, a hot start occurs if the exhaust gas temperature exceeds specified limits (answer A).

8127. Answer C. AC 65-12A

The two basic turbine section elements are the stator and the rotor (answer C). The stator includes the stationary vanes located in front of the rotor that make up the turbine nozzle or nozzle diaphragm. The rotor includes the rotating vanes, or turbine blades. The impeller and diffuser (answer A) are contained in a centrifugal compressor, while the hot and cold sections (answer B) refer to the turbine and compressor sections.

8128. Answer C. AC 65-12A

A jet engine exhaust cone collects the exhaust gases discharged from the turbine buckets and gradually converts them into a relatively straight and solid stream. Answer (A) is wrong because the exhaust cone does not aid in noise suppression and answer (B) is wrong because the exhaust cone straightens the exhaust rather than swirling it.

8129. Answer C. AC 65-12A

The two parts that make up a centrifugal compressor are the impeller and the diffuser. The impeller accelerates the flow of air to the diffuser which is designed to direct the flow of air to the manifold at an angle that returns the maximum amount of energy.

8130. Answer C. AC 65-12A

After a fuel control has been replaced on a turbine engine, it is often necessary to retrim the engine. Retrimming consists of adjusting both the idle and maximum speed. On some newer turbine engines, such as the GE T700, retrimming may not be necessary after the fuel control is replaced. Answer (A) is incorrect because a full power engine run is only part of the engine trimming process. Answer (B) is wrong because fuel nozzles are patterned to determine their flow characteristics but are not calibrated.

8131. Answer C. AC 65-9A

If a bearing becomes magnetized, metal particles would be attracted to the bearing surfaces and cause premature wear. Therefore, if a bearing has magnetism present, it must be removed with a suitable degausser before the bearing can be reused.

8132.   **B01**

A turbine engine compressor which contains vanes on both sides of the impeller is a

A — double entry centrifugal compressor.
B — double entry axial-flow compressor.
C — single entry axial-flow compressor.

8133.   **B01**

What is the first engine instrument indication of a successful start of a turbine engine?

A — A rise in the engine fuel flow.
B — A rise in oil pressure.
C — A rise in the exhaust gas temperature.

8134.   **B01**

Some engine manufacturers of twin spool gas turbine engines identify turbine discharge pressure in their maintenance manuals as

A — Pt7.
B — Pt2.
C — Tt7.

8135.   **B01**

Who establishes the recommended operating time between overhauls (TBO) of a turbine engine used in general aviation?

A — The engine manufacturer.
B — The operator (utilizing manufacturer data and
      trend analysis) working in conjunction with the
      FAA.
C — The FAA.

8136.   **B01**

The basic gas turbine engine is divided into two main sections: the cold section and the hot section.
(1) The cold section includes the engine inlet, com
      pressor, and turbine sections.
(2) The hot section includes the combustor, diffuser,
      and exhaust sections.

Regarding the above statements,

A — only No.1 is true.
B — only No.2 is true.
C — neither No.1 nor No.2 is true.

8132. Answer A. AC 65-12A

A double-sided centrifugal compressor has vanes on both sides of the impeller. Answers (B) and (C) are incorrect because axial-flow compressors do not utilize impellers.

8133. Answer C. AC 65-12A

The first indication in the cockpit that a successful start has occurred is an abrupt rise in temperature indicated on the exhaust gas temperature gauge. Although engine fuel flow (answer A) and oil pressure (answer B) will also rise, they will lag behind the exhaust gas temperature.

8134. Answer A. AC 65-12A

Turbine discharge pressure is identified in service manuals and on engine instruments by the standardized abbreviation Pt_7. Answer (B), Pt_2, is incorrect because it represents the pressure at the second stage and answer (C) is wrong because the abbreviation Tt_7 is not used.

8135. Answer A. AC 65-12A

Engine manufacturers always establish an engine's recommended time between overhaul (TBO). Answer (B) is wrong because the operator, working in conjunction with the FAA, can only get permission to operate beyond an established TBO, and answer (C) is wrong because the FAA does not establish recommended TBO times.

8136. Answer C. AC 65-12A

Neither statement (1) nor (2) is correct. The cold section includes the engine inlet, compressor, and diffuser sections. The hot section, on the other hand, includes the combustor, turbine, and exhaust sections.

8137.　　　B01

(1) Welding and straightening of turbine engine rotating airfoils does not require special equipment.
(2) Welding and straightening of turbine engine rotating airfoils is commonly recommended by the manufacturer.

Regarding the above statements,

A — only No.1 is true.
B — only No.2 is true.
C — neither No.1 nor No.2 is true.

8137. Answer C. AC 65-12A
Neither statement (1) nor (2) is correct. Welding and straightening of rotating airfoils typically requires very specialized equipment. Furthermore, only authorized overhaul facilities and manufacturer are typically authorized to weld or straighten a damaged rotating airfoil.

8138.　　　B01
Turbine engine components exposed to high temperatures generally may NOT be marked with

1. layout dye.
2. commercial felt tip marker.
3. wax or grease pencil.
4. chalk.
5. graphite lead pencil.

A — 1, 2, and 3.
B — 3 and 5.
C — 4 and 5.

8138. Answer B. AC 65-12A
Only certain materials may be used to mark combustion and turbine components during assembly and disassembly. For example, layout dye, chalk, and some commercial felt tip markers are typically used to mark parts that are directly exposed to an engine's gas path such as turbine blades and disks, turbine vanes, and combustion chamber liners. However, the question asks what may NOT be used. Therefore, answer (B) is correct. Wax or grease pencils, when used on turbine engine components, can cause hot spots to occur, and graphite lead pencils can cause dissimilar metal corrosion. This eliminates answers (A) and (C).

8139.　　　B01
Who establishes mandatory replacement times for critical components of turbine engines?

A — The FAA.
B — The operator working in conjunction with the FAA.
C — The engine manufacturer.

8139. Answer C. Part 33, Appendix A
Within a turbine engine, all critical components have mandatory replacement times that are established by the engine manufacturer and approved by the FAA.

8140.　　　B01
Main bearing oil seals used with turbine engines are usually what type(s)?

A — Labyrinth and/or carbon rubbing.
B — Teflon and synthetic rubber.
C — Labyrinth and/or silicone rubber.

8140. Answer A. AC 65-12A
Turbine main bearing oil seals are generally either the labyrinth or carbon rubbing (carbon ring) type. The labyrinth seal relies on pressure to prevent oil from leaking along the compressor shaft. Carbon rubbing seals, on the other hand, are usually spring loaded and are similar in material and application to the carbon brushes used in electrical motors. These seals rest against the surface provided and create a sealed bearing cavity or void that prevents oil leakage. Answers (B) and (C) are wrong because Teflon, synthetic rubber, and silicone rubber are not used in a main bearing oil seal.

8141.   B02

How does a dual axial-flow compressor improve the efficiency of a turbojet engine?

A — More turbine wheels can be used.
B — Higher compression ratios can be obtained.
C — The velocity of the air entering the combustion chamber is increased.

8142.   B02

Three types of turbine blades are

A — reaction, converging, and diverging.
B — impulse, reaction, and impulse-reaction.
C — impulse, vector, and impulse-vector.

8143.   B02

Which statements are true regarding aircraft engine propulsion?

1. An engine driven propeller imparts a relatively small amount of acceleration to a large mass of air.
2. Turbojet and turbofan engines impart a relatively large amount of acceleration to a smaller mass of air.
3. In modern turboprop engines, nearly 50 percent of the exhaust gas energy is extracted by turbines to drive the propeller and compressor with the rest providing exhaust thrust.

A — 1, 2, 3.
B — 1, 2.
C — 1, 3.

8144.   B02

An advantage of the axial-flow compressor is its

A — low starting power requirements.
B — low weight.
C — high peak efficiency.

8145.   B02

What is one purpose of the stator blades in the compressor section of a turbine engine?

A — Stabilize the pressure of the airflow.
B — Control the direction of the airflow.
C — Increase the velocity of the airflow.

8141. Answer B. AC 65-12A

One of the advantages of a dual spool axial compressor over a single spool is the ability to have two separate compressors rotate at their own optimum rpm. By having two compressors rotate at different speeds, higher compression ratios are obtained. Answer (A) is wrong because adding more turbine wheels will not necessarily improve efficiency and answer (C) is wrong since air flow is not increased in a dual axial-flow compressor.

8142. Answer B. ITP-P2

Turbine blades are classified as impulse, reaction, or a combination impulse-reaction type. Most engines incorporate a blade design utilizing an impulse-reaction combination. Answers (A) and (C) are wrong because there is no such thing as a converging, diverging, vector, or impulse-vector turbine blade.

8143. Answer B. AC 65-12A

A propeller generates thrust by imparting a relatively small amount of acceleration to a large quantity of air. Turbojet and turbofan engines, on the other hand, generate thrust by imparting a relatively large amount of acceleration to a smaller quantity of air. Based on this, statements 1 and 2 are correct. Answers (A) and (C) are incorrect because the turbine section of a modern turboprop engine extracts between 75 and 86 percent of the exhaust gas energy to drive the propeller and compressor.

8144. Answer C. AC 65-12A

Although an axial-flow compressor does not give as high a compression rise per stage as a centrifugal compressor, its multiple stages and ability to take advantage of ram air pressure allow it to produce higher peak pressures. Both answers (A) and (B) are incorrect because an axial-flow compressor has relatively high starting power requirements and is heavier than a centrifugal compressor.

8145. Answer B. AC 65-12A

In an axial-flow compressor, the stator blades are fixed airfoils that are placed at the discharge end of each compressor stage. Their purpose is to control the direction of airflow (answer B) into the next compressor stage or combustion section and eliminate turbulence. The stationary airfoils in the axial flow compressor are most appropriately called stator vanes.

8146.   B02

What is the purpose of the diffuser section in a turbine engine?

A — To increase pressure and reduce velocity.
B — To convert pressure to velocity.
C — To reduce pressure and increase velocity.

8146. Answer A. AC 65-12A

In a centrifugal-flow compressor, the diffuser is placed at the outlet of the compressor. The purpose of the diffuser is to reduce the velocity of the gases and to increase their pressure. This prepares the air for entry into the burner cans at low velocity so combustion can occur with a flame that will not blow out. Both answers (B) and (C) are wrong because the diffuser converts velocity to pressure not pressure to velocity.

8147.   B02

Where do stress rupture cracks usually appear on turbine blades?

A — Across the blade root, parallel to the fir tree.
B — Along the leading edge, parallel to the edge.
C — Across the leading or trailing edge at a right angle to the edge length.

8147. Answer C. AC 65-12A

Stress rupture cracks on turbine blades usually appear as minute hairline cracks on or across the leading or trailing edge at a right angle to the edge length. Stress rupture cracks located on the first stage turbine indicate either an over-temperature condition or centrifugal loading. Answers (A) and (B) are incorrect because stress rupture cracks typically do not occur across the blade root or parallel to the blade edge.

8148.   B02

In which type of turbine engine combustion chamber is the case and liner removed and installed as one unit during routine maintenance?

A — Can.
B — Can annular.
C — Annular.

8148. Answer A. AC 65-12A

Both the case and liner of can-type combustion chambers are self-contained and placed externally around the circumference of an engine. These features allow the individual chambers to be removed and installed as one unit during routine maintenance operations. Answer (B) is incorrect because the outer case of the can annular combustion chamber encircles the entire engine, making it impossible to remove both the case and liner simultaneously. Answer (C) is wrong because both the outer case and liner of an annular system encircle the engine.

8149.   B02

The diffuser section of a jet engine is located between

A — the burner section and the turbine section.
B — station No.7 and station No.8.
C — the compressor section and the burner section.

8149. Answer C. AC 65-12A

The diffuser section of a centrifugal-flow compressor is located between the outlet of the compressor section and the inlet of the burner section. The purpose of the diffuser is to reduce the velocity of the air exiting the compressor, thereby increasing air pressure. This prepares the air for entry into the burner cans. Answer (A) is wrong because there is no diffuser between the burner and turbine sections and answer (B) is incorrect because station seven does not always identify the outlet of the compressor.

8150.   B02

When the leading edge of a first-stage turbine blade is found to have stress rupture cracks, which of the following should be suspected?

A — Faulty cooling shield.
B — Overtemperature condition.
C — Overspeed condition.

8150. Answer B. AC 65-12A

Stress rupture cracks on turbine blades usually appear as minute hairline cracks on or across the leading or trailing edge at a right angle to the edge length. Stress rupture cracks located on the first stage turbine indicate either an over-temperature condition or centrifugal loading. Answer (A) is incorrect because a faulty cooling shield would lead to damage of accessories surrounding the hot section. Answer (C) is incorrect because on overspeed condition is likely to cause blade creep rather than stress rupture cracks in turbine blades.

8151.   B02
Turbine blades are generally more susceptible to operating damage than compressor blades because of

A — higher centrifugal loading.
B — exposure to high temperatures.
C — high pressure and high velocity gas flow.

8152.   B02
Which of the following is the ultimate limiting factor of turbine engine operation?

A — Compressor inlet air temperature.
B — Turbine inlet temperature.
C — Burner-can pressure.

8153.   B02
The recurrent ingestion of dust or other fine airborne particulates into a turbine engine can result in

A — foreign object damage to the compressor section.
B — the need for less frequent abrasive grit cleaning of the engine.
C — erosion damage to the compressor and turbine sections.

8154.   B02
Which of the following engine variables is the most critical during turbine engine operation?

A — Compressor inlet air temperature.
B — Compressor RPM.
C — Turbine inlet temperature.

8155.   B02
Reduced blade vibration and improved airflow characteristics in gas turbines are brought about by

A — fir-tree blade attachment.
B — impulse type blades.
C — shrouded turbine rotor blades.

8151. Answer B. AC 65-12A
Turbine blades are usually inspected and cleaned in the same manner as compressor blades. However, because turbine blades are consistently exposed to extreme temperatures, they are more susceptible to damage. Answer (A) is wrong because compressor blades and turbine blades experience the same degree of centrifugal loading. Answer (C) is wrong because pressure in the turbine section is lower than that in the compressor.

8152. Answer B. AC 65-12A
The materials within the turbine section of an engine will deteriorate rapidly if exposed to extreme temperatures. Therefore, the turbine inlet temperature is the limiting factor for a turbine engine. Answer (A) is incorrect because the air entering the compressor is nowhere near hot enough to cause damage to internal engine parts and answer (C) is wrong because burner can pressure is nowhere near high enough to cause damage.

8153. Answer C. AC 65-12A
The ingestion of dust and other fine particulates in a turbine engine causes erosion damage to compressor and turbine blades over a period of time. Answer (A) is wrong because foreign object damage is caused by ingestion of objects larger than dust particles and the damage to the blades is immediate rather than cumulative. Answer (B) is wrong because the ingestion of fine particulates has little impact on how often an engine needs to be grit blasted.

8154. Answer C. AC 65-12A
The materials within the turbine section of an engine will deteriorate rapidly if exposed to extreme temperatures. Therefore, the turbine inlet temperature is the limiting factor for a turbine engine. Answer (A) is incorrect because changes in compressor inlet temperature cause minor losses in engine thrust with little effect on engine operation. Answer (B) is incorrect because, although compressor rpm is a critical engine parameter, it is not the most critical parameter.

8155. Answer C. AC 65-12A
The use of shrouded turbine rotor blades reduces blade vibration and improves turbine efficiency. With shrouded blades the blade tips contact each other and provide additional support. This added support reduces vibration substantially. The shrouds also prevent air from escaping over the blade tips making the entire turbine more efficient. Although the type of blade used (answer B) and the means of attaching a blade (answer A) can affect a blade's vibration characteristics, neither has the degree of impact that using shrouded blades does.

8156.   B02
Which turbine engine compressor offers the greatest advantages for both starting flexibility and improved high-altitude performance?

A — Dual-stage, centrifugal-flow.
B — Split-spool, axial-flow.
C — Single-spool, axial-flow.

8157.   B02
Jet engine turbine blades removed for detailed inspection must be reinstalled in

A — a specified slot 180° away.
B — a specified slot 90° away in the direction of rotation.
C — the same slot.

8158.   B02
An advantage of the centrifugal-flow compressor is its high

A — pressure rise per stage.
B — ram efficiency.
C — peak efficiency.

8159.   B02
The highest heat-to-metal contact in a jet engine is the

A — burner cans.
B — turbine inlet guide vanes.
C — turbine blades.

8160.   B02
Which two elements make up the axial-flow compressor assembly?

A — Rotor and stator.
B — Compressor and manifold.
C — Stator and diffuser.

8156. Answer B. AC 65-12A
Of the choices given in this question, the split-spool, axial-flow compressor offers the greatest advantages. For example, since the compressor and turbine are split, starting speed is easily obtained. Furthermore, high altitude performance is better because the two separately rotating compressors are able to seek their own optimum rpm. Centrifugal-flow compressors (answer A) and single-spool axial-flow compressors (answer C) lack this flexibility to optimize compressor performance.

8157. Answer C. AC 65-12A
In order to maintain the balance of the turbine assembly, when a turbine blade is removed for inspection, it must be reinstalled in the same slot. Inserting the blade in any other position (answers A and B) will result in an unbalanced condition.

8158. Answer A. AC 65-12A
Although peak efficiency of the centrifugal compressor is not as great as in the axial-flow type, it does give a higher pressure rise per stage (answer A). Modern day centrifugal compressors produce as much as 8 or 10 to 1 compression ratios, while axial-flow compressors produce approximately a 1.3 to 1 compression ratio. Centrifugal compressors have poor ram efficiency (answer B), since they must redirect the airflow direction 90 degrees during each stage of compression. In addition, the design is limited to three stages and thus has low peak efficiencies (answer C).

8159. Answer B. AC 65-12A
The highest heat-to-metal contact in a turbine engine occurs as the heated gases leave the combustion section and enter the turbine inlet vanes. Although the highest temperatures occur in the middle of the flame zone within the burner can (answer A), the high temperature is shielded from heat-to-metal contact by an insulating blanket of air. Answer (C) is incorrect because by the time the gases reach the turbine, the high combustor temperatures have cooled considerably.

8160. Answer A. AC 65-12A
An axial-flow compressor assembly is made up of two principle elements, the rotor and the stator. The rotor consists of a set of blades installed on a spindle that rotates at a high speed and impels intake air through a series of stages. The stator blades, on the other hand, act as diffusers at each stage, changing high velocity to pressure. Answer (B) is wrong because there is no manifold in an axial-flow compressor, and answer (C) is incorrect because stator and diffuser are synonymous.

8161.   **B02**

The two types of centrifugal compressor impellers are

A — single entry and double entry.
B — rotor and stator.
C — impeller and diffuser.

8162.   **B02**

Between each row of rotating blades in a turbine engine compressor, there is a row of stationary blades which act to diffuse the air. These stationary blades are called

A — buckets.
B — rotors.
C — stators.

8163.   **B02**

Standard sea level pressure is

A — 29.00″ Hg.
B — 29.29″ Hg.
C — 29.92″ Hg.

8164.   **B02**

Using standard atmospheric conditions, the standard sea level temperature is

A — 59 °F.
B — 59 °C.
C — 29 °C.

8165.   **B02**

When aircraft turbine blades are subjected to excessive heat stress, what type of failures would you expect?

A — Bending and torsion.
B — Torsion and tension.
C — Stress rupture.

8166.   **B02**

In an axial-flow compressor, one purpose of the stator vanes at the discharge end of the compressor is to

A — straighten the airflow and eliminate turbulence.
B — increase the velocity and prevent swirling and eddying.
C — decrease the velocity, prevent swirling, and decrease pressure.

8161. Answer A. AC 65-12A

The two types of centrifugal-flow compressor impellers are the single entry and the double entry. The single entry has vanes on only one side of the impeller, while the double entry has vanes on both sides of the impeller. Answers (B) and (C) are incorrect because they identify components within the compressor.

8162. Answer C. AC 65-12A

Between each row of rotating blades in an axial-flow compressor there is a set of stationary airfoils called stator vanes. The stator vanes direct the air between stages and diffuse, or slow down the air causing pressure to increase. Answer (A) is incorrect because "bucket" is a slang term that refers to a turbine blade, and answer (B) is wrong because rotors are the rotating blades within the compressor and turbine.

8163. Answer C. AC 65-12A

A standard day is defined by a sea level pressure of 29.92 inches of mercury, or 14.7 psi. Both answers (A) and (B) are wrong because they are less than 29.92 inches.

8164. Answer A. AC 65-12A

A standard day is defined by an atmospheric pressure of 29.92 inches of mercury, or 14.7 psi, and a temperature of 59°F or 15°C.

8165. Answer C. AC 65-12A

When turbine blades are subjected to excessive temperatures, stress rupture cracks are likely to develop. Stress rupture cracks usually appear as minute hairline cracks on or across the leading or trailing edge at a right angle to the edge length. Bending, torsion, and tension (answers A and B) are forms of stress and do not describe actual types of blade failure.

8166. Answer A. AC 65-12A

At the discharge end of an axial-flow compressor, the air is extremely turbulent. To help eliminate this turbulence, as well as slow the air flow, stator vanes are installed. These vanes are sometimes called straightening vanes or the outlet vane assembly. Answer (B) is incorrect because the last stage of stator vanes does not increase the airflow velocity, and answer (C) is wrong because the decrease in airflow velocity causes an increase in pressure, not a decrease.

8167.   B02
Compressor field cleaning on turbine engines is performed primarily in order to

A — prevent engine oil contamination and subsequent engine bearing wear or damage.
B — facilitate flight line inspection of engine inlet and compressor areas for defects or FOD.
C — prevent engine performance degradation, increased fuel costs, and damage or corrosion to gas path surfaces.

8168.   B02
Hot section inspections for many modern turbine engines are required

A — only at engine overhaul.
B — only when an overtemperature or overspeed has occurred.
C — on a time or cycle basis.

8169.   B02
A purpose of the shrouds on the turbine blades of an axial-flow engine is to

A — reduce vibration.
B — increase tip speed.
C — reduce air entrance.

8170.   B02
In a dual axial-flow compressor, the first stage turbine drives

A — N2 compressor.
B — N1 compressor.
C — low pressure compressor.

8171.   B02
What should be done initially if a turbine engine catches fire when starting?

A — Turn off the fuel and continue engine rotation with the starter.
B — Continue engine start rotation and discharge a fire extinguisher into the intake.
C — Continue starting attempt in order to blow out the fire.

8167. Answer C. AC 65-12A
Accumulation of dirt on the compressor blades reduces the aerodynamic efficiency of the blades, with resultant deterioration in engine performance. Furthermore, dirt deposits can retain moisture and other chemicals that cause corrosion. Answer (A) is wrong because dirt in the compressor section typically should not be able to work its way into the engine oil and answer (B) is incorrect because a typical line inspection can only detect relatively large areas of damage at the engine inlet and, therefore, the cleanliness of the compressor is irrelevant.

8168. Answer C. AC 65-12A
Almost all of the components on a turbine engine, including the hot section, are required to be inspected on a time or cycle basis. Additional times when a hot section must be inspected include during an overhaul or when an overtemperature or overspeed incident occurs. Answers (A) and (B) are incorrect because they do not represent the only time a hot section inspection is required.

8169. Answer A. AC 65-12A
The use of shrouded turbine rotor blades reduces blade vibration and improves turbine efficiency. With shrouded blades, the tips of the blades contact each other and provide support. This added support reduces vibration substantially. The shrouds also prevent air from escaping over the blade tips making the turbine more efficient. Answer (B) is incorrect because the purpose of shrouded blades is not to increase tip speed and answer (C) is wrong because, although shrouds reduce air leakage over the blade tips, they do nothing to reduce air entrance.

8170. Answer A. AC 65-12A
In a dual spool axial-flow compressor the first compressor (N1) is driven by the second turbine, while the second compressor (N2) is driven by the first turbine.

8171. Answer A. AC 65-12A
If a turbine engine catches fire during an attempted start, you should immediately turn off the fuel and continue to turn the engine with the starter. By continuing to rotate the engine, the fire is likely to be drawn into the engine and discharged out the tailpipe. Answer (B) is incorrect because it does not indicate that you should cut off the fuel. In addition, a fire extinguisher should be discharged only if the fire fails to go out after continued cranking. Answer (C) is wrong because the engine will not blow the fire out.

8172.   B02

What is the proper starting sequence for a turbojet engine?

A — Ignition, starter, fuel.
B — Starter, ignition, fuel.
C — Starter, fuel, ignition.

8173.   B02

A weak fuel to air mixture along with normal airflow through a turbine engine may result in

A — a rich flameout.
B — a lean die-out.
C — high EGT.

8174.   B02

What is used in turbine engines to aid in stabilization of compressor airflow during low thrust engine operation?

A — Stator vanes and rotor vanes.
B — Variable guide vanes and/or compressor bleed valves.
C — Pressurization and dump valves.

8175.   B02

In a turbine engine with a dual-spool compressor, the low speed compressor

A — always turns at the same speed as the high speed compressor.
B — is connected directly to the high speed compressor.
C — seeks its own best operating speed.

8176.   B02

What is the function of the inlet guide vane assembly on an axial-flow compressor?

A — Directs the air into the first stage rotor blades at the proper angle.
B — Converts velocity energy into pressure energy.
C — Converts pressure energy into velocity energy.

8172. Answer B. AC 65-12A

The first step in starting a typical turbine engine is to engage the starter. Once this is done, the ignition is turned on. Then, when the N1 compressor obtains a pre-determined rpm, the fuel lever is moved to the idle position. Normal lightoff is indicated by a rise in the exhaust gas temperature (EGT). Both answers (A) and (C) are wrong because the three events are in the wrong order.

8173. Answer B. AC 65-12A

If you operate a turbine engine with a weak or lean fuel to air mixture, you risk encountering what is known as a lean die-out. In other words, the amount of fuel supplied is insufficient to support combustion. Answer (A) is wrong because a rich flameout occurs when the amount of oxygen in the air supply is insufficient to support combustion and when the mixture is cooled below the combustion temperature. Answer (C) is incorrect because a weak fuel mixture coupled with normal airflow through an engine results in low, not high, EGT.

8174. Answer B. TEP2

Airflow through some turbine engines during low thrust operations must be stabilized to prevent the compressor from stalling. To do this, variable inlet guide vanes or compressor bleed valves are used. Variable guide vanes rotate to maintain the correct angle of attack relationship between inlet air flow and compressor speed. Compressor bleed valves, on the other hand, dump away unwanted air. Answer (A) is incorrect because there are no such thing as rotor vanes, and answer (C) is wrong because pressurization and dump valves are fuel metering components.

8175. Answer C. AC 65-12A

Most modern gas turbine engines use a dual-spool compressor that utilizes two axial-flow rotors or one axial and one centrifugal-flow rotor. An advantage of the dual-spool compressor is the ability of the first compressor (N_1) to seek its own best operating speed. Therefore, when the engine is operated at altitude where the air is less dense, the reduced drag on the first stage compressor allows the compressor to speed up thereby increasing efficiency. Answer (A) is wrong because the two compressors rotate at different speeds, and answer (B) is incorrect because the low speed compressor is connected to the low pressure turbine, not the high speed compressor.

8176. Answer A. AC 65-12A

The guide vanes direct the airflow into the first stage rotor blades at the proper angle and induce a swirling motion to the air entering the compressor. Answers (B) and (C) are incorrect because inlet guide vanes do not alter the pressure or velocity of incoming air.

8177. **B02**
Hot spots on the tail cone of a turbine engine are possible indicators of a malfunctioning fuel nozzle or

A — a faulty combustion chamber.
B — a faulty igniter plug.
C — an improperly positioned tail cone.

8178. **B02**
The stator vanes in an axial-flow compressor

A — convert velocity energy into pressure energy.
B — convert pressure energy into velocity energy.
C — direct air into the first stage rotor vanes at the proper angle.

8179. **B02**
The velocity of subsonic air as it flows through a convergent nozzle

A — increases.
B — decreases.
C — remains constant.

8180. **B02**
The velocity of supersonic air as it flows through a divergent nozzle

A — increases.
B — decreases.
C — is inversely proportional to the temperature.

8177. Answer A. AC 65-12A
When inspecting the hot section of a turbine engine, the exhaust cone and tailpipe should be inspected for cracks, warping, buckling, or hotspots. Hotspots on the tail cone are a good indication of a malfunctioning fuel nozzle or combustion chamber. For example, if a fuel nozzle is spraying a solid stream of fuel instead of an atomized spray, the fuel continues to burn as it passes through the exhaust section, producing burn marks on the tail cone. By the same token, a combustion chamber which is not properly controlling the flame zone may allow the flame to come in contact with the tail cone. Answer (B) is wrong because the interconnector tubes in the burner cans allow normal flame propagation when a single igniter plug malfunctions. Answer (C) is wrong because no matter how the tail cone is positioned, the flame within the combustion chamber should not touch it.

8178. Answer A. AC 65-12A
Each set of rotor blades within an axial-flow compressor has a corresponding set of stator vanes. The stator vanes direct the airflow to the next set of rotor blades at the proper angle and partially convert velocity energy to pressure energy. Answer (B) is incorrect since stator vanes have a diverging profile that changes velocity into pressure, and answer (C) is wrong because inlet guide vanes direct air into the first stage rotor.

8179. Answer A. AC 65-15A
According to Bernoulli's Principle, any time a fluid passes through a constriction at subsonic speeds pressure decreases while velocity increases. The diameter of a convergent nozzle decreases as the exhaust gases move aft. Therefore, as exhaust gases pass through a convergent nozzle the velocity of the gases increases while the pressure decreases. Answers (B) and (C) are incorrect because subsonic airflow increases in velocity when passing through a convergent nozzle.

8180. Answer A. AC 65-15A
A supersonic flow of air differs from a subsonic flow in that as a supersonic flow passes through an expanding tube its speed increases while pressure decreases. The diameter of a divergent nozzle increases, or expands, as exhaust gases move aft. Therefore, as supersonic gases pass through a divergent nozzle, gas velocity increases and pressure decreases. Answer (C) is wrong because temperature has no bearing on the velocity of supersonic air.

8181.   B02

The pressure of subsonic air as it flows through a convergent nozzle

A — increases.
B — decreases.
C — remains constant.

8181. Answer B. AC 65-15A

According to Bernoulli's Principle, any time a fluid passes through a constriction at subsonic speeds pressure decreases while velocity increases. The diameter of a convergent nozzle decreases, or constricts, as the exhaust gases move aft. Therefore, as exhaust gases pass through a convergent nozzle the velocity of the gases increases while the pressure decreases. Answers (A) and (C) are incorrect because subsonic airflow increases in velocity when passing through a convergent nozzle.

8182.   B02

The pressure of supersonic air as it flows through a divergent nozzle

A — increases.
B — decreases.
C — is inversely proportional to the temperature.

8182. Answer B. AC 65-15A

A supersonic flow of air differs from a subsonic flow in that as a supersonic flow passes through an expanding tube its speed increases while pressure decreases. The diameter of a divergent nozzle increases, or expands, as exhaust gases move aft. Therefore, as supersonic gases pass through a divergent nozzle, gas velocity increases and pressure decreases. Answer (C) is wrong because temperature has no bearing on the velocity of supersonic air.

8183.   B02

Anti-icing of jet engine air inlets is commonly accomplished by

A — electrical heating elements inside the inlet guide vanes.
B — engine bleed air ducted through the critical areas.
C — electrical heating elements located within the engine air inlet cowling.

8183. Answer B. AC 65-12A

Anti-icing of turbine engine inlets is typically accomplished by routing warm engine bleed air through the inside of the inlets. In fact, engine bleed air is used to accomplish a variety of things including: cabin pressurization and heating, deicing and anti-icing, pneumatic starting, and powering auxiliary drive units, control-booster servo systems, and instruments. The exact location where the bleed air is taken from the engine depends on the pressure and temperature required for a particular job. Answers (A) and (C) are incorrect because, although electrical heating elements are used in some installations, engine bleed air is most commonly used for inlet anti-icing.

8184.   B02

Generally, when starting a turbine engine, the starter should be disengaged

A — after the engine has reached self-accelerating speed.
B — only after the engine has reached full idle RPM.
C — when the ignition and fuel system are activated.

8184. Answer A. AC 65-12A

When starting a turbine engine you should always follow the manufacturer's instructions. However, as a general guideline for a nonautomatic system, the starter is disengaged after the engine reaches its self-accelerating speed. Answer (B) is incorrect because keeping the starter engaged up to full idle rpm could cause damage, and answer (C) is wrong because disengaging the starter immediately after supplying ignition and fuel could result in a hot start or no start.

8185.   B02

What is the primary advantage of an axial-flow compressor over a centrifugal compressor?

A — High frontal area.
B — Less expensive.
C — Greater pressure ratio.

8185. Answer C. AC 65-12A

Although an axial-flow compressor does not provide a high pressure rise per stage, it is capable of greater peak pressure ratios. The higher peak ratios are made possible by increasing the number of stages. Answer (A) is incorrect because high frontal area is a characteristic of centrifugal compressors, and answer (B) is wrong because axial-flow compressors are generally more expensive to manufacture than centrifugal compressors.

8186. **B02**

The purpose of a bleed valve, located in the beginning stages of the compressor, in an aircraft gas turbine engine is to

A — vent some of the air overboard to prevent a compressor stall.
B — control excessively high RPM to prevent a compressor stall.
C — vent high ram air pressure overboard to prevent a compressor stall.

8186. Answer A. TEP2

A compressor stall occurs when the angle of attack between the compressor vanes and the air moving through a turbine engine's compressor becomes excessive. When this happens, the compressor blades can no longer move air at a sufficient rate. To prevent this, some turbine engines are equipped with a bleed valve located at the first compressor stages that vents air overboard to maintain the correct effective angle of attack and prevent a compressor stall. Answer (B) is incorrect because engine rpm is primarily determined by fuel flow through the engine, not by air flow. Answer (C) is wrong because high ram air pressure effectively lowers the angle of attack between the compressor blades and the inlet airflow thereby eliminating the need for air to be bled away.

8187. **B02**

What is meant by a double entry centrifugal compressor?

A — A compressor that has two intakes.
B — A two-stage compressor independently connected to the main shaft.
C — A compressor with vanes on both sides of the impeller.

8187. Answer C. AC 65-12A

A double entry centrifugal compressor is one that has vanes on both sides of the impeller. Answer (A) is incorrect because a double entry centrifugal compressor can have a single intake, and answer (B) is wrong because two single centrifugal compressor stages require a single inlet.

8188. **B02**

What is the major function of the turbine assembly in a turbojet engine?

A — Directs the gases in the proper direction to the tailpipe.
B — Supplies the power to turn the compressor.
C — Increases the temperature of the exhaust gases.

8188. Answer B. AC 65-12A

The purpose of the turbine section in a gas turbine engine is to extract energy from the gases coming off the combustor. The energy extracted drives the turbine which, in turn, drives the compressor and all accessories. Answer (A) is incorrect because directing exhaust gases to the tailpipe is a minor function of the turbine section, while answer (C) is wrong because the gas temperature actually drops as it passes through the turbine section.

8189. **B02**

Stator blades in the compressor section of an axial-flow turbine engine

A — increase the air velocity and prevent swirling.
B — straighten the airflow and accelerate it.
C — decrease the air velocity and prevent swirling.

8189. Answer C. AC 65-12A

Each set of rotor blades within an axial-flow compressor has a corresponding set of stator vanes. The stator vanes help prevent swirling as they direct airflow to the next set of rotor blades and decrease air velocity by converting velocity energy to pressure energy. Answers (A) and (B) are incorrect because stator vanes have a diverging profile that reduces velocity and increases pressure.

8190. **B02**

A gas turbine engine comprises which three main sections?

A — Compressor, diffuser, and stator.
B — Turbine, combustion, and stator.
C — Turbine, compressor, and combustion.

8190. Answer C. AC 65-12A

The three main sections of a gas turbine engine are the compressor, combustor, and turbine. Both answers (A) and (B) are incorrect because the stator and diffuser are part of the compressor.

8191.   **B02**

What type of turbine blade is most commonly used in aircraft jet engines?

A — Reaction.
B — Impulse.
C — Impulse-reaction.

8192.   **B02**

What is the primary factor which controls the pressure ratio of an axial-flow compressor?

A — Number of stages in compressor.
B — Compressor inlet pressure.
C — Compressor inlet temperature.

8193.   **B02**

The non-rotating axial-flow compressor airfoils in an aircraft gas turbine engine are called

A — pressurization vanes.
B — stator vanes.
C — bleed vanes.

8194.   **B02**

(1) In a turbine engine axial-flow compressor, each consecutive pair of rotor and stator blades constitutes a pressure stage.
(2) In a turbine engine axial-flow compressor, the number of rows of stages is determined by the amount of air and total pressure rise required.

Regarding the above statements,

A — only No.1 is true.
B — only No.2 is true.
C — both No.1 and No.2 are true.

8195.   **B02**

The air passing through the combustion chamber of a turbine engine is

A — used to support combustion and to cool the engine.
B — entirely combined with fuel and burned.
C — speeded up and heated by the action of the turbines.

8191. Answer C. ITP-P2

The most common type of turbine blade used in jet engines is the impulse-reaction type. This type of blade is constructed with an impulse section at its base and a reaction section at its tip. This design distributes the workload evenly along the blade's length. Answers (A) and (B) are incorrect because very few engines use plain impulse or reaction blades.

8192. Answer A. AC 65-12A

The primary factor in determining the pressure ratio in an axial-flow compressor is the number of stages within the compressor. Additional factors that affect pressure ratio include overall compressor efficiency and the pressure ratio produced by each stage. Answers (B) and (C) are wrong because pressure ratio is unaffected by compressor inlet temperature or pressure.

8193. Answer B. AC 65-12A

The two main elements of an axial-flow compressor are the rotor and stator. The rotor blades are attached to a rotating spindle while the stator vanes (answer B) are fixed and act as diffusers at each stage. Answers (A) and (C) are incorrect because neither pressurization vanes nor bleed vanes exist.

8194. Answer C. AC 65-12A

Both statements (1) and (2) are correct. Each consecutive pair of rotor and stator blades constitutes a single pressure stage that produces a given pressure rise. Therefore, the total amount of air and pressure rise required dictates the number of rows or stages needed in a particular engine.

8195. Answer A. AC 65-12A

As air leaves the compressor and enters the combustion section it is divided into a primary and secondary path. The primary path consists of approximately 25 to 35 percent of the total airflow and is routed to the area around the fuel nozzle to support combustion. The secondary path consists of the remaining 65 to 75 percent of the total airflow and is used to form an air blanket on either side of the combustion liner that cools the engine and centers the flames so they do not contact any metal. Answer (B) is incorrect because only a small fraction of the airflow supports combustion and answer (C) is wrong because the air is slowed and cooled as it passes through the turbine section.

8196.   B02

The stators in the turbine section of a gas turbine engine

A — increase the velocity of the gas flow.
B — decrease the velocity of the gas flow.
C — increase the pressure of the gas flow.

8197.   B02

The compressor stators in a gas turbine engine act as diffusers to

A — decrease the velocity of the gas flow.
B — increase the velocity of the gas flow.
C — increase the velocity and decrease the pressure of the gas.

8198.   B02

The procedure for removing the accumulation of dirt deposits on compressor blades is called

A — the soak method.
B — field cleaning.
C — the purging process.

8199.   B02

Which of the following may be used to accomplish internal inspection of an assembled turbine engine?

1. Infrared photography.
2. Ultrasound.
3. A borescope.
4. Fluorescent penetrant and ultraviolet light.

A — 1, 2, 3.
B — 1, 3.
C — 3.

8200.   B03

What is the possible cause when a turbine engine indicates no change in power setting parameters, but oil temperature is high?

A — High scavenge pump oil flow.
B — Engine main bearing distress.
C — Turbine damage and/or loss of turbine efficiency.

8196. Answer A. AC 65-12A

The fixed stator vanes in the turbine section of a gas turbine engine are located ahead of the turbine rotor. The turbine stators act as nozzles to increase gas velocity and decrease pressure. Answer (B) is incorrect because gas flow velocity increases and answer (C) is incorrect because stators cause a decrease in gas pressure.

8197. Answer A. AC 65-12A

A set of stator blades is placed immediately behind each set of rotor blades in an axial-flow compressor. The stators act as diffusers to decrease air velocity and increase pressure before the airflow is allowed to continue to the next stage or to the burners. Answers (B) and (C) are incorrect because airflow velocity decreases and pressure rises.

8198. Answer B. TEP2

Compressor field cleaning is the process of removing an accumulation of contaminants from compressor blades. Dirty compressor blades reduce aerodynamic efficiency and engine performance. Two common methods used for removing dirt deposits are a fluid wash and an abrasive grit blast. The soak method (answer A) and purging process (answer C) do not refer to any known powerplant cleaning process.

8199. Answer C. TEP2

In recent years the borescope has become one of the most effective ways of inspecting the inner parts of the engine. Both answers (A) and (B) are incorrect because none of the other methods listed allows you to inspect internal components while the engine is still assembled.

8200. Answer B. AC 65-12A

In the early stages of engine main bearing distress, increased friction can cause oil temperatures to rise while power parameters remain within normal limits. However, as a main bearing gets closer to failing, the engine's power parameters will change. Answer (A) is incorrect because high scavenge pump oil flow will most likely give a low or fluctuating oil pressure indication before oil temperature becomes elevated. Answer (C) is wrong because turbine damage and/or loss of turbine efficiency causes changes in power setting parameters

8201.   B03

Newton's First Law of Motion, generally termed the Law of Inertia, states:

A — To every action there is an equal and opposite reaction.
B — Force is proportional to the product of mass and acceleration.
C — Every body persists in its state of rest, or of motion in a straight line, unless acted upon by some outside force.

8202.   B03

A turbine engine hot section is particularly susceptible to which kind of damage?

A — Scoring.
B — Cracking.
C — Galling.

8203.   B03

Dirt particles in the air being introduced into the compressor of a turbine engine will form a coating on all but which of the following?

A — Turbine blades.
B — Casings.
C — Inlet guide vanes.

8204.   B03

Severe rubbing of turbine engine compressor blades will usually cause

A — bowing.
B — cracking.
C — galling.

8205.   B03

Which of the following influences the operation of an automatic fuel control unit on a turbojet engine?

A — Burner pressure.
B — Mixture control position.
C — Exhaust gas temperature.

8201. Answer C. AC 65-9A

Newton's First Law of Motion states that any body at rest will remain at rest and any body in motion will remain in a straight line motion, unless acted upon by some outside force. Answer (A) is Newton's Third Law of Motion and answer (B) is a statement from Newton's Second Law.

8202. Answer B. AC 65-12A

Due to the extremely high temperatures and vibration that exist in a hot section, cracking is the most common problem encountered. Answer (A), scoring, consists of deep scratches that are caused by foreign particles between moving parts and is rarely found in turbine sections. Answer (C), galling, is the transfer of metal from one surface to another and is more common in compressor sections.

8203. Answer A. AC 65-12A

As air passes through a compressor, centrifugal force throws particles of dirt, oil, soot, and other foreign matter outward so that they build up on the casing, guide vanes, and compressor blades. However, because of the high temperatures present in the hot section, the turbine blades are not susceptible to this problem. Answers (B) and (C) are wrong because these areas are subject to contamination from dust and dirt.

8204. Answer C. AC 65-12A

Galling is a transfer of metal from one surface to another usually caused by severe rubbing. Answer (A) is wrong because compressor blades will abrade or break before they bow and answer (B), cracking, is unlikely to occur on compressor blades in the absence of a hard impact or extreme heat.

8205. Answer A. AC 65-12A

Some of the variables that an automatic fuel control unit senses include the power lever position, engine rpm, either compressor inlet pressure or temperature, and burner pressure or compressor discharge pressure. Answer (B) is incorrect because there is no mixture control on a turbine engine and exhaust gas temperature (answer C) does not influence the operation of an automatic fuel control unit.

8206.   B03

If a turbine engine is unable to reach takeoff EPR before its EGT limit is reached, this is an indication that the

A — fuel control must be replaced.
B — EGT controller is out of adjustment.
C — compressor may be contaminated or damaged.

8206. Answer C. AC 65-12A

If the compressor blades of a turbine engine are dirty or damaged, the engine will run at a higher internal temperature. Whenever an engine's internal temperature increases, the corresponding exhaust gas temperature (EGT) also increases. Under these circumstances, an engine's EGT limits may be reached before its maximum or takeoff engine pressure ratio (EPR) is obtained. It is unlikely that a fuel control (answer A) could cause the conditions indicated, since the engine is receiving enough fuel to reach its EGT limit, and answer (B) is incorrect because turbine engines do not have EGT controllers.

8207.   B03

The Brayton cycle is known as the constant

A — pressure cycle.
B — temperature cycle.
C — mass cycle.

8207. Answer A. AC 65-12A

The Brayton cycle describes the combustion process in a turbine engine. This process is also known as the constant pressure cycle because the pressure across the combustion section in a turbine engine remains relatively constant. Answers (B) and (C) are incorrect because temperature and mass flow vary substantially in a turbine engine.

8208.   B03

Continued and/or excessive heat and centrifugal force on turbine engine rotor blades is likely to cause

A — profile.
B — creep.
C — galling.

8208. Answer B. AC 65-12A

Creep, or growth, are terms used to describe the permanent elongation of rotating parts. Creep is most pronounced in turbine blades because they are continually subjected to extreme heat and centrifugal loads. Profile (answer A) refers to a blade's contour, while galling (answer C) is the result of two surfaces rubbing together. Neither of these is the result of heat and centrifugal force.

8209.   B03

If the RPM of an axial-flow compressor remains constant, the angle of attack of the rotor blades can be changed by

A — changing the velocity of the airflow.
B — changing the compressor diameter.
C — increasing the pressure ratio.

8209. Answer A. TEP2

Although the orientation of compressor blades in a turbine engine is fixed, their angle of attack relative to the airflow is variable. Angle of attack is affected by the speed of the compressor, the direction of the airflow coming off the stator vanes, and the velocity of the airflow coming off the stator vanes. Answer (B) is wrong because changing the compressor diameter will result in a greater mass of airflow with no change in its velocity, and answer (C) is incorrect because increasing the pressure ratio has no effect on compressor speed or airflow velocity.

8210.   B03

The compression ratio of an axial-flow compressor is a function of the

A — number of compressor stages.
B — rotor diameter.
C — air inlet velocity.

8210. Answer A. AC 65-12A

The primary factor in determining the pressure ratio in an axial-flow compressor is the number of stages within the compressor. Additional factors that affect pressure ratio include overall compressor efficiency and the pressure ratio produced by each stage. Answer (B) is incorrect because changing the rotor diameter affects mass flow, not pressure. Answer (C) is wrong because compression ratio is not affected by changing inlet air velocity.

8211.   B03

Which of the following variables affect the inlet air density of a turbine engine?

1. Speed of the aircraft.
2. Compression ratio.
3. Turbine inlet temperature.
4. Altitude of the aircraft.
5. Ambient temperature.
6. Turbine and compressor efficiency.

A — 1, 3, 6.
B — 1, 4, 5.
C — 4, 5, 6.

8211. Answer B. AC 65-12A

The power produced by a turbine engine is directly proportional to the density of the air at the inlet. The factors which affect air density at the inlet are the speed of the aircraft, the altitude at which the aircraft is flying, and the ambient air temperature. Both answers (A) and (C) are wrong because items 2, 3, and 6 impact engine thermal efficiency and do not affect inlet air density.

8212.   B03

Which of the following factors affect the thermal efficiency of a turbine engine?

1. Turbine inlet temperature.
2. Compression ratio.
3. Ambient temperature.
4. Speed of the aircraft.
5. Turbine and compressor efficiency.
6. Altitude of the aircraft.

A — 3, 4, 6.
B — 1, 2, 5.
C — 1, 2, 6.

8212. Answer B. AC 65-12A

Thermal efficiency refers to the ratio of net work produced by a turbine engine to the chemical energy supplied in the form of fuel. The three most important factors affecting thermal efficiency are turbine inlet temperature, compression ratio, and the efficiency of the compressor and turbine. All of these factors are included in answer (B). Other factors that affect thermal efficiency are compressor inlet temperature and burner efficiency. Answers (A) and (C) are wrong because items 3, 4, and 6 are the determining factors of inlet air density.

8213.   B03

Why do some turbine engines have more than one turbine wheel attached to a single shaft?

A — To facilitate balancing of the turbine assembly.
B — To help stabilize the pressure between the compressor and the turbine.
C — To extract more power from the exhaust gases than a single wheel can absorb.

8213. Answer C. AC 65-12A

The number of turbine wheels used in a gas turbine engine is determined by the amount of energy that must be extracted to drive the compressor and all accessories. Both turbofan and turboprop engines require more turbine wheels than a turbojet, because more energy is required to drive the fan or prop. Answer (A) is wrong because turbine assembly balance is as easily achieved with one turbine wheel as with two. Answer (B) is incorrect because the number of turbine wheels has no relation to stabilizing pressure between the compressor and turbine.

8214.   B03

The exhaust section of a turbine engine is designed to

A — impart a high exit velocity to the exhaust gases.
B — increase temperature, therefore increasing velocity.
C — decrease temperature, therefore decreasing pressure.

8214. Answer A. AC 65-12A

The exhaust section of a turbine engine installed on a subsonic aircraft is comprised of several components performing multiple functions. However, all components must work together to direct the flow of hot gases rearward and impart a high exit velocity. Answer (B) is true for afterburning engines but not for conventional applications and answer (C) is incorrect because a properly designed exhaust section should increase the pressure of the exhaust gas.

8215.   B03

Which of the following types of combustion sections are used in aircraft turbine engines?

A — Annular, variable, and cascade vane.
B — Can, multiple-can, and variable.
C — Multiple-can, annular, and can-annular.

8216.   B03

A cool-off period prior to shutdown of a turbine engine is accomplished in order to

A — allow the turbine wheel to cool before the case contracts around it.
B — prevent vapor lock in the fuel control and/or fuel lines.
C — prevent seizure of the engine bearings.

8217.   B03

What type of igniter plug is used in the low tension ignition system of an aircraft turbofan engine?

A — Low voltage, high amperage glow plug.
B — Self-ionizing or shunted-gap type plug.
C — Recessed surface gap plug.

8218.   B03

What is meant by a shrouded turbine?

A — The turbine blades are shaped so that their ends form a band or shroud.
B — The turbine wheel is enclosed by a protective shroud to contain the blades in case of failure.
C — The turbine wheel has a shroud or duct which provides cooling air to the turbine blades.

8215. Answer C. AC 65-12A

The three types of combustion chambers used in gas turbine engines are the multiple-can, annular, and can-annular. In modern day engines, the annular is the most popular. Answers (A) and (B) are wrong because the terms variable and cascade vane do not refer to types of combustion sections.

8216. Answer A. AC 65-12A

Prior to shutting down some turbine engines, a cool-off period is required to allow the turbine wheel to cool and contract before the case contracts around it. Although the turbine case and turbine wheels operate at approximately the same temperature when the engine is running, the turbine wheels are relatively massive compared to the case and, therefore, cool and contract more slowly. Answer (B) is incorrect because vapor lock is a problem associated with reciprocating engines, and answer (C) is wrong because engine bearings are unlikely to seize unless their lubrication is interrupted.

8217. Answer B. TEP 2

Some turbine engines are equipped with low tension ignition systems that typically utilize self-ionizing or shunted-gap igniter plugs. Shunted-gap igniters contain a semiconductor material between the center and ground electrodes. The plug fires when current flows from a storage capacitor in the ignition exciter through the center electrode, the semiconductor, and to the plugs outer casing. Answer (A) is incorrect because low voltage glow plugs are actually small heating coils that do not require a coil-type ignition system. Answer (C) is wrong because recessed surface gap igniter plugs require high voltage and cannot be used in low tension systems.

8218. Answer A. AC 65-12A

The term shrouded turbine refers to a gas turbine engine that uses shrouded turbine blades. The use of shrouded turbine rotor blades reduces blade vibration and improves turbine efficiency. With shrouded blades the tips of the blades contact each other, thereby providing support. This added support reduces vibration substantially. The shrouds also prevent air from escaping over the blade tips making the turbine more efficient. Answer (B) is incorrect because although some compressor sections are reinforced to contain a blade failure, this is rarely done in turbine sections. Answer (C) is wrong because when turbine blades are cooled, they receive cooling air from the compressor and release it through holes in their leading and trailing edges.

8219.   B03

What term is used to describe a permanent and cumulative deformation of the turbine blades of a turbojet engine?

A — Stretch.
B — Distortion.
C — Creep.

8220.   B03

What is the purpose of the dump valve used on aircraft gas turbine engines?

A — The fuel is quickly cut off to the nozzles and the manifolds are drained preventing fuel boiling as a result of residual engine heat.
B — The valve controls compressor stalls by dumping compressor bleed air from the compressor discharge port under certain conditions.
C — Maintains minimum fuel pressure to the engine fuel control unit inlet and dumps excessive fuel back to the inlet of the engine driven fuel pump.

8221.   B03

At what stage in a turbine engine are gas pressures the greatest?

A — Compressor inlet.
B — Turbine outlet.
C — Compressor outlet.

8222.   B03

In what section of a turbojet engine is the jet nozzle located?

A — Combustion.
B — Turbine.
C — Exhaust.

8223.   B03

(1) Accumulation of contaminates in the compressor of a turbojet engine reduces aerodynamic efficiency of the blades.
(2) Two common methods for removing dirt deposits from turbojet engine compressor blades are a fluid wash and an abrasive grit blast.

Regarding the above statements,

A — only No. 1 is true.
B — only No. 2 is true.
C — both No. 1 and No. 2 are true.

8219. Answer C. AC 65-12A

Creep, or growth, are terms used to describe the permanent elongation and deformation of rotating parts. Creep is most pronounced in turbine blades because they continually must operate in extreme heat while being subjected to excessive centrifugal loads.

8220. Answer A. AC 65-12A

The dump valve is part of the fuel system in a turbine engine that automatically dumps fuel pressure at engine shut down. This prevents fuel boiling due to residual engine heat. Answer (B) is incorrect because a special bleed valve dumps compressor air on some engines to help prevent a compressor stall and answer (C) is wrong because the dump valve forces excess fuel back into the combustion chamber, not back into the fuel pump inlet.

8221. Answer C. AC 65-12A

The highest pressure in a gas turbine engine is at the compressor outlet. This point in the engine is known as the diffuser. Answers (A) and (B) are incorrect because pressures are lower at the compressor inlet and turbine outlet.

8222. Answer C. AC 65-12A

The jet nozzle of a gas turbine engine is attached to the rear of the tailpipe or rear flange of the exhaust duct and represents the last component the exhaust gases pass through. Therefore, the jet nozzle is part of the exhaust section.

8223. Answer C. AC 65-12A

Both statements (1) and (2) are correct. The accumulation of dirt, oil, and soot on compressor blades reduces the aerodynamic efficiency of the blades which, in turn, decreases engine performance. The two most common methods for removing dirt deposits are a fluid wash and an abrasive grit blast. The fluid cleaning procedure is accomplished by first spraying an emulsion type surface cleaner into the compressor as it is turning and then applying a rinse. Grit blasting, on the other hand, requires the injection of an abrasive grit into the engine operating at a selected power setting.

8224. **B03**
Hot spots in the combustion section of a turbojet engine are possible indicators of

A — faulty igniter plugs.
B — dirty compressor blades.
C — malfunctioning fuel nozzles.

8225. **B03**
Which of the following can cause fan blade shingling in a turbofan engine?

1. Engine overspeed.
2. Engine overtemperature.
3. Large, rapid throttle movements.
4. FOD.

A — 1, 2.
B — 1, 2, 3, 4.
C — 1, 4.

8226. **B03**
Compressor stall is caused by

A — a low angle of attack airflow through the first stages of compression.
B — a high angle of attack airflow through the first stages of compression.
C — rapid engine deceleration.

8227. **B03**
A condition known as "hot streaking" in turbine engines is caused by

A — a partially clogged fuel nozzle.
B — a misaligned combustion liner.
C — excessive fuel flow.

8224. Answer C. AC 65-12A
Hot spots within the combustion section are possible indicators of a serious condition, such as malfunctioning fuel nozzles or other fuel system malfunctions. Therefore, whenever hotspots are present they must be interpreted carefully.

8225. Answer C.
Fan blade shingling is the term used to describe the overlapping of midspan shrouds on fan blades. Any time rotating fan blades encounter a resistance that forces a blade sideways shingling occurs. Shingling is typically caused by an overspeed, FOD, a bird strike, or a compressor stall.

8226. Answer B. TEP2
A compressor stall occurs when the inlet airflow strikes the compressor blades at an excessive angle of attack causing the blades to momentarily lose the ability to compress inlet air. Answer (A) is incorrect because low angle of attack airflow can cause compressor choke, not compressor stall. Answer (C) is incorrect because, although rapid engine deceleration is one action that can cause compressor stall, high angle of attack airflow is the primary cause.

8227. Answer A. AC 65-12A
The term hot streaking describes a condition where a fuel nozzle shoots out an unatomized stream of fuel which can contact the combustion liner or other components creating hot spots. Answer (B) is incorrect because although a misaligned combustion liner could disrupt the airflow pattern within the liner and create hot spots, it would not create the distinctive streaking associated with a clogged fuel nozzle. Answer (C) is wrong because excessive fuel flow, if distributed through a properly working fuel nozzle, will result in high EGT but will not lead to hot streaking.

CHAPTER 3

ENGINE INSPECTION

The chapter on engine inspection presents information on the procedures used to conduct conformity and airworthiness inspections on powerplants. Particular attention is devoted to maintenance publications used as sources of approved data. The FAA exam questions that apply to this chapter include:

8228, 8229, 8230, 8231, 8232, 8233, 8234, 8235, 8236, 8237, 8238, 8239, 8240, 8241, 8242, 8243, 8244, 8245, 8246, 8247, 8248, 8249, 8250, 8251, 8252, 8253, 8254, 8255, 8256.

8228 C01
(Refer to figure 1 on page 3-2) Determine which portion of the AD is applicable for Model 0-690 series engine, serial No.5863-40 with 283 hours time in service.

A — (B), (1).
B — (A).
C — (B), (2).

8229. C01
A Cessna 180 aircraft has a McCauley propeller Model No.2A34C50/90A. The propeller is severely damaged in a ground accident, and this model propeller is not available for replacement. Which of the following should be used to find an approved alternate replacement?

A — Summary of Supplemental Type Certificates.
B — Aircraft Specifications/Type Certificate Data Sheets.
C — Aircraft Engine and Propeller Specifications/ Type Certificate Data Sheets.

8230. C01
Which of the following is used to monitor the mechanical integrity of the turbines, as well as to check engine operating conditions of a turbine engine?

A — Engine oil pressure.
B — Exhaust gas temperature.
C — Engine pressure ratio.

8228. Answer A. AC39-7B
Paragraph B in the AD applies to all model 0-690 engines with serial numbers 5265-40 to 6129-40. The engine and serial number listed in the question fall within this listing. Paragraph 1 also applies to the listed engine because it identifies engines with more than 275 hours time in service. Answer (B) is wrong because paragraph A of the AD applies only to serial numbers 101-40 through 5264-40 for the model O-690 engine and the engine in this question falls outside this range. Answer (C) is wrong because subparagraph 2 applies to engines with less than 275 hours time in service, and the engine in the example has 283 hours.

8229. Answer B. AC 65-9A
The Aircraft Specifications or Type Certificate Data Sheet for an aircraft lists the engines and propellers approved for use on the aircraft. If there is more than one approved propeller for the Cessna 180, it will be listed in one of these documents. This information can also be found in the Summary of Supplemental Type Certificates. Therefore, there are two correct answers for this question. However, it is our belief that the Aircraft Specifications or Type Certificate Data Sheets are better references to use. Answer (C) is incorrect because the Engine and Propeller Specifications/Type Certificate Data Sheets do not state which propellers may be installed on a given aircraft.

8230. Answer B. AC 65-12A
One of the most important indicators of how a turbine engine is performing as well as its mechanical integrity is exhaust gas temperature (EGT). If there is damage to the turbine section of an engine, it will show up as an increase in EGT. Answer (A) is incorrect because an engine oil pressure gauge indicates the presence and flow of oil. Answer (C) is wrong because engine pressure ratio represents overall engine efficiency and is not restricted to the turbine section only.

This is the compliance portion of an FAA Airworthiness Directive.

Compliance required as indicated:

(A)   For model O-690 series engines, serial Nos. 101-40 through 5264-40 and IO-690 series engines, serial Nos. 101-48 through 423-48, compliance with (C) required within 25 hours' time in service after the effective date of this AD and every 100 hours' time in service thereafter.

(B)   For model O-690 series engines, serial Nos. 5265-40 through 6129-40 and IO-690 series engines, serial Nos. 424-48 through 551-48, compliance with (C) required as follows:

   (1)   Within 25 hours' time in service after the effective date of this AD and every 100 hours' time in service thereafter for engines with more than 275 hours' time in service on the effective date of this AD.

   (2)   Prior to the accumulation of 300 hours total time in service and every 100 hours' time in service thereafter for engines with 275 hours or less time in service on the effective date of this AD.

(C)   Inspect the oil pump drive shaft (P/N 67512) on applicable engines in accordance with instructions contained in Connin Service Bulletin No. 295. Any shafts which are found to be damaged shall be replaced before further flight. These inspections shall be continued until Connin P/N 67512 (redesigned) or P/N 74641 oil pump drive shaft is installed at which time the inspections may be discontinued.

Figure 1.— Airworthiness Directive Excerpt.

8231.   C01

On a reciprocating engine aircraft using a shrouded exhaust muffler system as a source for cabin heat, the exhaust system should be

A — visually inspected for any indication of cracks or an operational carbon monoxide detection test should be done.
B — replaced at each reciprocating engine overhaul by a new or overhauled exhaust system or a hydro-static test should be accomplished.
C — removed and the exhaust muffler checked for cracks by using magnetic particle inspection method or a hydrostatic test should be done on the exhaust muffler.

8231. Answer A. AC 65-12A

Many piston engine powered aircraft use the engine exhaust as a source of cabin heat. This is done by installing a jacket, or shroud, around the exhaust system. With this type of system, air passes between the exhaust and the shroud and is heated by the exhaust manifold. When this type of system is used, it must be inspected on a regular basis to ensure that no leaks exist in the exhaust system. Furthermore, a carbon monoxide detection test should be performed periodically to verify that no exhaust fumes are entering the cabin area. Answer (B) is wrong because there is no requirement to replace a serviceable exhaust when an engine is overhauled, and answer (C) is wrong because there is no requirement to use magnetic particle inspection.

8232.   C01
(1) Airworthiness Directives are Federal Aviation Regulations and must be complied with unless specific exemption is granted.
(2) Most Airworthiness Directives of an emergency nature require immediate compliance upon receipt.

Regarding the above statements,

A — only No. 1 is true.
B — only No. 2 is true.
C — both No. 1 and No. 2 are true.

8233.   C01
Which of the following contains a minimum checklist for 100-hour inspections of engines?

A — FAR Part 33, Appendix A.
B — FAR Part 43, Appendix D.
C — Engine Specifications or Type Certificate Data Sheets.

8234.   C01
When must an Airworthiness Directive (AD) be complied with after it becomes effective?

A — As specified in the AD.
B — During the next scheduled inspection.
C — At the next scheduled overhaul.

8235.   C01
Which of the following contains a table that lists the engines to which a given propeller is adaptable?

A — Aircraft Type Certificate Data Sheets.
B — Propeller Type Certificate Data Sheets.
C — Engine Type Certificate Data Sheets.

8236.   C01
Which of the following component inspections is to be accomplished on a 100-hour inspection?

A — Check internal timing of magneto.
B — Check cylinder compression.
C — Check valve timing.

8237.   C01
You are performing a 100-hour inspection on an R985-22 aircraft engine. What does the "985" indicate?

A — The total piston displacement of the engine.
B — The pistons will pump a maximum of 985 cubic inches of air per crankshaft revolution.
C — The total piston displacement of one cylinder.

8232. Answer C. AC 65-9A
Both statements (1) and (2) are correct. Airworthiness Directives (ADs) are part of FAR Part 39 and must be complied with unless a specific exemption is granted. Statement (2) is also true on most occasions, because emergency ADs generally do require immediate compliance. Furthermore, if an AD is issued that identifies an emergency condition, compliance is typically required upon receipt.

8233. Answer B. Part 43, Appendix D
FAR Part 43 contains the minimum checklist for a 100-hour inspection of an engine and airframe. Answers (A) and (C) are incorrect because neither Appendix A of FAR Part 33, nor the Type Certificate Data Sheets contain information on inspection checklists.

8234. Answer A. FAR 39.3
After an AD has become effective, it must be complied with as specified in the AD. Answers (B) and (C) are wrong because although an AD can specify that compliance is required at the next inspection or overhaul, AD compliance is not an inspection or overhaul requirement.

8235. Answer B. AC 65-12A
To find out what engines a particular propeller is adaptable to, you must look at the propeller's Type Certificate Data Sheet. Answer (A) is incorrect because Aircraft Type Certificate Data Sheets give the propeller that is acceptable for use on a given aircraft, and answer (C) is wrong because Engine Type Certificate Data Sheets list the propellers that are acceptable for use on a given engine.

8236. Answer B. Part 43, Appendix D
According to Appendix D of FAR Part 43 a 100-hour inspection on an engine requires that a cylinder compression check be performed. Although it is good practice to also check the internal timing of the magnetos (answer A) and the valve timing (answer C), neither is required to be checked during a 100-hour inspection.

8237. Answer A. AC 65-12A
In the designation for an engine R985-22, the 985 indicates the total piston displacement of the engine in cubic inches. Answers (B) and (C) are incorrect because the correct definition of piston displacement is the total volume swept by the pistons of an engine in one revolution of the crankshaft.

8238.   C01

Where would one find type design information for an R1830-92 engine certificated under the Civil Air Regulations (CAR) and installed on a DC-3?

A — The Aircraft Specifications and Type Certificate Data Sheet.
B — The Aircraft Engine Specifications.
C — The Aircraft Engine Type Certificate Handbook.

8238. Answer B. JSGT

Both the R1830-92 and DC-3 were certified under the older Civil Aeronautics Regulations and, therefore, Type Certificate Data Sheets were not published for either the engine or the aircraft. Therefore, the only place to find type design information for an R1830-92 engine that is installed on a DC-3 is in the aircraft engine specifications. Answer (A) is incorrect because the Aircraft Specifications and Type Certificate Data Sheets do not contain engine type design information and answer (C) is incorrect because there are no Type Certificate Handbooks.

8239.   C01

Straightening nitrided crankshafts is

A — recommended.
B — not recommended.
C — approved by the manufacturer.

8239. Answer B. AC 65-12A

A bent nitrided crankshaft should not be straightened. Any attempt to do so will result in a rupture of the nitrided surface of the bearing journals and eventual crankshaft failure. Answers (A) and (C) are incorrect because straightening nitrided crankshafts is neither recommended nor approved.

8240.   C01

The breaking loose of small pieces of metal from coated surfaces, usually caused by defective plating or excessive loads, is called

A — flaking.
B — chafing.
C — brinelling.

8240. Answer A. AC 65-12A

Flaking is defined as the breaking loose of small pieces of metal from coated surfaces. It is usually caused by defective plating or excessive loading. Answer (B) is wrong because chafing is wear caused by light rubbing between two parts that does not produce small pieces of metal. Answer (C) is incorrect because brinelling refers to the indentations found on bearing races that are caused by high static loads or the application of force during component installation or removal.

8241.   C01

Each powerplant installed on an airplane with a Standard Airworthiness Certificate must have been

A — type certificated.
B — manufactured under the TSO system.
C — originally certificated for that aircraft.

8241. Answer A. FAR 23.903

Each airplane having a standard airworthiness certificate must be equipped with an engine which is type certificated and, if it is prop driven, a type certificated propeller. Answer (B) is incorrect because an engine that is type certificated does not need to be manufactured under a TSO, and answer (C) is wrong since Supplemental Type Certificates permit the installation of components and appliances that were not originally certificated for a given aircraft.

8242.   C01

A severe condition of chafing or fretting in which a transfer of metal from one part to another occurs is called

A — scoring.
B — burning.
C — galling.

8242. Answer C. AC 65-12A

Galling is defined as a severe condition of chafing or fretting in which a transfer of metal from one part to another occurs. It is usually caused by a slight movement of mated parts under high loads and having limited relative motion. Answer (A) is incorrect because scoring results in deep scratching and is the result of foreign particles between moving parts. Answer (B) is wrong because burning is surface damage caused by excessive heat and rarely results in the transfer of metal.

8243.   C01
Indentations on bearing races caused by high static loads are known as

A — fretting.
B — brinelling.
C — galling.

8243. Answer B. AC 65-12A
Brinelling is defined as one or more indentations on bearing races, usually caused by high loads or the application of force during installation or removal. The indentations are rounded or spherical due to the impression left by the contacting ball or roller bearings. Answer (A) is incorrect because fretting is a form of surface corrosion that is caused by movement between two parts that are clamped together under pressure. Answer (C) is wrong because galling is a severe chafing that results in transfer of metal.

8244.   C01
When inspecting an aircraft reciprocating engine what document is used to determine if the proper magnetos are installed?

A — Instructions for continued airworthiness issued by the engine manufacturer.
B — Engine Manufacturer's Maintenance Manual.
C — Aircraft Engine Specifications or Type Certificate Data Sheets.

8244. Answer C. AC 65-9A
When inspecting an engine, it is important to make sure that it conforms to its original type design. The original type design for an engine manufactured before 1959 is contained in the Aircraft Engine Specifications. However, for engines that were manufactured after 1959 the type design information is in the Type Certificate Data Sheet. Answer (A) is wrong because instructions for continued airworthiness consist of maintenance manuals, installation instructions, and servicing information. Answer (B) is wrong because maintenance manuals do not reference approved components for a given engine or aircraft.

8245.   C01
Which of the following can inspect and approve an engine major repair for return to service?

A — Certificated mechanic with airframe and powerplant ratings.
B — Certificated mechanic with a powerplant rating.
C — Certificated mechanic with inspection authorization.

8245. Answer C. FAR 65.95
Although a certified airframe and powerplant technician is authorized to perform a major repair, it takes a person with the inspection authorization to return the repair to service. Answers (A) and (B) are incorrect because a mechanic certificate alone is not sufficient to inspect and approve a major repair for return to service.

8246.   C01
What publication is used for guidance to determine whether a powerplant repair is major or minor?

A — Airworthiness Directives.
B — Federal Aviation Regulations, Part 43, appendix A.
C — Technical Standard Orders.

8246. Answer B. Part 43, Appendix A
A list of what constitutes a powerplant major repair or alteration is provided in FAR Part 43, Appendix A. However, this list is only a guide and does not identify all possible repairs and alterations. Answer (A) is incorrect because Airworthiness Directives give no guidance on the status of repairs and alterations and answer (C) is incorrect because a technical standard order merely certifies that a part meets certain quality standards.

8247.   C01

The airworthiness standards for the issue of type certificates for small airplanes with nine or less passenger seats in the normal, utility, and acrobatic categories may be found in the

A — Supplemental Type Certificate.
B — Federal Aviation Regulations, Part 23.
C — Federal Aviation Regulations, Part 25.

8248.   C01

Which of the following contains approved data for performing a major repair to an aircraft engine?

A — Engine Type Certificate Data Sheets.
B — Supplemental Type Certificates.
C — Manufacturer's maintenance instructions when FAA approved.

8249.   C01

What maintenance record(s) is/are required following a major repair of an aircraft engine?

A — Entries in engine maintenance records and a list of discrepancies for the FAA.
B — Entries in the engine maintenance record and FAA Form 337.
C — Entry in logbook.

8250.   C01

A ground incident that results in propeller sudden stoppage may require a crankshaft runout inspection. What publication would be used to obtain crankshaft runout tolerance?

A — Current Manufacturer's maintenance instructions.
B — Type Certificate Data Sheet.
C — AC 43.13-1A, Acceptable Methods, Techniques, and Practices Aircraft Inspection and Repair.

8247. Answer B. FAR 23.1

FAR Part 23 entitled, Airworthiness Standards: Normal, Utility, Acrobatic and Commuter Category Airplanes, prescribes the airworthiness standards for the issue of type certificates for small airplanes in the normal, utility, and acrobatic categories that have a passenger seating configuration, excluding pilot seats, of 9 seats or less. Answer (A) is incorrect because a Supplemental Type Certificate allows the alteration of an aircraft, powerplant, or component and contains no airworthiness information beyond the requirements for the alteration. Answer (C) is wrong because Part 25 of the FARs gives airworthiness standards for transport category airplanes.

8248. Answer C. AC 65-19E

Manufacturer's maintenance instructions are acceptable to use when performing a major repair to an engine, providing they are FAA approved. FAA approval must be stamped on the manual before it can be used as approved data. Answer (A) is incorrect because Engine Type Certificate Data Sheets contain information such as power rating, fuel grade, and weight for a given engine model but contain no approved data for major repairs. Answer (B) is incorrect because Supplemental Type Certificates contain approved data for major alterations, not repairs.

8249. Answer B. FAR 43.9

When a major repair is performed on an engine, an entry must be made in the engine's maintenance records and an FAA Form 337 must be filled out. One copy of the Form 337 stays with the maintenance records and a second copy is sent to the FAA. An exception to this would be if the repair was done by a certified repair station. If approved data was used, the repair station would not be required to fill out a Form 337. Answer (A) is wrong because there is no requirement that the FAA receive a list of discrepancies found during a major repair, and answer (C) is incorrect because an FAA Form 337 must be completed in addition to an entry in the engine's maintenance record.

8250. Answer A. AC 43.13-1A

When an engine has been subjected to a sudden stoppage requiring a crankshaft run-out check, it should be done in accordance with the manufacturer's technical data. Therefore, the manufacturer's maintenance instructions would typically be used. Answers (B) and (C) are incorrect because neither the Type Certificate Data Sheets nor AC 43.13-1A gives specific limits or tolerances for engine overhauls.

8251.   C01
Select the Airworthiness Directive applicability statement which applies to an IVO-355 engine, serial number T8164, with 2,100 hours total time and 300 hours since rebuilding.

A — Applies to all IVO-355 engines, serial numbers T8000 through T8300, having less than 2,400 hours total time.

B — Applies to all IVO-355 engines, serial numbers T8000 through T8900 with 2,400 hours or more total time.

C — Applies to all I.O. and TV10-355 engines, all serial numbers regardless of total time or since overhaul.

8251. Answer A. AC 65-9A
Answer (A) applies to the engine identified because it gives the model number as IVO-355; the serial numbers include the number of the listed engine; and the hours of time in service apply to the listed engine. The number of hours the engine has accumulated since rebuilding does not matter in relation to this question. Answer (B) is incorrect since it specifies engines with more total time than the given engine has, and answer (C) is wrong because it specifies IO and TVIO-355 engines while the given engine is an IVO-355.

8252.   C01
What publication contains time and/or cycle limitations for components or parts of a turbine engine installed on a specific aircraft?

A — Engine Manufacturer's service instructions.
B — Engine Manufacturer's maintenance manual.
C — Airworthiness directive issued by the engine manufacturer.

8252. Answer B. Part 33, Appendix A
Appendix A of FAR Part 33 specifies what must be included in an engine manufacturer's maintenance manuals. Paragraph A33.3 states that recommended overhaul periods must be included in the Airworthiness Limitations section of engine maintenance manuals. Answer (A) is incorrect because service instructions are used to communicate with owners and service personnel and generally do not contain time limitations for engine components. Answer (C) is incorrect because if an Airworthiness Directive contains a time or cycle limitation it will be for a specific part only.

8253.   C01
How are discharge nozzles in a fuel injected reciprocating engine identified to indicate the flow range?

A — By an identification letter stamped on one of the hexes of the nozzle body.
B — By an identification metal tag attached to the nozzle body.
C — By color codes on the nozzle body.

8253. Answer A. AC 65-12A
Fuel discharge nozzles are calibrated for several different flow ranges. In order to help identify the flow range of a specific nozzle a letter is stamped on the hex of the nozzle body.

8254.   C01
What section in the instructions for continued airworthiness is FAA approved?

A — Engine maintenance manual or section.
B — Engine overhaul manual or section.
C — Airworthiness limitations section.

8254. Answer C. Part 33, Appendix A
According to FAR Part 33 Appendix A, the Instructions for Continued Airworthiness must contain a section titled Airworthiness Limitations that is segregated and clearly distinguishable from the rest of the document. This section is FAA approved and must list the mandatory replacement time, inspection interval, and related procedures required for certification. Answers (A) and (B) are incorrect because the FARs do not require engine maintenance and overhaul manuals to be FAA approved.

8255.   **C01**

Which of the following conditions is usually not acceptable to any extent in turbine blades?

A — Cracks.
B — Pits.
C — Dents.

8256.   **C01**

(1) Serviceability limits for turbine blades are much more stringent than are those for turbine nozzle vanes.
(2) A limited number of small nicks and dents can usually be permitted in any area of a turbine blade.

Regarding the above statements,

A — both No.1 and No. 2 are true.
B — neither No.1 nor No. 2 is true.
C — only No. 1 is true.

8255. Answer A. AC 65-12A

Any crack or sharp bend that may result in cracking is cause for rejection of a turbine blade. Answers (B) and (C) are wrong because most manufacturers allow some pits or dents in a turbine blade if the defect falls within certain limits.

8256. Answer C. AC 65-12A

Only statement number (1) is correct. Because the centrifugal stresses and gas temperatures imposed on turbine blades is greater than those imposed on turbine nozzle vanes, serviceability limits are more stringent for turbine blades than for nozzle vanes. Furthermore, any nicks or dents found in the root area of a turbine blade is cause for immediate replacement.

CHAPTER 4

ENGINE INSTRUMENT SYSTEMS

This chapter discusses the maintenance practices used to inspect, check, service, and troubleshoot electrical and mechanical engine indication systems. The engine indicating systems covered include engine and oil temperature and pressure systems, engine rpm, and fuel rate-of-flow systems. The following FAA exam questions are taken from this chapter:

8257, 8258, 8259, 8260, 8261, 8262, 8263, 8264, 8265, 8266, 8267, 8268, 8269, 8270, 8271, 8272, 8273, 8274, 8275, 8276, 8277, 8278, 8279, 8280, 8281, 8282, 8283, 8284, 8285, 8286, 8287, 8288, 8289, 8290, 8291, 8292, 8293, 8294, 8295, 8296, 8297, 8298, 8299, 8300, 8301, 8302, 8303, 8304, 8305, 8306, 8307, 8308, 8309.

8257.   H01
Which unit most accurately indicates fuel consumption of a reciprocating engine?

A — Fuel flowmeter.
B — Fuel pressure gauge.
C — Electronic fuel quantity indicator.

8257. Answer A. AC 65-12A
Electronic fuel flowmeters (vane-type or mass-flow type) are what many modern aircraft use to measure the amount of fuel consumed by an engine. Fuel flowmeters monitor the amount of fuel that flows past a given point and display this flow rate in the cockpit as pounds of fuel consumed per hour. Answer (B) is wrong because a fuel pressure gauge only indicates the fuel pressure within the fuel lines and answer (C) is incorrect because an electronic fuel quantity indicator displays the amount of fuel in the fuel tanks and does not directly indicate the amount of fuel consumption.

8258.   H01
The fuel flowmeter used with a continuous-fuel injection system installed on an aircraft horizontally opposed reciprocating engine measures the fuel pressure drop across the

A — manifold valve.
B — fuel nozzles.
C — metering valve.

8258. Answer B. ITP-A2
Most light aircraft equipped with continuous-fuel injection systems utilize a fuel flow indication system that measures the pressure drop across the injection nozzles to determine fuel flow (answer B). With this type of system, a higher fuel flow results in a greater pressure drop and a corresponding increase in fuel flow is indicated in the cockpit. Answer (A) and (C) are wrong because there is no pressure drop across either the manifold valve or metering valve.

8259.   H01
The principle fault in the pressure type fuel flowmeter indicating system, installed on a horizontally opposed continuous-flow fuel injected aircraft reciprocating engine, is that a plugged fuel injection nozzle will cause a

A — normal operation indication.
B — lower than normal fuel flow indication.
C — higher than normal fuel flow indication.

8259. Answer C. ITP-A2
Most light aircraft equipped with continuous-fuel injection systems utilize a fuel flow indication system that measures the pressure drop across the injection nozzles to determine fuel flow. With this type of system, a higher fuel flow results in a greater pressure drop and a corresponding increase in fuel flow is indicated in the cockpit. However, if an injector nozzle becomes restricted, the pressure drop across the nozzle becomes greater and produces a false or high fuel flow reading (answer C).

8260. **H01**

Motor driven impeller and turbine fuel flow transmitters are designed to transmit data

A — using aircraft electrical system power.
B — mechanically.
C — by fuel pressure.

8261. **H01**

The fuel-flow indicator rotor and needle for a motor-impeller and turbine indicating system is driven by

A — an electrical signal.
B — direct coupling to the motor shaft.
C — a mechanical gear train.

8262. **H01**

On a twin-engine aircraft with fuel-injected reciprocating engines, one fuel-flow indicator reads considerably higher than the other in all engine operating configurations. What is the probable cause of this indication?

A — Carburetor icing.
B — One or more fuel nozzles are clogged.
C — Alternate air door stuck open.

8263. **H01**

The fuel-flow indication system used with many fuel-injected opposed engine airplanes utilizes a measure of

A — fuel flow volume.
B — fuel pressure.
C — fuel flow mass.

8264. **H01**

In addition to fuel quantity, a computerized fuel system (CFS) with a totalizer-indicator provides indication of how many of the following?

1. Fuel flow rate.
2. Fuel used since reset or initial start-up.
3. Fuel time remaining at current power setting.
4. Fuel temperature.

A — Two.
B — Three.
C — Four.

8260. Answer A. AC 65-15A

In an autosyn system installed in the fuel system of turbine engine aircraft, fuel-flow data are transmitted using the aircraft's electrical system. Answers (B) and (C) are incorrect because mechanical connections or fuel lines between an engine and a cockpit indicator would be inaccurate, hazardous, and add unnecessary weight.

8261. Answer A. AC 65-15A

The only fuel flow indicating system that utilizes an impeller and turbine is the synchronous mass flow system. In this type of system both the indicator rotor and needle are driven by an electrical signal. Answers (B) and (C) are incorrect because there is no fuel flow indicating system that is driven directly off a motor shaft or through a mechanical gear train.

8262. Answer B. ITP-A2

Most light twin-engine aircraft utilize a fuel flow indication system that measures the pressure drop across the injection nozzles to determine fuel flow. With this type of system, a higher fuel flow results in a greater pressure drop and a corresponding increase in fuel flow is indicated in the cockpit. However, if an injector nozzle becomes restricted, the pressure drop across the nozzle becomes greater and produces a false or high fuel flow reading. Answer (A) is incorrect because you can not get carburetor icing with a fuel-injected engine, and answer (C) is wrong because, although having an alternate air door stick open will cause a decrease in power output, it will have little effect on fuel flow indications.

8263. Answer B. AC 65-15A

The fuel flow indication used for fuel injected opposed engines is actually a measure of the pressure drop across the fuel injection nozzles. With this type of system, a higher fuel flow creates a greater pressure drop and a corresponding increase in the indicated fuel flow. Answer (A) is incorrect because volume measuring systems (autosyn or vane) are used on large reciprocating engine aircraft and answer (C) is wrong because mass measuring systems are typically used on turbine engine aircraft.

8264. Answer B. ITP-P2

A computerized fuel system (CFS) utilizes a transducer mounted in the fuel line leading to the engine to provide fuel flow in gallons or pounds per hour, gallons or pounds remaining, time remaining for flight at the current power setting, and gallons used since startup or reset. Of the four items listed, three are provided by a CFS.

8265.   H01
The fuel-flow indication data sent from motor driven impeller and turbine, and motorless type fuel flow transmitters is a measure of

A — fuel mass-flow.
B — fuel volume-flow.
C — engine burner pressure drop.

8265. Answer A. AC 65-9A
In both a motor driven impeller and turbine, and a motorless fuel flow indication system a flow meter transmitter converts the fuel's mass-flow rate into electronic signals that produce a fuel flow indication in the cockpit. Answer (B) is incorrect because fuel volume-flow transmitters typically utilize a movable vane, and answer (C) is incorrect because engine burner can pressure is not a monitored engine parameter and, in any case, is only indirectly related to engine fuel flow.

8266.   H01
In an aircraft equipped with a pressure-drop type fuel-flow indicating system, if one of the injector nozzles becomes restricted, this would cause a decrease in fuel flow with

A — a decreased fuel flow indication on the gauge.
B — an increased fuel flow indication on the gauge.
C — no change in fuel flow indication on the gauge.

8266. Answer B. ITP-A2
If an injector nozzle becomes restricted in an aircraft equipped with a pressure-drop type fuel flow indicating system the pressure drop across the nozzle increases and produces a false or high fuel flow indication. Both answers (A) and (C) are wrong because a restricted injector nozzle will not cause a decrease or no change in the fuel flow indication.

8267.   H02
A manifold pressure gauge is designed to

A — maintain constant pressure in the intake manifold.
B — indicate differential pressure between the intake manifold and atmospheric pressure.
C — indicate absolute pressure in the intake manifold.

8267. Answer C. AC 65-12A
A manifold pressure gauge measures the absolute pressure in the induction system of a piston engine. Answer (A) is incorrect because a manifold pressure gauge has no role in maintaining pressure in the intake manifold, and answer (B) is wrong because a manifold pressure gauge indicates absolute pressure, not differential pressure.

8268.   H02
The purpose of an exhaust gas analyzer is to indicate the

A — brake specific fuel consumption.
B — fuel/air ratio being burned in the cylinders.
C — temperature of the exhaust gases in the exhaust manifold.

8268. Answer B.
The purpose of an exhaust gas analyzer is to indicate the fuel/air ratio being burned in the cylinders. It identifies cylinders that are running too rich or too lean, and can be used to fine tune the fuel metering system. Answer (A) is incorrect because brake specific fuel consumption is a calculated measure of the amount of fuel burned for each horsepower produced and cannot be determined by an exhaust gas analyzer. Answer (C) is incorrect because an EGT gauge measures the temperature of the exhaust gases in the exhaust manifold.

8269.   H02
Which of the following types of electric motors are commonly used in electric tachometers?

A — Direct current, series-wound motors.
B — Synchronous motors.
C — Direct current, shunt-wound motors.

8269. Answer B. AC 65-15A
A typical electric tachometer consists of a three-phase generator mounted to the engine that is connected electrically to a three-phase synchronous motor in the tachometer instrument. The engine-mounted generator produces a three-phase current that is sent to the synchronous motor where a rotating field is produced in the stator. The rotating field causes the rotor to turn which, in turn, moves the tachometer's indicating needle. Answers (A) and (C) are incorrect because these types of electric motors are not capable of sending position information since they are primarily used for power.

8270.   H02

Where are the hot and cold junctions located in an engine cylinder temperature indicating system?

A — Both junctions are located at the instrument.
B — Both junctions are located at the cylinder.
C — The hot junction is located at the cylinder and the cold junction is located at the instrument.

8270. Answer C. AC 65-15A

A thermocouple is a circuit of two dissimilar metals connected together at two junctions to form a loop. When there is a temperature difference between the two junctions an electromotive force is produced which can be measured with a galvanometer. Therefore, when a thermocouple temperature indicating system is used on a reciprocating engine, the thermocouple's hot junction is placed at the cylinder whereas the system's cold junction is at the instrument. Answers (A) and (B) are incorrect because a thermocouple must have a temperature differential in order to produce current flow, and there is no temperature difference if both junctions are located in the same place.

8271.   H02

Basically, the indicator of a tachometer system is responsive to change in

A — current flow.
B — frequency.
C — voltage.

8271. Answer B. AC 65-15A

The typical electric tachometer system utilizes a three-phase AC generator coupled to the aircraft engine and connected electrically to a synchronous motor indicator mounted to the instrument panel. The generator transmits three-phase power to the synchronous motor at a frequency that is proportional to the engine speed. The exact frequency determines the motor speed which, in turn, produces the instrument indication. Answers (A) and (C) are incorrect because changing the current or voltage to the tachometer indicator, as long as the values remain within the instrument's operating range, has no effect on the indicator.

8272.   H02

Which statement is correct concerning a thermocouple-type temperature indicating instrument system?

A — It is a balanced-type, variable resistor circuit.
B — It requires no external power source.
C — It usually contains a balancing circuit in the instrument case to prevent fluctuations of the system voltage from affecting the temperature reading.

8272. Answer B. AC 65-15A

Because a thermocouple produces its own milliamp current flow, a temperature indicating system using thermocouples does not require any external power. However, most systems do use external power and an amplifier to improve the response. Answer (A) is incorrect because a thermocouple produces a temperature indication by generating current, not by changing resistance, and answer (C) is wrong because the amplifier circuit in a typical indicator removes any transient voltage signals.

8273.   H02

Which statement is true regarding a thermocouple-type cylinder head temperature measuring system?

A — The resistance required for cylinder head temperature indicators is measured in farads.
B — The voltage output of a thermocouple system is determined by the temperature difference between the two ends of the thermocouple.
C — When the master switch is turned on, a thermocouple indicator will move off-scale to the low side.

8273. Answer B. AC 65-15A

A thermocouple is a circuit of two dissimilar metals connected together at two junctions to form a loop. When there is a temperature difference between the two junctions an electromotive force is produced which can be measured with a galvanometer. The greater the temperature difference the greater the voltage produced. Answer (A) is wrong because resistance is measured in ohms, not farads, and answer (C) is incorrect because turning on the master switch will have no effect on a thermocouple indication system.

8274.   H02
What basic meter is used to indicate cylinder head temperature in most aircraft?

A — Electrodynamometer.
B — Galvanometer.
C — Thermocouple-type meter.

8275.   H02
Which of the following is a primary engine instrument?

A — Tachometer.
B — Fuel flowmeter.
C — Airspeed indicator.

8276.   H02
A complete break in the line between the manifold pressure gauge and the induction system will be indicated by the gauge registering

A — prevailing atmospheric pressure.
B — zero.
C — lower than normal for conditions prevailing.

8277.   H02
Engine oil temperature gauges indicate the temperature of the oil

A — entering the oil cooler.
B — entering the engine.
C — in the oil storage tank.

8278.   H02
Why do helicopters require a minimum of two synchronous tachometer systems?

A — One indicates engine RPM and the other tail rotor RPM.
B — One indicates main rotor RPM and the other tail rotor RPM.
C — One indicates engine RPM and the other main rotor RPM.

8279.   H02
If the thermocouple leads were inadvertently crossed at installation, what would the cylinder temperature gauge pointer indicate?

A — Normal temperature for prevailing condition.
B — Moves off-scale on the zero side of the meter.
C — Moves off-scale on the high side of the meter.

8274. Answer B. AC 65-15A
A thermocouple is a circuit of two dissimilar metals connected together at two junctions to form a loop. When there is a temperature difference between the two junctions an electromotive force is produced which can be measured with a galvanometer.

8275. Answer A. FAR 91.205
On both reciprocating and turbine powered aircraft, the tachometer is the primary engine instrument. On turboprop and turboshaft powered aircraft that utilize a torque meter gauge, it also becomes a primary engine instrument. Answer (B) is wrong because the only fuel instrument considered a primary instrument is a fuel quantity indicator, and answer (C) is incorrect because an airspeed indicator is not an engine instrument.

8276. Answer A. AC 65-12A
A manifold pressure gauge measures the absolute pressure within an engine's intake manifold. However, if a break exists in the line between the manifold pressure gauge and the manifold, the gauge will only be able to display the prevailing atmospheric pressure. Answers (B) and (C) are incorrect because the gauge will still display atmospheric pressure.

8277. Answer B. AC 65-12A
In both wet and dry-sump lubricating systems, the oil temperature bulb is located somewhere in the oil inlet line between the supply tank and the engine. This means the oil temperature gauge in the cockpit indicates the temperature of the oil entering the engine. Neither answer (A) nor (C) is correct because the temperature of the oil entering the oil cooler and in the storage tank are not measured on aircraft.

8278. Answer C. AC 65-15A
Helicopters require a minimum of two tachometers to monitor both the engine rpm and the rotor rpm. Answers (A) and (B) are wrong because the tail rotor is interconnected with the main rotor and, therefore, its speed is directly related to the main rotor rpm.

8279. Answer B. AC 65-15A
A thermocouple type of temperature indicating system produces a current flow in one direction when there is a difference in temperature between the hot junction and the cold junction. Therefore, if the leads to the temperature gauge are reversed, the temperature gauge pointer movement will reverse and the needle will peg out at the meter's zero side.

8280.   H02

A common type of electrically operated oil temperature gauge utilizes

A — either a wheatstone bridge or ratiometer circuit.
B — a thermocouple type circuit.
C — vapor pressure and pressure switches.

8280. Answer A. AC 65-15A

The two types of circuits typically used in electrically operated oil temperature gauges are the wheatstone bridge circuit and the ratiometer circuit. Answer (B) is incorrect because thermocouple indicators are typically used to measure cylinder head temperatures and answer (C) is wrong because vapor pressure oil temperature gauges are not electrically operated.

8281.   H02

The indication on a thermocouple-type cylinder head temperature indicator is produced by

A — resistance changes in two dissimilar metals.
B — a difference in the voltage between two dissimilar metals.
C — a current generated by the temperature difference between dissimilar metal hot and cold junctions.

8281. Answer C. AC 65-12A

A thermocouple is a circuit of two dissimilar metals connected together at two junctions to form a loop. When there is a temperature difference between the two junctions an electromotive force is produced which can be measured with a galvanometer. The greater the temperature difference the greater the voltage produced. Answer (A) is wrong because the resistance of the dissimilar metals does not change, and answer (B) is wrong because there is no voltage "difference" between the two dissimilar metals.

8282.   H02

(1) Powerplant instrument range markings show whether the current state of powerplant operation is normal, acceptable for a limited time, or unauthorized.
(2) Powerplant instrument range markings are based on installed engine operating limits which may not exceed (but are not necessarily equal to) those limits shown on the engine Type Certificate Data Sheet.

Regarding the above statements,

A — both No.1 and No.2 are true.
B — neither No.1 nor No.2 is true.
C — only No.1 is true.

8282. Answer A. AC 65-12A

Both statements (1) and (2) are correct. Powerplant range markings show minimum, continuous, limited, and maximum ranges. These ranges may not exceed the engine's Type Certificate Data Sheet specifications and, in some cases, may be less than those specified.

8283.   H02

Thermocouple leads

A — may be installed with either lead to either post of the indicator.
B — are designed for a specific installation and may not be altered.
C — may be repaired using solderless connectors.

8283. Answer B. AC 65-15A

Thermocouple leads are designed for a specific installation. For example, in order to function properly there must be a specific amount of resistance in the thermocouple circuit. Thus, their length or cross sectional size cannot be altered unless some compensation is made for the change in total resistance. A thermocouple system for a typical turbine engine, for example, has eight ohms of resistance. Answer (A) is incorrect because thermocouple leads are polarized and can only be installed one way. Answer (C) is wrong because thermocouple leads have precise resistances that are matched to each installation and cannot be repaired.

8284.   **H02**

(1) Engine pressure ratio (EPR) is a ratio of the exhaust gas pressure to the engine inlet air pressure, and indicates the thrust produced.

(2) Engine pressure ratio (EPR) is a ratio of the exhaust gas pressure to the engine inlet air pressure, and indicates volumetric efficiency.

Regarding the above statements,

A — only No.1 is true.
B — only No.2 is true.
C — both No.1 and No.2 are true.

8285.   **H02**

What unit in a tachometer system sends information to the indicator?

A — The three-phase ac generator.
B — The two-phase ac generator.
C — The synchronous motor.

8286.   **H02**

(1) Generally, when a turbine engine indicates high EGT for a particular EPR (when there is no significant damage), it means that the engine is out of trim.

(2) Some turbine-powered aircraft use RPM as the primary indicator of thrust produced, others use EPR as the primary indicator.

Regarding the above statements,

A — only No.1 is true.
B — only No.2 is true.
C — both No.1 and No.2 are true.

8287.   **H02**

Engine pressure ratio is determined by

A — multiplying engine inlet total pressure by turbine outlet total pressure.
B — dividing turbine outlet total pressure by engine inlet total pressure.
C — dividing engine inlet total pressure by turbine outlet total pressure.

8284. Answer A. AC 65-12A

Only statement number (1) is correct (answer A). By definition, engine pressure ratio (EPR) is the ratio of the total turbine discharge pressure to the total compressor inlet pressure and indicates the thrust being produced. The EPR reading is displayed in the cockpit on the EPR gauge and is used by the pilot to set the power levers. Statement number (2) is false because EPR does not indicate an engine's volumetric efficiency.

8285. Answer A. AC 65-15A

The typical electric tachometer system uses a three-phase AC generator coupled to the engine to send information to an AC synchronous motor that is attached to the indicator. Answer (B) is wrong because two-phase AC is not used in aircraft tachometers. Answer (C) is incorrect because a synchronous motor is located in the tachometer indicator and receives the signal sent by a three-phase AC generator.

8286. Answer C. AC 65-12A

Both statements (1) and (2) are correct. If a turbojet engine is undamaged and the turbine blades are clean a high exhaust gas temperature (EGT) for a given engine pressure ratio (EPR) identifies an out-of-trim condition. Furthermore, on turbine engines that utilize centrifugal flow compressors, compressor rpm is a direct indication of the thrust being produced. Therefore, on some turbine-powered aircraft, rpm is the primary indicator of the thrust produced.

8287. Answer B. AC 65-12A

Engine pressure ratio (EPR) is the ratio of the total pressure leaving the turbine to the total pressure entering the engine and indicates the amount of thrust produced by an engine. EPR is calculated by dividing the total turbine outlet pressure by the total compressor inlet pressure. Answer (A) is wrong because a ratio is basically a fraction that compares two values, not the product of the two values. Answer (C) is wrong because dividing engine inlet total pressure by turbine outlet total pressure would produce a negative value, which would indicate the engine is producing negative thrust.

8288. **H02**
Jet engine thermocouples are usually constructed of

A — chromel-alumel.
B — iron-constantan.
C — alumel-constantan.

8289. **H02**
Which of the following instrument discrepancies require replacement of the instrument?

1. Red line missing from glass.
2. Glass cracked.
3. Case paint chipped.
4. Will not zero out.
5. Pointer loose on shaft.
6. Mounting screw loose.
7. Leaking at line B nut.
8. Fogged.

A — 2, 3, 7, 8.
B — 2, 4, 5, 8.
C — 1, 2, 4, 7.

8290. **H02**
A Bourdon-tube instrument may be used to indicate

1. pressure.
2. temperature.
3. position.
4. quantity.

A — 1 and 2.
B — 1 and 3.
C — 2 and 4.

8291. **H02**
An indication of unregulated power changes that result in continual drift of manifold pressure indication on a turbosuper-charged aircraft engine is known as

A — Overshoot.
B — Waste gate fluctuation.
C — Bootstrapping.

8288. Answer A. AC 65-15A
The thermocouples used in turbine engines are usually constructed of chromel, a nickel/chromium alloy; and alumel, a nickel/aluminum alloy. These are dissimilar metals which produce a milliamp current flow when heated. Answer (B) is incorrect because iron-constantan thermocouples are used for lower-temperature applications on reciprocating engines and answer (C) is wrong because alumel and constantan are not compatible for use in thermocouples.

8289. Answer B. AC 65-15A
Items 2, 4, 5 and 8 cannot be repaired by a maintenance technician and, therefore, the instrument must be removed from the aircraft and sent to a certified instrument repair station. The remaining items (items 1, 3, 6, and 7) can be repaired by an aviation technician and do not require the removal and replacement of the instrument. Therefore, answer (B) is correct.

8290. Answer A. AC 65-15A
A Bourdon tube is a metal tube that is formed in a circular shape with an oval or flattened cross section and is used to measure both pressure and temperature (answer A). When air or liquid pressure enters the open end of a Bourdon tube, the tube has a tendency to straighten out. By the same token, if a Bourdon tube is filled with a gas and sealed at both ends, changes in temperature will cause the sealed gas to expand and contract thereby causing the tube to move. Through a series of gears, this movement is then used to move an indicating needle.

8291. Answer C. AC 65-12A
Bootstrapping occurs when a turbocharger system senses small changes in temperature or rpm and continually changes the turbocharger output in an attempt to establish an equilibrium. Bootstrapping typically occurs during part-throttle operation and is characterized by a continual drift of manifold pressure. Answer (A) is wrong because overshoot is indicated by an excessive manifold pressure, not a drifting manifold pressure reading. Answer (B) is incorrect because although a fluctuating manifold pressure can be caused by a fluctuating waste gate, the term used to describe this occurrence is bootstrapping

8292.   H02
Which of the following instrument conditions is acceptable and does NOT require immediate correction?

1. Red line missing.
2. Pointer loose on shaft.
3. Glass cracked.
4. Mounting screws loose.
5. Case paint chipped.
6. Leaking at line B nut.
7. Will not zero out.
8. Fogged.

A — 1.
B — 4.
C — 5.

8293.   H02
A change in engine manifold pressure has a direct effect on the

A — piston displacement.
B — compression ratio.
C — mean effective cylinder pressure.

8294.   H02
What instrument on a gas turbine engine should be monitored to minimize the possibility of a "hot" start?

A — RPM indicator.
B — Turbine inlet temperature.
C — Torquemeter.

8295.   H02
In regard to using a turbine engine oil analysis program, which of the following is NOT true?

A — Generally, an accurate trend forecast may be made after an engine's first oil sample analysis.
B — It is best to start an oil analysis program on an engine when it is new.
C — A successful oil analysis program should be run over an engine's total operating life so that normal trends can be established.

8296.   H02
On an aircraft turbine engine operating at a constant power, the application of engine anti-icing will result in

A — noticeable shift in EPR.
B — a false EPR reading.
C — an increase in EPR.

8292. Answer C. AC 65-15A
Chipped paint on an instrument case has no effect on an instrument's operational condition and, therefore, no immediate corrective action is required. Answer (A) is incorrect because a missing red line (item 1) could threaten operating safety and answer (B) is wrong because loose mounting screws (item 4) could subject the instrument to vibration damage. Both items require immediate attention.

8293. Answer C. AC 65-12A
The mean effective cylinder pressure in an engine is the average pressure produced in the combustion chamber during an operating cycle. Therefore, the higher the manifold pressure, the higher the mean effective cylinder pressure.

8294. Answer B. AC 65-12A
A "hot" start is a start in which the turbine temperature exceeds specific limits. To minimize the chance of a hot start the temperature at the turbine should always be monitored when starting a gas turbine engine. Depending on the aircraft, turbine temperature is monitored by watching the turbine inlet temperature, exhaust gas temperature, or interstage gas temperature. Answers (A) and (C) are incorrect because neither the rpm indicator nor the torquemeter will alert you to a hot start.

8295. Answer A. AC 65-12A
Spectrometric Oil Analysis programs must include samples taken at regular intervals and should begin when an engine is new. The ability of an analysis program to predict problems is based on comparing data taken from a number of samples over a known time period. Therefore, an accurate trend forecast cannot be made after an engine's first oil analysis (answer A).

8296. Answer A. TEP2
Inlet anti-ice systems use compressor bleed air to prevent ice formation on inlet ducts. When air is bled off the compressor, less pressure is available at all stations downstream, and EPR drops. Therefore, the application of engine anti-ice will cause a noticeable shift in the EPR indication in the cockpit. Answer (B) is incorrect because the EPR reading with anti-ice activated is accurate and answer (C) is wrong because EPR decreases when anti-ice is activated.

8297.   H02

Engine pressure ratio is the total pressure ratio between the

A — aft end of the compressor and the aft end of the turbine.
B — front of the compressor and the rear of the turbine.
C — front of the engine inlet and the aft end of the compressor.

8298.   H02

What would be the possible cause if a gas turbine engine has high exhaust gas temperature, high fuel flow, and low RPM at all engine power settings?

A — Fuel control out of adjustment.
B — Loose or corroded thermocouple probes for the EGT indicator.
C — Turbine damage or loss of turbine efficiency.

8299.   H02

What is the primary purpose of the tachometer on an axial-compressor turbine engine?

A — Monitor engine RPM during cruise conditions.
B — It is the most accurate instrument for establishing thrust settings under all conditions.
C — Monitor engine RPM during starting and to indicate overspeed conditions.

8300.   H02

The engine pressure ratio (EPR) indicator is a direct indication of

A — engine thrust being produced.
B — pressure ratio between the front and aft end of the compressor.
C — ratio of engine RPM to compressor pressure.

8297. Answer B. AC 65-12A

By definition, engine pressure ratio is the ratio of the total pressure leaving the turbine to the total pressure entering the compressor.

8298. Answer C. AC 65-12A

A possible cause of high EGT, high fuel flow, and low RPM in a gas turbine engine is turbine section damage or loss of turbine efficiency (answer C). The purpose of the turbine blades is to convert the energy from the gases coming off the combustor into rotary motion to drive the compressor. If the turbine is damaged, it won't convert as much energy and the rpm will remain low, the exhaust gas temperature will increase, and the engine will burn more fuel at given rpm settings. Answer (A) is wrong because a fuel control unit out of adjustment could cause high fuel flow, but not high fuel flow and low rpm. Answer (B) is incorrect because although loose or corroded probes for the EGT indicator could cause a high EGT indication, the fact that fuel flow is high and rpm is low eliminate the possibility of a faulty EGT indicator.

8299. Answer C. AC 65-12A

A tachometer on an axial-flow compressor turbine engine is used to monitor the engine during starting and during possible overspeed conditions. However, a tachometer on a centrifugal-flow compressor presents a direct indication of the amount of engine thrust being produced (answer B). Answer (A) is incorrect because the engine pressure ratio gauge is used to monitor engine performance during cruise conditions.

8300. Answer A. AC 65-12A

The engine pressure ratio (EPR) indicator is, for the majority of turbine powered airplanes, the primary indicator of engine thrust (answer A). EPR represents the ratio of the total pressure aft of the turbines to the total pressure at the engine inlet.

8301. H02

The exhaust gas temperature (EGT) indicator on a gas turbine engine provides a relative indication of the

A — exhaust temperature.
B — temperature of the exhaust gases as they pass the exhaust cone.
C — turbine inlet temperature.

8301. Answer C. AC 65-12A

The exhaust gas temperature (EGT) indicator provides a relative indication of the turbine inlet temperature (TIT). Engineers who design an engine know how much heat energy the turbine section will absorb from the gases flowing through it. Therefore, TIT can be calculated as a function of EGT. Answer (A) is wrong because EGT provides direct indication of exhaust gas temperature and answer (B) is incorrect because EGT probes monitor the exhaust temperature at the rear of the turbine section, not the inlet.

8302. H02

What instrument indicates the thrust of a gas turbine engine?

A — Exhaust gas temperature indicator.
B — Turbine inlet temperature indicator.
C — Engine pressure ratio indicator.

8302. Answer C. AC 65-12A

The engine pressure ratio (EPR) indicator is, for the majority of turbine powered airplanes, the primary indicator of engine thrust. EPR represents the ratio of the total pressure aft of the turbines to the total pressure at the engine inlet. Answers (A) and (B) are wrong because temperature readings do not indicate thrust.

8303. H02

In a turbine engine, where is the turbine discharge pressure indicator sensor located?

A — At the aft end of the compressor section.
B — At a location in the exhaust cone that is determined to be subjected to the highest pressures.
C — Immediately aft of the last turbine stage.

8303. Answer C. AC 65-12A

In a gas turbine engine, the turbine discharge pressure sensor is located immediately aft of the last turbine stage. The readings taken from this sensor and the compressor inlet pressure sensor are used to determine the engine pressure ratio. Answer (A) is wrong because it is impossible to monitor turbine discharge pressure at the compressor outlet and answer (B) is wrong because the sensor in the exhaust cone would not allow turbine discharge pressure to be read accurately.

8304. H02

In what units are turbine engine tachometers calibrated?

A — Percent of engine RPM.
B — Actual engine RPM.
C — Percent of engine pressure ratio.

8304. Answer A. AC 65-12A

Gas turbine engine tachometers are usually calibrated in percent rpm. This allows various types of engines to be operated on the same basis of comparison.

8305. H02

Instruments that provide readings of low or negative pressure, such as manifold pressure gauges, are usually what type?

A — Vane with calibrated spring.
B — Bourdon tube.
C — Diaphragm or bellows.

8305. Answer C. AC 65-15A

Typically, instruments that provide low or negative pressure readings utilize a sensitive diaphragm or bellows that expands and contracts to drive an indicator needle. Answer (A) is incorrect because vanes are typically used to measure volume flow or high pressure air flow. Answer (B) is incorrect because the shape of a Bourdon tube does not allow it to accurately indicate low or negative pressures.

8306.   **H02**

Instruments that measure relatively high fluid pressures, such as oil pressure gauges, are usually what type?

A — Vane with calibrated spring.
B — Bourdon tube.
C — Diaphragm or bellows.

8306. Answer B. AC 65-15A

Oil pressure gauges typically utilize a Bourdon tube type indicator. A Bourdon tube is a metal tube that is formed in a circular shape with an oval or flattened cross section. When air or liquid pressure enters the open end of a Bourdon tube, the tube has a tendency to straighten out. Through a series of gears, this movement is used to move an indicating needle. Answer (A) is incorrect because vane type transmitters are used in fluid flow systems and measure volume of flow. Answer (C) is wrong because diaphragm or bellows type indicators are generally used to measure relatively low air pressures.

8307.   **H02**

The RPM indication of a synchronous ac motor-tachometer is governed by the generator

A — voltage.
B — current.
C — frequency.

8307. Answer C. AC 65-15A

Modern AC tachometers utilize a three-phase AC generator coupled to an engine and connected electrically to an indicator mounted in the instrument panel. As an engine runs, the three-phase generator transmits a frequency that is proportional to the engine speed of a synchronous motor mounted to the indicator. The transmitted frequency causes the synchronous motor to turn at a specific rpm and provide a specific indication. Answers (A) and (B) are incorrect because changing voltage or current will have no effect on a synchronous motor tachometer, providing the values of current or voltage do not exceed the operating limits of the instrument.

8308.   **H02**

The EGT gauge used with reciprocating engines is primarily used to furnish temperature readings in order to

A — obtain the best mixture setting for fuel efficiency.
B — obtain the best mixture setting for engine cooling.
C — prevent engine overtemperature.

8308. Answer A. AC 65-15A

The exhaust gas temperature (EGT) gauge provides a pilot with a means of properly adjusting the fuel/air mixture for efficient operation. Answers (B) and (C) are incorrect because the oil temperature and cylinder head temperature gauges are typically used to monitor engine cooling and prevent an overtemperature condition.

8309.   **H02**

A red triangle, dot, or diamond mark on an engine instrument face or glass indicates

A — the maximum operating limit for all normal operations.
B — the maximum limit for high transients such as starting.
C — a restricted operating range.

8309. Answer B. AC 20-88A

A red mark on an instrument face designates the maximum limit for a high transient condition. Answer (A) is incorrect because a red radial line is used to indicate a maximum operating limit, and answer (C) is wrong because a restricted operating range is indicated by a yellow arc.

ENGINE FIRE PROTECTION SYSTEMS

The chapter on fire protection systems describes the different types of fire detection and extinguishing systems used in aircraft powerplants. In addition, it includes information on the inspection, servicing, troubleshooting, and repair of these systems. The FAA exam questions taken from this chapter include:

8310, 8311, 8312, 8313, 8314, 8315, 8316, 8317, 8318, 8319, 8320, 8321, 8322, 8323, 8324, 8325, 8326, 8327, 8328, 8329, 8330, 8331, 8332, 8333, 8334, 8335, 8336, 8337, 8338, 8339, 8340, 8341.

8310.   I01
Which of the following fire detectors are commonly used in the power section of an engine nacelle?

A — CO detectors.
B — Smoke detectors.
C — Rate-of-temperature-rise detectors.

8310. Answer C. AC 65-12A
A typical fire detection system used in reciprocating engine aircraft incorporates a thermocouple system that uses a series of rate-of-temperature-rise detectors. With this type of system a warning will not sound when an engine warms up slowly or when a short circuit develops. However, if temperatures in the engine compartment should rise rapidly, such as when a fire exists, the detectors will sound a warning horn in the cockpit. Answers (A) and (B) are incorrect because neither a CO detector nor a smoke detector is used in engine nacelles.

8311.   I01
What is the function of a fire detection system?

A — To discharge the powerplant fire-extinguishing system at the origin of the fire.
B — To activate a warning device in the event of a powerplant fire.
C — To identify the location of a powerplant fire.

8311. Answer B. AC 65-12A
The function of a fire detection system is to activate a warning device in the event of a powerplant fire. It is important to remember that a fire detection system only warns the pilot of a fire, it does not pinpoint a fire's location (answer C) or try to extinguish it (answer A).

8312.   I01

(Refer to figure 2.) Determine the fire-extinguisher container pressure limits when the temperature is 75 °F.

A — 326 minimum and 415 maximum.
B — 330 minimum and 419 maximum.
C — 338 minimum and 424 maximum.

8312. Answer C. AC 65-12A

Since the question specifies a temperature of 75°C you must interpolate between the minimum and maximum limits for both 70°F and 80°F. To interpolate find the difference between the two readings, divide the difference by two and add the quotient to the lower pressure. The minimum container pressure at 70°F is 319 psig and 356 psig at 80°F. Therefore, the minimum pressure at 75°F is 338 psig (356 – 319 = 37 ÷ 2 = 18.5 + 319 = 337.5). The maximum pressure at 70°F is 405 psig and 443 psig at 80°F. Therefore, the maximum pressure at 75°F is 424 psig (443 – 405 = 38 ÷ 2 = 19 + 405 = 424).

CONTAINER PRESSURE VERSUS TEMPERATURE		
TEMPERATURE °F	CONTAINER PRESSURE (PSIG)	
	MINIMUM	MAXIMUM
−40	60	145
−30	83	165
−20	105	188
−10	125	210
0	145	230
10	167	252
20	188	275
30	209	295
40	230	317
50	255	342
60	284	370
70	319	405
80	356	443
90	395	483
100	438	523

Figure 2.— Fire Extinguisher Pressure Chart.

8313.   I01

How are most aircraft turbine engine fire-extinguishing systems activated?

A — Electrically discharged cartridges.
B — Manual remote control valve.
C — Pushrod assembly.

8313. Answer A. AC 65-12A

In a turbine engine powered aircraft, the fire extinguishing portion of a fire protection system typically includes a cylinder of extinguishing agent for each engine and nacelle area. The container of agent is normally equipped with two discharge valves that are operated by electrically discharged cartridges. The electrical current needed to discharge the cartridges is released by the fire handles in the cockpit. Answers (B) and (C) are incorrect because a high rate discharge extinguishing system used on turbine engines requires an explosive detonator that cannot be triggered manually.

8314.   I01

How does carbon dioxide (CO2) extinguish an aircraft engine fire?

A — Contact with the air converts the liquid into snow and gas which smothers the flame.

B — By lowering the temperature to a point where combustion will not take place.

C — The high pressure spray lowers the temperature and blows out the fire.

8315.   I01

What retains the nitrogen charge and fire-extinguishing agent in a high rate of discharge (HRD) container?

A — Breakable disk and fusible disk.

B — Pressure switch and check tee valve.

C — Pressure gauge and cartridge.

8316.   I01

A continuous-loop fire detector is what type of detector?

A — Spot detector.

B — Overheat detector.

C — Rate-of-temperature-rise detector.

8317.   I01

What is the operating principle of the spot detector sensor in a fire detection system?

A — Resistant core material that prevents current flow at normal temperatures.

B — A conventional thermocouple that produces a current flow.

C — A bimetallic thermoswitch that closes when heated to a high temperature.

8318.   I01

How is the fire-extinguishing agent distributed in the engine section?

A — Spray nozzles and fluid pumps.

B — Nitrogen pressure and slinger rings.

C — Spray nozzles and perforated tubing.

8314. Answer A. AC 65-12A

When liquid CO_2 leaves the fire extinguisher nozzle under pressure, it converts into a gas that extinguishes flame by displacing the oxygen around the flame and smothering it. Answers (B) and (C) are wrong because a CO_2 extinguisher cannot cool a fire sufficiently to extinguish it or simply blow a fire out.

8315. Answer A. AC 65-12A

The nitrogen charge within a typical high rate of discharge container is retained, or held in by a discharge plug and a safety discharge connection. The discharge plug is sealed with a breakable disk combined with an explosive charge that is electrically detonated to discharge the contents of the bottle. The safety discharge connection, or fusible disk, is capped at the inboard side of the engine strut with a red indication disk. If the temperature rises beyond a predetermined safe value, the disk will rupture, dumping the agent overboard.

8316. Answer B. AC 65-12A

A continuous-loop fire detection system consists of a loop of one or two conductors installed around an engine compartment that, when overheated, sends electrical current to a warning indicator in the cockpit. Answer (A) is wrong because a spot detector only senses in one spot, whereas a continuous-loop acts as a detector along its entire length. Answer (C) is incorrect because a continuous-loop system does not detect the rate of temperature rise.

8317. Answer C. AC 65-12A

Spot detector fire detection systems consist of a bimetallic thermoswitch installed between two loops of wire. When the thermoswitch is heated to a predetermined temperature, the switch closes and completes the circuit between the two wire loops. With the circuit completed, electrical current flows to the fire warning horn in the cockpit. Answers (A) and (B) are incorrect because a spot detector contains neither resistant core material nor a thermocouple.

8318. Answer C. AC 65-12A

In a typical engine fire extinguishing system, the extinguishing agent is distributed through spray nozzles and perforated tubing. The perforated tubing distribution system is more common with reciprocating engines, while spray nozzles are typically used with turbine engines. Answer (A) is incorrect because virtually all extinguisher systems use a compressed gas to spray the extinguishing agent onto a fire and answer (B) is wrong because a slinger ring distributes deicing fluid on propellers and has nothing to do with fire extinguishers.

8319.   I01

Which of the following is the safest fire-extinguishing agent to use from a standpoint of toxicity and corrosion hazards?

A — Dibromodifluoromethane (Halon 1202).
B — Bromochlorodifluoromethane (Halon 1211).
C — Bromotrifluoromethane (Halon 1301).

8320.   I01

Which of the following is NOT used to detect fires in reciprocating engine nacelles?

A — Smoke detectors.
B — Rate-of-temperature-rise detectors.
C — Flame detectors.

8321.   I01

What is the principle of operation of the continuous-loop fire detector system sensor?

A — Fuse material which melts at high temperatures.
B — Core resistance material which prevents current flow at normal temperatures.
C — A bimetallic thermoswitch which closes when heated to a high temperature.

8322.   I01

The most satisfactory extinguishing agent for a carburetor or intake fire is

A — carbon dioxide.
B — dry chemical.
C — methyl bromide.

8323.   I01

The explosive cartridge in the discharge valve of a fire-extinguisher container is

A — a life-dated unit.
B — not a life-dated unit.
C — mechanically fired.

8319. Answer C. AC 65-15A

Bromotrifluoromethane (Halon 1301) is one of the most effective fire extinguishing agents. In addition, it is non-toxic and non-corrosive. Both answers (A) and (B) are wrong because Halon 1202 and Halon 1211 are more toxic than Halon 1301. Furthermore, Halon 1202 can be corrosive.

8320. Answer A. AC 65-12A

Some of the common devices used to detect fires on reciprocating engine aircraft include: overheat detectors, rate-of-temperature-rise detectors, flame detectors, and observation by crewmembers. Smoke detectors, on the other hand, are only effective in relatively still air where materials burn slowly or smolder and, therefore, are not used in reciprocating engine nacelles.

8321. Answer B. AC 65-12A

In a continuous-loop fire detection system, an electrical wire or wires are surrounded by a material with a resistance value that prevents the flow of current at normal temperatures. However, when the material is heated, the resistance decreases and allows current within the wires to find a path to ground. This completes the circuit and allows current to flow to the warning horn in the cockpit. Answer (A) is wrong because continuous-loop fire detectors contain no fusible elements and answer (C) is wrong because spot detectors, not loop detectors, utilize bimetallic thermoswitches.

8322. Answer A. AC 65-9A

Carbon dioxide is the most satisfactory agent to use for a carburetor or intake fire and, when used properly, will not damage the engine. Dry chemical (answer B) and methyl bromide (answer C), on the other hand, can cause damage when used to extinguish intake fires.

8323. Answer A. AC 65-15A

The service life of fire extinguisher discharge cartridges is specified by the manufacturer and stated in hours. The service life of a typical discharge cartridge is 5,000 hours. Since discharge cartridges are life-dated units, answer (B) is incorrect. Furthermore, answer (C) is wrong because discharge cartridges are fired electrically, not mechanically.

8324.   I01

Why does one type of Fenwal fire detection system use spot detectors wired in parallel between two separate circuits?

A — To provide an installation that is equal to two separate systems: a primary system and a secondary, or back-up system.

B — So that a double fault may exist in the system without sounding a false alarm.

C — So that a single fault may exist in the system without sounding a false alarm.

8325.   I01

Which of the following fire detection systems measures temperature rise compared to a reference temperature?

A — Thermocouple.

B — Thermal switch.

C — Lindberg continuous element.

8326.   I01

The pulling out (or down) of an illuminated fire handle in a typical large jet aircraft fire protection system commonly accomplishes what events?

A — Closes all firewall shutoff valves, disconnects the generator, and discharges a fire bottle.

B — Closes fuel shutoff, closes hydraulic shutoff, disconnects the generator field, and arms the fire-extinguishing system.

C — Closes fuel shutoff, closes hydraulic shutoff, closes the oxygen shutoff, disconnects the generator field, and arms the fire-extinguishing system.

8324. Answer C. AC 65-12A

The Fenwal fire-detection system utilizes spot detectors that are wired in parallel between two separate circuits so that a short or fault in either leg of the system will not cause a false fire warning. The system is wired so that one leg of the circuit supplies current to the detectors while the other leg serves as a path to ground. If the ground leg should develop a short, a false fire warning will not occur because this portion of the circuit is already grounded. If the powered leg shorts, the rapid increase in current flow will trip a relay which causes the powered leg to become the ground and the grounded leg to become powered. Answer (A) is incorrect because the purpose of the Fenwal system is to prevent false alarms, not to provide a back-up system. Answer (B) is wrong because a double fault renders the fire detection system inoperative.

8325. Answer A. AC 65-12A

The thermocouple fire warning system senses the rate of temperature rise and, therefore, only provides a warning when the temperature increases rapidly. In each thermocouple, there is a cold, or reference junction that is enclosed in an insulated air space and a hot junction which is installed in an uninsulated space. If both of these junctions heat up at the same rate, no fire warning is given regardless of the temperature. However, if the hot junction should be exposed to an extreme amount of heat, a temperature imbalance between the two junctions will exist causing current to flow to the warning horn. Answers (B) and (C) are incorrect because thermal switches and Lindberg continuous element detectors are activated when temperatures reach a maximum level and do not measure a temperature rise.

8326. Answer B. AC 65-12A

When the pilot pulls the fire handle it arms the fire extinguisher system, disconnects the generator field relay, and shuts off the fuel and hydraulics to the engine. Answer (A) is wrong because pulling the fire handle arms the fire bottle but does not fire it, while answer (C) is wrong because the fire handle is not connected to an oxygen shutoff.

8327.   I01

A fire detection system operates on the principle of a buildup of gas pressure within a tube proportional to temperature. Which of the following systems does this statement define?

A — Kidde continuous-loop system.
B — Lindberg continuous-element system.
C — Thermal switch system.

8327. Answer B. AC 65-15A

The Lindberg continuous-element fire detection system is a continuous-element type detector consisting of a stainless steel tube filled with an inert gas, typically helium. The principle of operation is based on the fact that if the volume of the gas is held constant, its pressure will increase as temperature increases. Thus the helium within the enclosed tube will exert a pressure proportional to the temperature along the entire length of the tube. If the pressure within the tube becomes excessive, it mechanically actuates a diaphragm in a responder unit which sets off the fire alarm. The Kidde continuous-loop system (answer A) uses two conductors embedded in a ceramic core; when the ceramic core becomes hot, its resistance changes and current flows between the two conductors. A thermal switch (answer C) uses a bimetallic spring that expands to complete a warning circuit when heated.

8328.   I01

The fire detection system that uses a single wire surrounded by a continuous string of ceramic beads in a tube is the

A — Fenwal system.
B — Kidde system.
C — thermocouple system.

8328. Answer A. AC 65-12A

The Fenwal fire detection system consists of an inconel tube with one wire running through it. The wire carries an electrical potential and the tube is the source to ground. The potential and ground are separated by a core material which, when cold, acts as a resistor. However, when the core material is heated to a specified temperature, it acts as a conductor and allows the potential to find a path to ground. When this circuit is completed, it causes a fire alarm to sound. Answer (B) is wrong because the Kidde fire detection system consists of an inconel tube with two wires running through it. Answer (C) is incorrect because a thermocouple fire detection system consists of two dissimilar metal strips joined at both ends that generate electricity when one junction is hotter than the other.

8329.   I01

The fire detection system that uses two wires imbedded in a ceramic core within a tube is the

A — Fenwal system.
B — Lindberg system.
C — Kidde system.

8329. Answer C. AC 65-12A

The Kidde fire detection system consists of an inconel tube with two wires running through it. One of the wires has a positive electrical potential while the other is a source to ground. The two wires are separated by a core material which, when cold, acts as a resistor. However, when the core material is heated to a specific temperature it acts as a conductor and allows the potential to find a path to ground. Answer (A) is wrong because the Fenwal system consists of an inconel tube with one wire running through it while answer (B) is wrong because the Lindbergh fire detection system consists of a stainless steel tube that is filled with an inert gas.

8330.   I01

A fuel or oil fire is defined as a

A — class B fire.
B — class A fire.
C — class C fire.

8330. Answer A. AC 65-15A

Class B fires involve combustible liquids such as gasoline, engine oil, turbine fuel, hydraulic oil, and many solvents and paint thinners used in aviation maintenance. Answer (B) is incorrect because a class A fire involves ordinary combustible materials such as wood and paper while answer (C) is wrong because a class C fire involves energized electrical equipment.

8331.   **I01**

A fire detection system that operates on the rate-of-temperature rise is a

A — continuous-loop system.
B — thermocouple system.
C — thermal switch system.

8331. Answer B. AC 65-12A

The thermocouple fire warning system senses the rate of temperature rise and, therefore, only provides a warning when the temperature increases rapidly. In each thermocouple, there is a cold, or reference junction that is enclosed in an insulated air space and a hot junction which is installed in an uninsulated space. If both of these junctions heat up at the same rate, no fire warning is given regardless of the temperature. However, if the hot junction should be exposed to an extreme amount of heat, a temperature imbalance between the two junctions will exist causing current to flow to the warning horn. Answers (A) and (C) are incorrect because thermal switches and Lindberg continuous element detectors are activated when temperatures reach a maximum level and do not measure a temperature rise.

8332.   **I01**

A fire involving energized electrical equipment is defined as a

A — class B fire.
B — class D fire.
C — class C fire.

8332. Answer C. AC 65-15A

Class C fires are those which involve electrical equipment. When attempting to extinguish a class C fire, special care must be exercised because of the dangers of electricity, as well as those from the fire itself. Answer (A) is wrong because a class B fire involves flammable liquids such as gasoline or oil and answer (B) is incorrect because a class D fire involves flammable metals such as magnesium.

8333.   **I01**

Two continuous-loop fire detection systems that will not test due to a broken detector element are the

A — Kidde system and the Lindberg system.
B — Kidde system and the Fenwal system.
C — thermocouple system and the Lindberg system.

8333. Answer B. AC 65-15A

Both the Kidde and Fenwal systems are continuous-loop fire detection systems that rely on a complete, unbroken circuit to allow the press-to-test operation to function. However, both systems can experience a break and still give a fire warning.

8334.   **I01**

In a fixed fire-extinguishing system, there are two small lines running from the system and exiting overboard. These line exit ports are covered with a blowout type indicator disc. Which of the following statements is true?

A — When the red indicator disc is missing, it indicates the fire-extinguishing system has been normally discharged.
B — When the yellow indicator disc is missing, it indicates the fire-extinguishing system has been normally discharged.
C — When the green indicator disc is missing, it indicates the fire-extinguishing system has had a thermal discharge.

8334. Answer B. AC 65-15A

In a typical fixed fire extinguishing system, a yellow and a red colored disk are used to indicate the status of the extinguishing agent. The yellow disk blows when the agent has been emptied by a normal discharge (answer B) and the red disk blows when the agent is blown overboard due to an over-temperature condition. Answer (A) is wrong because a missing red disk indicates an overtemperature discharge and answer (C) is wrong because green indicator disks are used as overpressure indicators in oxygen systems.

8335.   **I01**

The most satisfactory extinguishing agent for an electrical fire is

A — carbon tetrachloride.
B — carbon dioxide.
C — methyl bromide.

8336.   **I01**

Which of the following fire detection systems will detect a fire when an element is inoperative but will not test when the test circuit is energized?

A — The Kidde system and the thermocouple system.
B — The Kidde system and the Fenwal system.
C — The thermocouple system and the Lindberg system.

8337.   **I01**

Which of the following fire detection systems uses heat in the normal testing of the system?

A — The thermocouple system and the Lindberg system.
B — The Kidde system and the Fenwal system.
C — The thermocouple system and the Fenwal system.

8338.   **I01**

After a fire is extinguished, or overheat condition removed in aircraft equipped with a Systron-Donner fire detector, the detection system

A — must be manually reset.
B — automatically resets.
C — sensing component must be replaced.

8339.   **I01**

The use of water on class D fires

A — is most effective if sprayed in a fine mist.
B — will cause the fire to burn more violently and can cause explosions.
C — has no effect.

8340.   **I01**

For fire detection and extinguishing purposes, aircraft powerplant areas are divided into fire zones based on

A — hot and cold sections of the engine.
B — the volume and smoothness of the airflow through engine compartments.
C — engine type and size.

8335. Answer B. AC 65-15A

Of the choices given, carbon dioxide is the most satisfactory extinguishing agent for fires involving electrical equipment. However, halogenated hydrocarbon and dry powder extinguishers may also be used. Answers (A) and (C) are incorrect because carbon tetrachloride and methyl bromide are banned from use as extinguishing agents because they become extremely toxic when exposed to heat.

8336. Answer B. AC 65-15A

Both the Kidde and Fenwal systems are continuous-loop fire detection systems that rely on a complete, unbroken circuit to allow the press-to-test operation to function. However, both systems can experience a break and still give a fire warning.

8337. Answer A. AC 65-15A

When testing either the thermocouple or the Lindbergh fire detection systems, heat must be applied to the detectors to simulate a fire condition and sound the warning horn in the cockpit. Answers (B) and (C) are incorrect because Kidde and Fenwal detectors must be provided with a path to ground in order to be tested.

8338. Answer B. ITP-A2

The Systron-Donner fire detector system continuously monitors temperatures and automatically resets after an overheat condition is removed or the fire extinguished. Answer (A) is wrong since the Systron-Donner system automatically resets and answer (C) is wrong because the sensing component is replaced only when it malfunctions, not after every warning.

8339. Answer B. AC 65-9A

A class D fire is one in which some metal, such as magnesium, is burning. Class D fires are put out using dry powder or halogenated extinguishers and under no circumstances should water be used. The application of water to a class D fire will cause the fire to burn more violently and can cause explosions.

8340. Answer B. AC 65-15A

For fire detection and extinguishing purposes, aircraft powerplant areas are divided into fire zones based on the volume and smoothness of airflow passing through the area (answer B). Answers (A) and (C) are incorrect because characteristics such as engine type and size, or whether an area is a hot or cold section have no bearing on the ability of a fire to start and spread.

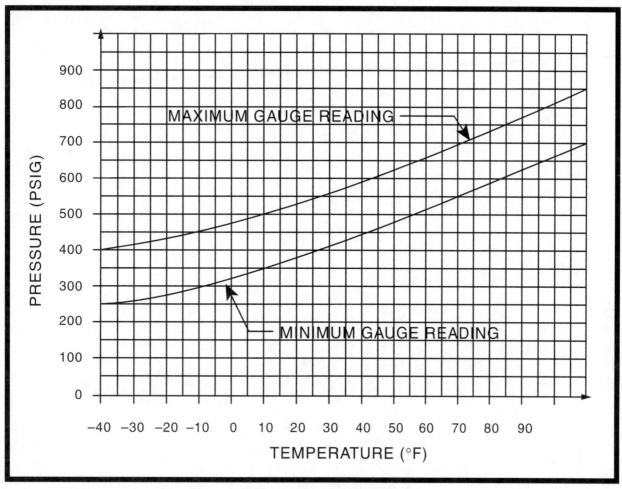

Figure 3.— Fire Extinguisher Pressure Chart.

8341.   I01

(Refer to figure 3.) What are the fire-extinguisher container pressure limits when the temperature is 50 °F?

A — 425 - 575 PSIG.
B — 435 - 605 PSIG.
C — 475 - 625 PSIG.

8341. Answer C. AC 65-12A

To answer this question, begin by locating 50°F at the bottom of the chart. From here, follow the line up to intersect the minimum gauge reading curve. From this intersection, draw a horizontal line to the left that intersects the pressure axis at 475 psig. Next, go back to the 50°F line and follow it up to intersect the maximum gauge reading curve. From this intersection, draw a horizontal line to the left that intersects the pressure axis at 625 psig. Based on this chart, the minimum and maximum container pressure at 50°F is 475 psig and 625 psig respectively.

ENGINE ELECTRICAL SYSTEMS

This chapter describes the components commonly found in engine electrical systems and provides information on the techniques used to inspect and repair these components. In addition, this chapter discusses the maintenance practices used to install, check, and service electrical wiring, controls, switches, indicators, and protective devices. The following FAA exam questions pertain to this chapter:

8342, 8343, 8344, 8345, 8346, 8347, 8348, 8349, 8350, 8351, 8352, 8353, 8354, 8355, 8356, 8357, 8358, 8359, 8360, 8361, 8362, 8363, 8364, 8365, 8366, 8367, 8368, 8369, 8370, 8371, 8372, 8373, 8374, 8375, 8376, 8377, 8378, 8379, 8380, 8381, 8382, 8383, 8384, 8385, 8386, 8387, 8388, 8389, 8390, 8391, 8392, 8393, 8394, 8395, 8396, 8397, 8398, 8399, 8400, 8401, 8402, 8403, 8404, 8405, 8406, 8407, 8408, 8409, 8410.

8342.   J01

What device is used to convert alternating current, which has been induced into the loops of the rotating armature of a dc generator, to direct current?

A — A rectifier.
B — A commutator.
C — An inverter.

8342. Answer B. AC 65-9A

By replacing the slip rings of a basic AC generator with two half-cylinders, called a commutator, DC current is obtained. As the generator's armature rotates, the commutator elements act as a switch causing the current to flow in the same direction through the external circuit. Although a rectifier (answer A) changes AC to DC, rectifiers are not used in DC generators. Answer (C) is incorrect because an inverter changes DC to AC.

8343.   J01

A certain direct current series motor mounted within an aircraft draws more amperes during start than when it is running under its rated load. The most logical conclusion that may be drawn is

A — the starting winding is shorted.
B — the brushes are floating at operating RPM because of weak brush springs.
C — the condition is normal for this type of motor.

8343. Answer C. AC 65-9A

Because the windings in a series motor have such a low resistance, it is normal for these motors to draw a large amount when started. However, when this starting current passes through both the field and armature windings, a high starting torque is produced.

8344.   J01

The stationary field strength in a direct current generator is varied

A — by the reverse-current relay.
B — because of generator speed.
C — according to the load requirements.

8344. Answer C. AC 65-9A

The stationary field strength in a direct-current generator is varied according to the load requirements. For example, as the load increases, the voltage regulator automatically increases the field current to allow the generator to provide the required current load. Answer (A) is incorrect because a reverse-current relay takes the generator off-line when its voltage drops below battery voltage. Answer (B) is wrong because there is no relationship between generator speed and stationary field strength.

8345.   **J01**

What type of electric motor is generally used with a direct-cranking engine starter?

A — Direct current, shunt-wound motor.
B — Direct current, series-wound motor.
C — Synchronous motor.

8345. Answer B. AC 65-12A

A series-wound motor produces the highest torque of any of the motors listed. Furthermore, a typical starter motor is operated by a 12- or 24-volt direct current battery. Therefore, the most common starter found on reciprocating engines is a direct current series-wound motor. Answer (A) is incorrect because shunt motors develop less torque on starting than series-wound motors do. Answer (C) is wrong because synchronous motors produce insufficient torque for starting applications.

8346.   **J01**

Upon what does the output frequency of an ac generator (alternator) depend?

A — The speed of rotation and the strength of the field.
B — The speed of rotation, the strength of the field, and the number of field poles.
C — The speed of rotation and the number of field poles.

8346. Answer C. AC 65-9A

The output frequency of an alternator depends on the rotational speed of the rotor and the number of poles. The faster the rotor turns, the higher the frequency generated. By the same token, the more poles on a rotor, the higher the frequency for any given speed.

8347.   **J01**

A high surge of current is required when a dc electric motor is first started. As the speed of the motor increases,

A — the counter emf decreases proportionally.
B — the applied emf increases proportionally.
C — the counter emf builds up and opposes the applied emf, thus reducing the current flow through the armature.

8347. Answer C. AC 65-9A

When an armature in a motor rotates in a magnetic field, a voltage is induced into the windings that opposes the applied voltage. This back, or counter electromotive force (EMF) increases with motor speed and, therefore, reduces the current flowing through the armature.

8348.   **J01**

Alternators (ac generators) that are driven by a constant-speed drive (CSD) mechanism are used to regulate the alternator to a constant

A — voltage output.
B — amperage output.
C — hertz output.

8348. Answer C. AC 65-9A

Components that utilize alternators (AC generators) as a source for power, require a specific frequency or hertz output to function properly. One way to ensure that an alternator produces a specified frequency is to have the alternator driven by a constant speed drive (CSD) unit. Answers (A) and (B) are incorrect because voltage and amperage output are governed by an alternator regulator.

8349.   **J01**

What is used to polish commutators or slip rings?

A — Very fine sandpaper.
B — Crocus cloth or fine oilstone.
C — Aluminum oxide or garnet paper.

8349. Answer A. AC 65-9A

A rough or pitted commutator should be smoothed using very fine sandpaper, such as 000, and then cleaned and polished with a clean, dry cloth. Answers (B) and (C) are incorrect because these materials can leave conductive grit in the commutator that can cause shorting between commutator segments.

8350.   **J01**

If a generator is malfunctioning, its voltage can be reduced to residual by actuating the

A — rheostat.
B — generator master switch.
C — master solenoid.

8350. Answer B. AC 65-9A

A generator master switch is provided in most aircraft so that a malfunctioning generator may be disconnected from the aircraft electrical system to prevent damage to the generator or to the rest of the system. Operation of this switch deactivates the voltage coil in the voltage regulator, resulting in generator output being reduced to residual voltage.

8351. **J01**

If the points in a vibrator-type voltage regulator stick in the closed position while the generator is operating, what will be the probable result?

A — Generator output voltage will decrease.
B — Generator output voltage will not be affected.
C — Generator output voltage will increase.

8352. **J01**

Why is a constant-speed drive used to control the speed of some aircraft engine-driven generators?

A — So that the voltage output of the generator will remain within limits.
B — To eliminate uncontrolled surges of current to the electrical system.
C — So that the frequency of the alternating current output will remain constant.

8353. **J01**

According to the electron theory of the flow of electricity, when a properly functioning dc alternator and voltage regulating system is charging an aircraft's battery, the direction of current flow through the battery

A — is into the negative terminal and out the positive terminal.
B — is into the positive terminal and out the negative terminal.
C — cycles back and forth with the number of cycles per second being controlled by the rotational speed of the alternator.

8354. **J01**

Aircraft that operate more than one generator connected to a common electrical system must be provided with

A — automatic generator switches that operate to isolate any generator whose output is less than 80 percent of its share of the load.
B — an automatic device that will isolate nonessential loads from the system if one of the generators fails.
C — individual generator switches that can be operated from the cockpit during flight.

8355. **J01**

The most effective method of regulating aircraft direct current generator output is to vary, according to the load requirements, the

A — strength of the stationary field.
B — generator speed.
C — number of rotating armature loops in use.

8351. Answer C. AC65-9A

The opening and closing of the points in a vibrating-type voltage regulator controls the generator output. When the points are open, generator output decreases and when the points are closed, generator output increases. Therefore, if the points stick closed, the generator's output will increase to its maximum.

8352. Answer C. AC 65-9A

Components that utilize alternators (AC generators) as a source of power require a specific frequency or number of cycles per second to function properly. One way to ensure that an alternator produces a specified frequency is to have the alternator driven by a constant speed drive (CSD) unit. Answers (A) and (B) are incorrect because voltage and amperage output are governed by an alternator regulator.

8353. Answer A. AC 65-9A

The electron theory of the flow of electricity states that the flow of electrons is from negative to positive. When this theory is applied to a charging battery, the current flow through the battery is from the negative terminal to the positive terminal. The theory of conventional flow states that electrons flow from the positive terminal to the negative terminal (answer B) and is generally considered incorrect. Answer (C) is incorrect because DC electricity does not cycle back and forth nor does it have a frequency that varies with alternator rotational speed.

8354. Answer C. FAR 25.1351

According to FAR 25.1351, aircraft equipped with more than one generator connected to a common electrical system must have individual generator switches which can be operated from the cockpit during flight.

8355. Answer A. AC 65-9A

Although all of the choices listed can be used to regulate generator output, varying the strength of the stationary field is the most effective and convenient means.

8356. **J01**
Electric motors are often classified according to the method of connecting the field coils and armature. Aircraft engine starter motors are generally of which type?

A — Compound.
B — Series.
C — Shunt (parallel).

8357. **J01**
As the generator load is increased (within its rated capacity), the voltage will

A — decrease and the amperage output will increase.
B — remain constant and the amperage output will increase.
C — remain constant and the amperage output will decrease.

8358. **J01**
As the flux density in the field of a dc generator increases and the current flow to the system increases, the

A — generator voltage decreases.
B — generator amperage decreases.
C — force required to turn the generator increases.

8359. **J01**
What is the purpose of a reverse-current cutout relay?

A — It eliminates the possibility of reversed polarity of the generator output current.
B — It prevents fluctuations of generator voltage.
C — It opens the main generator circuit whenever the generator voltage drops below the battery voltage.

8360. **J01**
Generator voltage will not build up when the field is flashed and solder is found on the brush cover plate. These are most likely indications of

A — an open armature.
B — excessive brush arcing.
C — armature shaft bearings overheating.

8356. Answer B. AC 65-12A
Of the types of motors listed, the series-wound motor develops the most torque. Therefore, series motors are generally used as starter motors.

8357. Answer B. AC 65-9A
Generators are designed to operate at a specified voltage while generator ratings are usually given as the number of amperes a generator can supply at its rated voltage. Therefore, as the load on a generator increases, the amperage output increases up to the generator's limit, while the voltage remains constant. Answers (A) and (C) are incorrect because a voltage regulator maintains a constant output voltage and varies current to meet the load demand. In other words, as load demand rises, amperage output increases.

8358. Answer C. AC 65-15A
The greater the flux density in the field of a generator the greater the resistance to rotation. The greater the resistance to rotation the greater the force required to turn the generator (answer C). Answers (A) and (B) are wrong because both output voltage and current increase when field current increases.

8359. Answer C. AC 65-9A
The purpose of the reverse-current cutout relay is to automatically disconnect the battery from the generator when generator output voltage is less than battery voltage. This prevents the battery from discharging through the generator and trying to drive it as a motor. Answer (A) is incorrect because polarity is a function of a generator's internal wiring and commutator design, while answer (B) is wrong because eliminating voltage fluctuation is a function of the voltage regulator.

8360. Answer A. AC 65-9A
If voltage does not build when a generator's field is flashed, check for an open armature. To do this, remove the generator cover and inspect the commutator cover. If melted solder is found, then the armature is open. Answer (B) is wrong because brush arcing leads to commutator pitting and excessive brush wear and does not prevent voltage build up in the field. Answer (C) is wrong because armature shaft bearings contain no solder and defective bearings are not likely to prevent voltage from building.

8361.   J01

Why is it unnecessary to flash the field of the exciter on a brushless alternator?

A — The exciter is constantly charged by battery voltage.
B — Brushless alternators do not have exciters.
C — Permanent magnets are installed in the main field poles.

8361. Answer C. AC 65-9A

A brushless alternator utilizes permanent magnet interpoles in the exciter stator to provide enough magnetic flux to start producing electricity. Therefore, there is no need to flash the field to put residual magnetism into the field frame. Answer (A) is incorrect because the exciter of a brushless alternator receives direct current from the GCU, not from the battery, and answer (B) is wrong because brushless alternators do have exciter units.

8362.   J01

One way that the automatic ignition relight systems are activated on gas turbine engines is by a

A — drop in compressor discharge pressure.
B — sensing switch located in the tailpipe.
C — drop in fuel flow.

8362. Answer A. ITP-P2

The automatic ignition relight system is activated differently on different aircraft. One popular method of activating the system is to use pressure sensors installed at the compressor discharge. When used this way, a drop in discharge pressure automatically activates the ignition system. Answer (B) is wrong because the only sensor in a turbine engine exhaust pipe measures exhaust gas temperature, and answer (C) is incorrect because power lever movements from the cockpit can produce fuel flow drops that do not require an ignition relight.

8363.   J01

How are the rotor windings of an aircraft alternator usually excited?

A — By a constant ac voltage from the battery.
B — By a constant ac voltage.
C — By a variable direct current.

8363. Answer C. AC 65-9A

In most brush-type alternators, the rotor winding is excited by direct current supplied by the battery and varied by a regulator. When the alternator load increases, the regulator supplies more current to the rotor windings and when the load decreases, less current is supplied. Answers (A) and (B) are incorrect because if an alternator's rotor windings were supplied with constant voltage, the output would be constant regardless of load requirements.

8364.   J01

What precaution is usually taken to prevent electrolyte from freezing in a lead acid battery?

A — Place the aircraft in a hangar.
B — Remove the battery and keep it under constant charge.
C — Keep the battery fully charged.

8364. Answer C. AC 65-9A

As the specific gravity of the electrolyte solution within a battery rises, its freezing point drops. Therefore, in cold climates, the state of charge in a storage battery should be kept at a maximum so it does not freeze. Answers (A) and (B) are impractical and wasteful and, therefore, should be avoided.

8365.   J01

What is the ampere-hour rating of a storage battery that is designed to deliver 45 amperes for 2.5 hours?

A — 112.5 ampere-hour.
B — 90.0 ampere-hour.
C — 45.0 ampere-hour.

8365. Answer A. AC 65-9A

The capacity of a storage battery is rated in ampere-hours which is the amount of electricity that can be taken out of a battery when a current of one ampere flows for one hour. This rating indicates the minimum amount of amperes that a battery can put out in one hour. Therefore, a battery which can deliver 45 amps for 2.5 hours has a 112.5 ampere-hour capacity (45 amps × 2.5 hours = 112.5 amp-hours).

8366.   **J01**

How many hours will a 140 ampere-hour battery deliver 15 amperes?

A — 1.40 hours.
B — 9.33 hours.
C — 14.0 hours.

8366. Answer B. AC 65-9A

The capacity of a storage battery is rated in ampere-hours which is the amount of electricity that can be taken out of a battery when a current of one ampere flows for one hour. This rating indicates the minimum amount of amperes that a battery can put out in one hour. Therefore, a battery that can supply 140 amperes in one hour can deliver 15 amps for 9.33 hours (140 amp-hour ÷ 15 amps = 9.33 hours).

8367.   **J01**

What is a basic advantage of using ac for electrical power for a large aircraft?

A — AC systems operate at higher voltage than dc systems and therefore use less current and can use smaller and lighter weight wiring.
B — AC systems operate at lower voltage than dc systems and therefore use less current and can use smaller and lighter weight wiring.
C — AC systems operate at higher voltage than dc systems and therefore use more current and can use smaller and lighter weight wiring.

8367. Answer A. AC 65-9A

Electrical power is the product of voltage and current. Since direct current systems produce low voltage, the corresponding current must be large enough to produce sufficient power to sustain heavy electrical loads. As a result, conductors carrying direct current must be large and heavy to carry the high current. Alternating current, on the other hand, utilizes much higher voltages and, therefore, lower currents. Since low current can be carried in smaller wire, the use of AC power on large aircraft produces substantial weight savings. Answer (B) is wrong because a lower voltage would require higher current to produce the same power, and answer (C) is incorrect because systems operating at higher voltages use less current.

8368.   **J01**

What are two types of ac motors that are used to produce a relatively high torque?

A — Shaded pole and shunt field.
B — Shunt field and single phase.
C — Three-phase induction and capacitor start.

8368. Answer C. AC 65-9A

The most common AC motors that produce a relatively high torque are the three-phase induction motor and the capacitor start motor. Answers (A) and (B) are incorrect because shunt field motors are powered by direct current.

8369.   **J01**

(1) Alternators are rated in volt-amps, which is a measure of the apparent power being produced by the generator.
(2) Alternating current has the advantage over direct current in that its voltage and current can easily be stepped up or down.

Regarding the above statements,

A — only No. 1 is true.
B — only No. 2 is true.
C — both No. 1 and No. 2 are true.

8369. Answer C. AC 65-9A

Both statements (1) and (2) are correct. Alternating current is used on large aircraft to take advantage of the weight savings and the fact that AC can be easily stepped up or down. The alternators used in these systems are rated in volt-amps which are generally expressed in kilo-volt amps (KVA). A typical Boeing 727 AC alternator is rated at 45 KVA.

8370.   **J01**

What is the frequency of most aircraft alternating current?

A — 115 Hertz.
B — 60 Hertz.
C — 400 Hertz.

8370. Answer C. AC 65-9A

Most aircraft systems use 400-hertz alternating current. At this high frequency, inductive reactance is high and current is low. As a result, motors can be wound with smaller wire, and transformers can be made much smaller and lighter. The use of 115-Hz AC (answer A) or 60-Hz AC (answer B) on aircraft is not desirable since it would require heavier wire to safely carry higher amperages.

8371.   J01

The reason for flashing the field in a generator is to

A — restore correct polarity and/or residual magnetism to the field poles.
B — increase generator capacity.
C — remove excessive deposits.

8371. Answer A. AC 65-9A

Generators use field coils wrapped around soft iron cores to produce the magnetic field required to generate current. Soft iron retains little or no residual magnetism when the magnetizing field is removed. As a result, generator fields must be flashed to restore residual magnetism. Answers (B) and (C) are incorrect because flashing the generator field does not increase generator capacity or remove deposits from the field coils.

8372.   J01

The part of a dc alternator power system that prevents reverse flow of current from the battery to the alternator is the

A — reverse current relay.
B — voltage regulator.
C — rectifier.

8372. Answer C. AC 65-9A

An alternator uses solid-state diodes in its rectifier circuit. These diodes act as electrical check valves and allow current to only flow in one direction. This isolates battery current from the alternator. Reverse current relays (answer A) are used only with DC generators and voltage regulators (answer B) supply current to the field to match the generator's output current to load demand.

8373.   J01

The generating system of an aircraft charges the battery by using

A — constant current and varying voltage.
B — constant voltage and varying current.
C — constant voltage and constant current.

8373. Answer B. AC 65-9A

A typical aircraft generating system produces a constant voltage that supplies power to the primary bus and charges the battery. This type of system utilizes a fixed voltage that is slightly higher than the battery voltage. Answer (A) is incorrect because a constant current charge is typically supplied by a battery charger and answer (C) is wrong because the current supplied by an aircraft charging system does not produce a constant current.

8374.   J01

The constant current method of charging a ni-cad battery

A — will bring it up to fully charged in the shortest amount of time.
B — will lead to cell imbalance over a period of time.
C — is the method most effective in maintaining cell balance.

8374. Answer C. AC 65-9A

A ni-cad battery can be charged using either the constant current or constant voltage method. With the constant current method the charge takes longer but is more effective in maintaining cell balance. Answer (A) is incorrect because constant-voltage charging is the fastest method for charging a battery, and answer (B) is wrong because the constant voltage method tends to lead to cell imbalance.

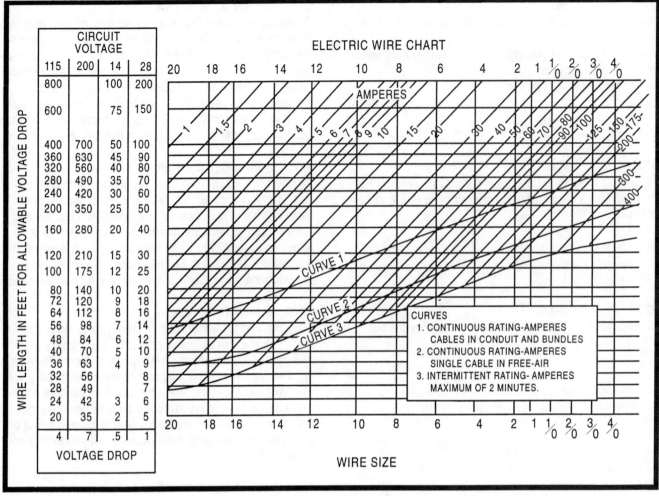

Figure 4.— Electric Wire Chart.

8375.   J02
(Refer to figure 4.) The following data concerning the installation of an electrical unit is known: current requirements for continuous operation – 11 amperes; measured cable length – 45 feet; system voltage – 28 volts (do not exceed 1 volt drop); cable in conduit and bundles. What is the minimum size copper electrical cable that may be selected?

A — No.10.
B — No.12.
C — No.14.

8376.   J02
Which of the following aircraft circuits does NOT contain a fuse/circuit breaker?

A — Generator circuit.
B — Air-conditioning circuit.
C — Starter circuit.

8375. Answer B. AC 43.13-1A
First, locate the column on the left side of the chart representing a 28V system with a 1 volt drop. Move down this column to a wire length of 45 feet, which is between the 40 and 50 foot callouts. From this point, project a line to the right just beyond the 10 amp diagonal line. Since this point is above curve 1, installation in a bundle carrying continuous current is permitted. Now, project a line down vertically to the bottom of the chart. The line falls on the #12 wire size. Therefore, a #12 wire is required.

8376. Answer C. AC 65-9A
An aircraft starter circuit does not have a fuse or circuit breaker because the current draw is so great that a fuse or circuit breaker would continually be blowing. Although generator circuits (answer A) and air conditioning circuits (answer B) draw high amperages, they use considerably less current than a starter and, therefore, use circuit breakers or fuses to protect the aircraft wiring.

8377.   J02

The maximum number of terminals that may be connected to any one terminal stud in an aircraft electrical system is

A — two.
B — three.
C — four.

8378.   J02

What is the maximum number of bonding jumper wires that may be attached to one terminal grounded to a flat surface?

A — Two.
B — Three.
C — Four.

8379.   J02

As a general rule, starter brushes are replaced when they are approximately

A — one-half their original length.
B — one-third their original length.
C — two-thirds their original length.

8380.   J02

When installing an electrical switch, under which of the following conditions should the switch be derated from its nominal current rating?

A — Conductive circuits.
B — Capacitive circuits.
C — Direct-current motor circuits.

8381.   J02

The resistance of the current return path through the aircraft is always considered negligible, provided the

A — voltage drop across the circuit is checked.
B — generator is properly grounded.
C — structure is adequately bonded.

8377. Answer C. AC 43.13-1A

According to AC 43.13-1A, no more than four terminals can be attached to a single terminal stud. If more than four terminals must be attached, use two adjacent studs connected by a small metal bus strap.

8378. Answer C. AC 43.13-1A

According to AC 43.13-1A, no more than four bonding jumper wires should be attached to one terminal that is grounded to a flat surface. If more than four jumper wires are used, a proper ground may not be obtained.

8379. Answer A. AC 65-12A

Manufacturers specify the exact wear limits for their parts. However, as a general rule, starter brushes should be replaced when they are worn to approximately one-half of their original length. Allowing the wear to progress much farther will affect the spring tension and the ability of the brush to stay in contact with the commutator.

8380. Answer C. AC 65-12A

Electrical switches should be derated from their nominal current rating when they are used to control direct current motors. The reason for this is that DC motors will draw several times their rated current during starting. Therefore, if the switch is not derated, it will not have enough of a safety factor to prevent overloading. Answer (A) is incorrect since all circuits are "conductive" and answer (B) is wrong because capacitive circuits do not draw high amperage and thus do not require derated switches.

8381. Answer C. AC 65-12A

One of the purposes of bonding and grounding an aircraft structure is to provide current return paths. If the bonding and grounding is properly done, there should be virtually no resistance in the return path. Bonding is accomplished using bonding straps and braids. Answers (A) and (B) are incorrect because neither a circuit's voltage drop nor the generator's grounding has any bearing on an aircraft's current return path resistance.

8382. J02

In order to reduce the possibility of ground shorting the circuits when the connectors are separated for maintenance, the AN and MS electrical connectors should be installed with the

A — socket section on the ground side of the electrical circuit.
B — pin section on the ground side of the electrical circuit.
C — pin section on the positive side of the electrical circuit.

8382. Answer B. AC 65-12A

AN and MS electrical connectors consist of a female socket and a male connector with a set of pins. When installing an electrical connector, the socket should be installed on the voltage side while the pin section should be attached to the ground side. When assembled this way, the recessed sockets make it extremely difficult to short or ground a circuit. Answers (A) and (C) are incorrect because installing the socket on the ground side and the pin section on the hot side will increase the possibility of shorting.

8383. J02

When does current flow through the coil of a solenoid-operated electrical switch?

A — Continually, as long as the aircraft's electrical system master switch is on.
B — Continually, as long as the control circuit is complete.
C — Only until the movable points contact the stationary points.

8383. Answer B. AC 65-9A

In a solenoid-operated electrical switch, part of the core is movable and is spring loaded open. When the control circuit to the solenoid is completed, a magnetic field pulls the solenoid closed. This completes the primary circuit. When power is removed from the control circuit the magnetic field dissipates causing the movable core to return to its original position and open the circuit. Therefore, as long as the control circuit is complete, current will flow through the coil and the switch will close. Although some solenoid-operated electrical switches are actuated by an aircraft's master switch (answer A), many switches have separate control circuits that must be complete before the solenoid closes. Answer (C) is incorrect because current flows through the coil when the movable points contact the stationary points, not when the points are separated.

8384. J02

It is necessary to determine that the electrical load limit of a 28-volt, 75-amp generator, installed in a particular aircraft, has not been exceeded. By making a ground check, it is determined that the battery furnished 57 amperes to the system when all equipment that can continuously draw electrical power in flight is turned on. This type of load determination

A — can be made, but the load will exceed the generator load limit.
B — can be made, and the load will be within the generator load limit.
C — cannot be made on direct current electrical systems.

8384. Answer B. AC 43.13-1A

The electrical load check described in this question is an acceptable method for determining an aircraft's total electrical load. According to AC 43.13-1A, unless the aircraft is placarded or contains monitoring devices, the total continuous electrical load may be held to approximately 80% of the total rated generator output capacity. The total load on the system is only 76 percent of the generator's capacity. Therefore, the load is considered to be within the generator's load limit.

8385. J02

What type of lubricant may be used to aid in pulling electrical wires or cables through conduits?

A — Silicone grease.
B — Soapstone talc.
C — Rubber lubricant.

8385. Answer B.

Prior to pulling electrical wires or cables through conduit, soapstone talc is dusted on the cables to act as a lubricant. The talc helps keep the wire from binding and chafing against the walls of the conduit. Answer (A) is incorrect because silicon grease can cause some types of insulation to soften and deteriorate. Answer (C) is wrong because rubber lubricants consist of highly viscous grease that will not assist in cable insertion.

8386. J02

Which of the following is regulated in a generator to control its voltage output?

A — Speed of the armature.
B — Number of windings in the armature.
C — The strength of the field.

8387. J02

Bonding jumpers should be designed and installed in such a manner that they

A — are not subjected to flexing by relative motion of airframe or engine components.
B — provide a low electrical resistance in the ground circuit.
C — prevent buildup of a static electrical charge between the airframe and the surrounding atmosphere.

8388. J02

When the starter switch to the aircraft gas turbine engine starter-generator is energized and the engine fails to rotate, one of the probable causes would be the

A — power lever switch is defective.
B — undercurrent solenoid contacts are defective.
C — starter solenoid is defective.

8389. J02

Arcing at the brushes and burning of the commutator of a motor may be caused by

A — weak brush springs.
B — excessive brush spring tension.
C — low mica.

8390. J02

The maximum allowable voltage drop between the generator and the bus bar is

A — 1 percent of the regulated voltage.
B — 2 percent of the regulated voltage.
C — less than the voltage drop permitted between the battery and the bus bar.

8386. Answer C. AC 65-9A

Although all of the choices listed can be used to regulate generator output, varying the strength of the stationary field is the most effective and convenient means. Answer (A) is incorrect because a generator's armature speed is not easily changed and answer (B) is wrong because an armature's number of windings is fixed and cannot be changed.

8387. Answer B. AC 65-12A

One of the purposes of bonding jumpers is to provide a ground for electrical circuits. If the bonding and grounding is properly done, there should be virtually no resistance in the return path. Some guidelines to follow when attaching bonding jumpers is to make them as short as possible and install them in such a manner that the resistance of each connection does not exceed 0.003 ohm. Answer (A) is incorrect because flexible jumpers are often used to ground movable objects such as flight control surfaces. Answer (C) is wrong because bonding jumpers do not prevent static buildup on airframe surfaces but instead provide a conductive path for static electricity to follow so it can be dissipated at the static dischargers.

8388. Answer C.

Although the FAA does not list a figure to refer to for this question, it may be helpful to use figure 5 on page 8-29 of this book. When the master switch is on and the start switch is placed in the start position, power is supplied to the starter generator. However, if the starter solenoid is defective, the starter will not rotate. Answers (A) and (B) are incorrect because the starter should rotate regardless of the condition of the power lever switch or the undercurrent solenoid

8389. Answer A. AC 65-9A

Weak or worn brush springs allow the brushes to bounce, resulting in arcing and burned or pitted commutator surfaces. Answer (B) is incorrect because excessive spring pressure causes rapid wear of the brushes, and answer (C) is wrong because low mica would have little or no effect on the commutator.

8390. Answer B. AC 43.13-1A

According to AC 43.13-1A, the voltage drop in the main power wires from the generator or the battery to the bus should not exceed 2 percent of the regulated voltage when the generator is carrying rated current or the battery is being discharged at the 5-minute rate. Restricting the voltage drop to 1 percent (answer A) is impractical and answer (C) is incorrect because the permitted voltage drop between the battery and the bus bar is the same as that for the generator.

8391.   J02
ON-OFF two position engine electrical switches should be installed

A — so that the toggle will move in the same direction as the desired motion of the unit controlled.
B — under a guard.
C — so the ON position is reached by a forward or upward motion.

8392.   J02
When selecting an electrical switch for installation in an aircraft circuit utilizing a direct current motor,

A — a switch designed for dc should be chosen.
B — a derating factor should be applied.
C — only switches with screw-type terminal connections should be used.

8393.   J02
When installing electrical wiring parallel to a fuel line, the wiring should be

A — in metal conduit.
B — in a non-conductive fire-resistant sleeve.
C — above the fuel line.

8394.   J02
(Refer to figure 4.) In a 28-volt system, what is the maximum continuous current that can be carried by a single No.10 copper wire 25 feet long, routed in free air?

A — 20 amperes.
B — 35 amperes.
C — 28 amperes.

8391. Answer C. AC 43.13-1A
Hazardous errors in switch operation can be avoided by logical and consistent installation. For example, when two-position on-off switches are installed, they should always be mounted so that the on position is reached by a forward or upward movement. Furthermore, when a switch controls movable aircraft elements such as landing gear or flaps, the switch should move in the same direction as the desired motion. Answer (A) is incorrect because it is impractical to install engine switches so their toggles move in the same direction as the unit controlled, and answer (B) is incorrect because switch guards are reserved for switches that control critical systems.

8392. Answer B. AC 43.13-1A
Switches should be derated from their nominal current rating when they are used to control direct current motors, inductive circuits, and high in-rush circuits. The reason for this is that these types of circuits can draw several times their rated current when closed, so the switch must be capable of handling this without the contacts burning or welding together. Answer (A) is wrong because switches can be used with direct or alternating current interchangeably, and answer (C) is incorrect because a switches' terminal connectors have no bearing on whether it is used with an AC or DC motor.

8393. Answer C. AC 43.13-1A
An arcing fault between an electric wire and a metallic fluid line can puncture the line and result in a serious fire. Consequently, every effort should be made to physically separate electrical wire from lines or equipment containing oil, fuel, hydraulic fluid, or alcohol. When separation is impractical, locate the electric wire above the flammable fluid line and securely clamp it to the structure. When installed in this manner, a leaking fluid line is less likely to drip onto the electrical wire and ignite.

8394. Answer B. AC 65-15A
Begin by locating the 28-volt column on the left side of the chart. Move down this column until you hit the number 25 which represents the wire length. From here, move horizontally left until you intersect the vertical line representing No. 10 copper wire. Since this intersection is above curve 2, the wire can carry a continuous current in free air. To determine the maximum continuous current that can be carried, interpolate between the 30 amp and 40 amp diagonal lines. The answer is 35 amperes.

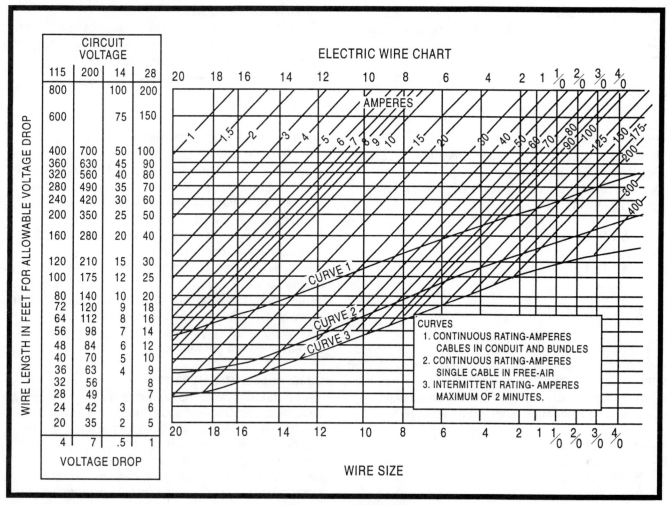

Figure 4.— Electric Wire Chart.

8395.   **J02**

What speed must an eight-pole ac generator turn to produce 400-Hertz ac?

A — 400 RPM.
B — 1,200 RPM.
C — 6,000 RPM.

8395. Answer C. AC 65-9A

The frequency of AC produced by an AC generator is determined by the number of poles and the speed of the rotor and can be calculated using the formula:

$$F = (P \div 2) \times (N \div 60)$$

Where:

F = frequency of the AC in Hertz
P = number of poles in the rotating field
N = rotational speed of the generator in rpm.

To solve for N, the formula becomes:

$$N = (F \times 60) \div (P \div 2)$$

Therefore:

$$N = 400 \text{ hz} \times 60 \text{ seconds} \div 8 \div 2$$
$$N = 24,000 \text{ hz/second} \div 4$$
$$N = 6,000 \text{ rpm}$$

8396.   J02
How many basic types of circuit breakers are used in powerplant installation electrical systems?

A — Two.
B — Three.
C — Four.

8396. Answer B. JSGT
The three basic types of circuit breakers used in aircraft electrical systems are the push-to-reset type, the push/pull type, and the toggle type.

8397.   J02
Which Federal Aviation Regulation specifies that each resettable circuit protective device requires a manual operation to restore service after the device has interrupted the circuit?

A — FAR Part 23.
B — FAR Part 43.
C — FAR Part 91.

8397. Answer A. FAR 23.1357
FAR Part 23, Airworthiness Standards: Normal, Utility, Acrobatic, and Commuter Category Airplanes, specifies the airworthiness standards for the issue of type certificates. Within this part, FAR 23.1357 states that each resettable circuit protection device requires a manual operation to restore service after the device has interrupted the circuit. Answer (B) is incorrect because FAR Part 43, Maintenance, Preventive Maintenance, Rebuilding, and Alteration, describes the regulations governing aircraft maintenance and repair. Answer (C) is incorrect because Part 91, General Operating and Flight Rules, gives rules and procedures for aircraft operations.

8398.   J02
Which Federal Aviation Regulation requirement prevents the use of automatic reset circuit breakers?

A — FAR Part 21.
B — FAR Part 23.
C — FAR Part 91.

8398. Answer B. FAR 23.1357
FAR Part 23, Airworthiness Standards: Normal, Utility, Acrobatic, and Commuter Category Airplanes, specifies the airworthiness standards for the issue of type certificates. Within this part, FAR 23.1357 states that each resettable circuit protection device (trip free device in which the tripping mechanism cannot be overridden by the operating control) must be designed so that:

1. A manual operation is required to restore service after tripping; and
2. If an overload or circuit fault exists, the device will open the circuit regardless of the position of the operating control.

Answer (A) is incorrect because Part 21, Certification Procedures for Products and Parts, describes procedures to obtain an airworthiness certificate for aircraft. Answer (C) is incorrect because Part 91, General Operating and Flight Rules, gives rules and procedures for aircraft operations.

8399.   J02
The time/current capacities of a circuit breaker or fuse must be

A — above those of the associated conductor.
B — equal to those of the associated conductor.
C — below those of the associated conductor.

8399. Answer C. AC 43.13-1A
A circuit breaker or fuse should open a circuit before the associated conductor reaches its maximum capacity. To accomplish this, the time/current characteristics of the protective device must fall below that of the associated conductor. Answers (A) and (B) are wrong because a protective device with a capacity equal to or higher than the conductor's could expose the conductor to excessive current and cause it to fail.

8400.   J02
(1) Most modern aircraft use circuit breakers rather than fuses to protect their electrical circuits.
(2) Federal Aviation Regulations Part 23 requires that all electrical circuits incorporate some form of circuit protective device.

Regarding the above statements,

A — only No. 1 is true.
B — only No. 2 is true.
C — both No. 1 and No. 2 are true.

8401.   J02
Electrical switches are rated according to the

A — voltage and the current they can control.
B — resistance rating of the switch and the wiring.
C — resistance and the temperature rating.

8402.   J02
Electrical circuit protection devices are installed primarily to protect the

A — switches.
B — units.
C — wiring.

8403.   J02
(1) Electrical circuit protection devices are rated based on the amount of current that can be carried without overheating the wiring insulation.
(2) A "trip-free" circuit breaker makes it impossible to manually hold the circuit closed when excessive current is flowing.

Regarding the above statements,

A — only No. 1 is true.
B — only No. 2 is true.
C — both No. 1 and No. 2 are true.

8404.   J02
Which of the following Federal Aviation Regulations require that all aircraft using fuses as the circuit protective devices carry "one spare set of fuses, or three spare fuses of each kind required"?

A — FAR Part 23.
B — FAR Part 43.
C — FAR Part 91.

8400. Answer A. FAR 23.1357
Only statement (1) is correct. Most modern aircraft use circuit breakers rather than fuses to protect their electrical circuits because fuses are typically more cumbersome to replace. However, according to FAR 23.1357, protective devices such as fuses or circuit breakers do not have to be installed in the main circuits of starter motors, or in nonhazardous circuits.

8401. Answer A. AC 43.13-1A
Switches are rated according to both the voltage and current they can control. A typical aircraft switch may be rated for 5 amps at 125 volts, or 35 amps at 24 volts. Answers (B) and (C) are incorrect because a switch does not have a resistance rating.

8402. Answer C. AC 65-9A
Circuit protection devices are installed primarily to protect the wiring. Therefore, circuit protection devices are rated based on the amount of current that can be safely carried in the wiring.

8403. Answer C. AC 65-9A
Both statements (1) and (2) are correct. Circuit protection devices are installed primarily to protect the wiring and, therefore, are rated based on the amount of current that can be carried without overheating the wire and insulation. A second requirement is that all aircraft circuit protection devices open the circuit regardless of the position of the operating control. This requirement is met by trip-free circuit breakers that cannot override an open circuit. In other words, this type of circuit breaker makes it impossible to manually hold the circuit closed when excessive current is flowing.

8404. Answer C. FAR 91.205
Within Part 91, FAR 91.205 specifically requires that one spare set of fuses, or three spare fuses of each type be carried in the aircraft during flight.

8405.   J02

What is the smallest terminal stud allowed for aircraft electrical power systems?

A — No.6.
B — No.8.
C — No.10.

8405. Answer C. AC 65-12A

The smallest terminal stud allowed for electrical power systems is a number 10. However, smaller studs are sometimes used with some smaller operational systems.

8406.   J02

A typical barrier type aircraft terminal strip is made of

A — paper-base phenolic compound.
B — polyester resin and graphite compound.
C — layered aluminum impregnated with compound.

8406. Answer A. ITP-P2

Most of the terminal strips in an aircraft electrical system are of the barrier type and are made of a strong paper-base phenolic compound. Answers (B) and (C) are wrong since graphite and aluminum are electrical conductors and, therefore, cannot be used in terminal strips.

8407.   J02

A term commonly used when two or more electrical terminals are installed on a single lug of a terminal strip is

A — strapping.
B — stepping.
C — stacking.

8407. Answer C. AC 65-12A

When attaching the terminal end of wires to a terminal strip, fan the wires out from the bundles so they will align with the terminal studs. If two or more electrical terminals must be installed on a single lug you must "stack" the terminals as necessary. Answers (A) and (B) are wrong since the terms "strapping" and "stepping" are not used in reference to electrical terminals.

8408.   J02

(1) Electrical wires larger than 10 gauge use uninsulated terminals.
(2) Electrical wires smaller than 10 gauge use uninsulated terminals.

Regarding the above statements,

A — only No. 1 is true.
B — only No. 2 is true.
C — neither No. 1 nor No. 2 is true.

8408. Answer A. AC 65-12A ITP-P2

Only statement (1) is correct. Terminals on wires up to 10-gauge are pre-insulated and color coded to identify the size of wire they fit. Wires larger than 10 gauge, on the other hand, use uninsulated terminals.

8409.   J02

Aircraft electrical wire size is measured according to the

A — Military Specification system.
B — American Wire Gauge system.
C — Technical Standard Order system.

8409. Answer B. AC 65-12A

Wire is measured according to the American Wire Gauge (AWG) system, with the smaller numbers used to identify the larger wire. The Military Specification system (answer A) does not provide a means of measuring wire size and Technical Standard Orders (answer C) certify that parts and appliances installed on aircraft meet certain quality standards.

8410.   J02

Aircraft copper electrical wire is coated with tin, silver, or nickel in order to

A — improve conductivity.
B — add strength.
C — prevent oxidization.

8410. Answer C. ITP-P2

Copper is a very corrosive metal. Therefore, aircraft electrical wire is coated with tin, silver, or nickel plating to help prevent oxidation. Answer (A) is wrong because copper is more conductive than tin or nickel and answer (B) is wrong because the thin coating provides no strength.

LUBRICATION SYSTEMS

Chapter 7 discusses the inspection, checking, troubleshooting, and repair of engine lubrication systems and their associated components. In addition, this chapter describes the correct manner in which to identify and select lubricants for use in various aircraft powerplants. The FAA exam questions taken from this subject include:

8411, 8412, 8413, 8414, 8415, 8416, 8417, 8418, 8419, 8420, 8421, 8422, 8423, 8424, 8425, 8426, 8427, 8428, 8429, 8430, 8431, 8432, 8433, 8434, 8435, 8436, 8437, 8438, 8439, 8440, 8441, 8442, 8443, 8444, 8445, 8446, 8447, 8448, 8449, 8450, 8451, 8452, 8453, 8454, 8455, 8456, 8457, 8458, 8459, 8460, 8461, 8462, 8463, 8464, 8465, 8466, 8467, 8468, 8469, 8470, 8471, 8472, 8473, 8474, 8475, 8476, 8477, 8478, 8479, 8480, 8481, 8482, 8483, 8484, 8485, 8486, 8487, 8488, 8489, 8490, 8491, 8492, 8493, 8494, 8495, 8496, 8497, 8498, 8499, 8500, 8501, 8502.

8411.   K01
What will be the result of operating an engine in extremely high temperatures using a lubricant recommended by the manufacturer for a much lower temperature?

A — The oil pressure will be higher than normal.
B — The oil temperature and oil pressure will be higher than normal.
C — The oil pressure will be lower than normal.

8411. Answer C. AC 65-12A
The viscosity, or the resistance of oil to flow, changes with temperature. For example, as the temperature drops, highly viscous oils become extremely thick and do not circulate. Therefore, low viscosity oils are typically recommended for use in reciprocating engines operating in cold climates. However, if a low viscosity oil is used when an engine is operated in extremely high temperatures, the oil can become so thin that a lower than normal oil pressure can result (answer C). Both answers (A) and (B) are wrong because using a low viscosity oil in extremely high temperatures results in lower than normal pressure indications, not higher.

8412.   K01
(1) Gas turbine and reciprocating engine oils can be mixed or used interchangeably.
(2) Most gas turbine engine oils are synthetic.
Regarding the above statements,

A — only No. 2 is true.
B — both No. 1 and No. 2 are true.
C — neither No.1 nor No. 2 is true.

8412. Answer A. AC 65-12A
Only statement (2) is correct. Because of the unique operating requirements, synthetic oils are typically used in gas turbine engines. Furthermore, because of the differences between turbine and reciprocating engine oils, they should not be mixed or used interchangeably.

8413.   K01
An oil separator is generally associated with which of the following?

A — Engine-driven oil pressure pump.
B — Engine-driven vacuum pump.
C — Cuno oil filter.

8413. Answer B. AC 65-15A
A wet-type engine-driven vacuum pump uses an air-oil separator to separate the oil that mixes with the air that passes through the pump. The separator is installed in the pump's discharge line where it removes oil from the air and returns it to the engine sump. Both answers (A) and (B) are incorrect because neither an engine-driven oil pressure pump nor a Cuno oil filter introduces air into the oil that would require separation.

8414.   K01

The time in seconds required for exactly 60 cubic centimeters of oil to flow through an accurately calibrated orifice at a specific temperature is recorded as a measurement of the oil's

A — flash point.
B — specific gravity.
C — viscosity.

8414. Answer C. AC 65-12A

The viscosity of commercial aviation oils is measured by a testing instrument called a Saybolt Universal Viscosimeter. This instrument consists of a tube that holds a specific oil quantity at an exact temperature and a calibrated orifice. The time in seconds required for exactly 60 cubic centimeters of oil to flow through the orifice is recorded as the oil's viscosity. Answer (A) is incorrect because flash point represents the temperature at which a fluid will momentarily flash without sustaining combustion. Answer (B) is wrong because specific gravity is the ratio of the weight of a given volume of material to the same volume of pure water.

8415.   K01

Upon what quality or characteristic of a lubricating oil is its viscosity index based?

A — Its resistance to flow at a standard temperature as compared to high grade paraffin-base oil at the same temperature.
B — Its rate of change in viscosity with temperature change.
C — Its rate of flow through an orifice at a standard temperature.

8415. Answer B.

Viscosity index is a measure of the change in an oil's viscosity for a given change in temperature. The smaller the change in viscosity for a given temperature change, the higher the viscosity index. Answer (A) is wrong because viscosity is the measure of resistance to flow at a standard temperature, while answer (C) is incorrect because viscosity, not viscosity index, is found by measuring a fluid's rate of flow through an orifice at a standard temperature.

8416.   K01

Lubricating oils with high viscosity index ratings are oils

A — in which the viscosity does not vary much with temperature change.
B — in which the viscosity varies considerably with temperature change.
C — which have high SAE numbers.

8416. Answer A.

Viscosity index is a measure of the change in an oil's viscosity for a given change in temperature. The smaller the change in viscosity for a given temperature change, the higher the viscosity index. In other words, a high viscosity index indicates that an oil's viscosity does not change very much with changes in temperature. Answer (B) is incorrect because oils whose viscosity varies considerably with temperature change have low viscosity index ratings. Answer (C) is wrong because a high SAE number indicates a high viscosity, not a high viscosity index rating.

8417.   K01

Compared to reciprocating engine oils, the types of oils used in turbine engines

A — are required to carry and disperse a higher level of combustion by-products.
B — may permit a somewhat higher level of carbon formation in the engine.
C — have less tendency to produce lacquer or coke.

8417. Answer C. AC 65-12A

Synthetic turbine engine oil has two principle advantages over petroleum oil. It has less tendency to deposit lacquer and coke, and is less likely to evaporate at high temperatures. Answer (A) is incorrect because turbine engine lubricants are required to disperse an extremely low level of combustion by-products, and answer (B) is wrong because synthetic turbine oils prevent the formation of carbon (coke) in engines.

8418. K01

The oil used in reciprocating engines has a relatively high viscosity due to

A — the reduced ability of thin oils to maintain adequate film strength at altitude. (reduced atmospheric pressure).
B — the relatively high rotational speeds.
C — large clearances and high operating temperatures.

8418. Answer C. AC 65-12A

Reciprocating engines require large engine operating clearances because of the relatively large size of the moving parts and high operating temperatures. Therefore, the oil used in reciprocating engines must have relatively high viscosity in order to maintain an adequate film between moving parts. Answer (A) is incorrect because reduced atmospheric pressure has little effect on an oil's film strength. Answer (B) is incorrect because the rotational speeds of reciprocating engine components are relatively low compared to those of turbine engines.

8419. K01

If all other requirements can be met, what type of oil should be used to achieve theoretically perfect engine lubrication?

A — The thinnest oil that will stay in place and maintain a reasonable film strength.
B — An oil that combines high viscosity and low demulsibility.
C — An oil that combines a low viscosity index and a high neutralization number.

8419. Answer A. AC 65-12A

The oil selected for aircraft engine lubrication must be thin enough to circulate freely, yet heavy enough to provide the proper film strength at operating temperatures (answer A). Answer (B) is wrong because oil should have high demulsibility, meaning that it tends to separate from water. Answer (C) is incorrect because neutralization number is a measure of an oil's acid content and a low neutralization number is preferred in lubricating oils.

8420. K01

In addition to lubricating (reducing friction between moving parts), engine oil performs what functions?

1. Cools.
2. Seals.
3. Cleans.
4. Prevents corrosion.
5. Cushions impact (shock) loads.

A — 1, 2, 3, 4.
B — 1, 2, 3, 4, 5.
C — 1, 3, 4.

8420. Answer B. AC 65-12A

In addition to reducing friction, one of the primary functions of oil is to circulate through the engine and absorb heat to aid in engine cooling. In addition, engine oil also helps to form a seal between the piston rings and cylinder walls, clean the engine interior by carrying foreign particles to the filter, coat engine parts to prevent corrosion, and act as a cushion between the metal parts during the combustion process. This cushioning effect is particularly important for such parts as crankshafts and connecting rods.

8421. K01

Which of these characteristics is desirable in turbine engine oil?

A — Low flash point.
B — High flash point.
C — High volatility.

8421. Answer B. AC 65-12A

The flash point of oil is an important characteristic when selecting a lubricant. Flash point is determined by laboratory tests and represents the temperature at which a liquid will begin to give off ignitable vapors. The safest liquids are those that expel ignitable vapors at very high temperatures (high flash point). Therefore, it is desirable for aircraft engine oils to have a high flash point (answer B). Answers (A) and (C) are incorrect because a low flash point and high volatility could cause a turbine engine lubricant to catch fire during engine operation and are therefore undesirable characteristics.

8422.   K01

The viscosity of a liquid is a measure of its

A — resistance to flow.
B — rate of change of internal friction with change in temperature.
C — weight or density.

8423.   K01

What type of oil system is usually found on turbine engines?

A — Dry sump, pressure, and spray.
B — Dry sump, dip, and splash.
C — Wet sump, spray, and splash.

8424.   K01

Which of the following factors helps determine the proper grade of oil to use in a particular engine?

A — Adequate lubrication in various attitudes of flight.
B — Positive introduction of oil to the bearings.
C — Operating speeds of bearings.

8425.   K01

Specific gravity is a comparison of the weight of a substance to the weight of an equal volume of

A — oil at a specific temperature.
B — distilled water at a specific temperature.
C — mercury at a specific temperature.

8426.   K01

Which of the following has the greatest effect on the viscosity of lubricating oil?

A — Temperature.
B — Pressure.
C — Volatility.

8427.   K01

What advantage do mineral base lubricants have over vegetable oil base lubricants when used in aircraft engines?

A — Cooling ability.
B — Chemical stability.
C — Friction resistance.

8422. Answer A. AC 65-12A

The resistance of an oil to flow is known as its viscosity. Answer (B) is incorrect because the rate of change of internal friction (viscosity) with a change in temperature is known as a liquid's viscosity index. Answer (C) is incorrect because there is no correlation between viscosity and weight or density.

8423. Answer A. AC 65-12A

Both wet- and dry-sump lubrication systems are used in gas turbine engines. However, most turbojet engines are of the axial flow configuration and use a dry-sump lubrication system. With this type of system, the engine's bearings are pressure lubricated and the gearboxes are pressure and spray lubricated. Answers (B) and (C) are incorrect because turbine engines lack reciprocating components that can provide splash lubrication.

8424. Answer C. AC 65-12A

Some of the factors considered when determining the proper grade of oil to use in a particular engine include the engine's operating loads, rotational speeds (answer C), and operating temperatures. Answers (A) and (B) are incorrect because adequate lubrication at various flight attitudes and positive bearing lubrication are functions of a lubrication system's design and have little impact in determining the proper oil grade.

8425. Answer B. AC 65-12A

All liquids have a specific gravity. Specific gravity is a comparison of the weight of a substance to the weight of an equal volume of distilled water at a specific temperature.

8426. Answer A. AC 65-12A

The viscosity of oil is a measure of its resistance to flow. The one factor which affects an oil's viscosity the most is temperature. The higher the temperature, the more an oil thins and the less viscous it becomes.

8427. Answer B. DSA-25

In general, vegetable based oils are chemically unstable at high temperatures, perform poorly at low temperatures, and are unsuited for aircraft engine lubrication. Mineral based oils, on the other hand, tend to be much more chemically stable and suited for aircraft use (answer B). Answer (A) is incorrect because the cooling ability of mineral based lubricants and vegetable based lubricants is about the same. Answer (C) is wrong because vegetable based lubricants actually result in lower friction coefficients than mineral based lubricants.

8428.   K01

Lubricants may be classified according to their origin. Satisfactory aircraft engine lubricants are

A — mineral or synthetic based.
B — vegetable, mineral, or synthetic based.
C — animal, mineral, or synthetic based.

8429.   K01

High tooth pressures and high rubbing velocities, such as occur with spur-type gears, require the use of

A — an EP lubricant.
B — straight mineral oil.
C — metallic ash detergent oil.

8430.   K01

Manufacturers normally require turbine engine oil servicing within a short time after engine shutdown primarily to

A — prevent overservicing.
B — help dilute and neutralize any contaminants that may already be present in the engine's oil system.
C — provide a better indication of any oil leaks in the system.

8431.   K01

What type of oil do most engine manufacturers recommend for new reciprocating engine break-in?

A — Ashless-dispersant oil.
B — Straight mineral oil.
C — Semi-synthetic oil.

8432.   K01

What type of oil do most engine manufacturers recommend after new reciprocating engine break-in?

A — Metallic-ash detergent oil.
B — Ashless-dispersant oil.
C — Straight mineral oil.

8428. Answer A. DSA-25

In general, animal and vegetable based lubricants (answers B and C) are chemically unstable at high temperatures, often perform poorly at low temperatures, and are unsuited for aircraft engine lubrication. However, neither mineral based nor synthetic based oils have these limitations and, therefore, perform well as aircraft engine lubricant.

8429. Answer A.

EP (extreme pressure) lubricants are intended for use with spur-type gears operating at high speeds and under high pressure loads. Under these conditions, straight mineral oil (answer B) would allow metal to metal contact resulting in excessive wear. Answer (C) is incorrect because there is no such thing as a "metallic ash detergent oil."

8430. Answer A. TEP2

In an operating turbine engine the oil scavenge pump returns oil from the main bearing galleries to the oil reservoir. However, after an engine is shut down, the oil in the tank tends to seep down to the engine's lower components. This causes the oil level in the reservoir to decrease and give a faulty oil level indication. Therefore, the best way to prevent overfilling the reservoir is to service the oil system within 30 minutes after engine shutdown. Answer (B) is wrong because if a substantial number of contaminants exist in an engine's oil system, the oil should be changed, not just diluted. Answer (C) is wrong because servicing an oil system within a short time does not provide any better indication of oil leaks than if the system were serviced at a later time interval.

8431. Answer B. ITP-P2

Most engine manufacturers recommend the use of straight mineral oil for at least the first 50 hours of the break-in period in new or newly overhauled reciprocating engines. Both answers (A) and (C) are incorrect because ashless-dispersant oils and semi-synthetic oils are typically used after the break-in period because they provide more effective lubrication than straight mineral oils.

8432. Answer B. ITP-P2

Ashless dispersant or AD oil is the most commonly used lubricant for reciprocating engines after break-in. Answer (A) is incorrect because there is no such thing as a metallic ash detergent oil and answer (C) is wrong because straight mineral oil is typically used during the engine break-in period.

8433.   K02

The type of oil pumps most commonly used on turbine engines are classified as

A — positive displacement.
B — variable displacement.
C — constant speed.

8433. Answer A. TEP2

The three most common types of oil pumps used on turbine engines are the vane, gerotor, and gear-types. All are classified as positive displacement pumps since they pump a fixed quantity of oil for each revolution. Answer (B) is wrong because variable displacement pumps are generally used in hydraulic systems, while answer (C) is incorrect because the speed at which an oil pump operates varies with engine speed and, therefore, an oil pump is not classified as a constant speed pump.

8434.   K02

As a general rule, the mixture setting on a reciprocating engine operating at or near takeoff power that provides the best cooling is

A — FULL RICH.
B — LEAN.
C — FULL LEAN.

8434. Answer A. AC 65-12A

Air-cooled aircraft engines rely to some degree on fuel to aid in cooling during high-power operations. Therefore, as a general rule the mixture should be set in the full rich position when operating at or near takeoff power. A rich mixture typically provides more fuel than is needed for combustion, leaving excess fuel to aid in engine cooling. Answers (B) and (C) are incorrect because the leaner the mixture the less fuel is available for cooling.

8435.   K02

The engine oil temperature regulator is usually located between which of the following on a dry sump reciprocating engine?

A — The engine oil supply pump and the internal lubrication system.
B — The scavenger pump outlet and the oil storage tank.
C — The oil storage tank and the engine oil supply pump.

8435. Answer B. AC 65-12A

The oil temperature regulator controls oil temperature by directing oil through the core of the cooler or to the oil tank without cooling. Therefore, the engine oil temperature regulator must sense the oil's temperature as it leaves the scavenger pump but before it proceeds to the storage tank (answer B). Answers (A) and (C) are incorrect because if the oil temperature regulator were installed at any point after the oil storage tank, there would be no way to direct the flow of oil to the oil cooler.

8436.   K02

What will happen to the return oil if the oil line between the scavenger pump and the oil cooler separates?

A — Oil will accumulate in the engine.
B — The return oil will be pumped overboard.
C — The scavenger return line check valve will close and force the oil to bypass directly to the intake side of the pressure pump.

8436. Answer B. AC 65-12A

If the return line between the scavenge pump and oil cooler should separate, the return oil would be pumped overboard. Answer (A) is incorrect because the only way oil would accumulate in the engine is if the return oil line was blocked, while answer (C) is incorrect because there is no check valve in the scavenger return line.

8437. K02

At cruise RPM, some oil will flow through the relief valve of a gear-type engine oil pump. This is normal as the relief valve is set at a pressure which is

A — lower than the pump inlet pressure.
B — lower than the pressure pump capabilities.
C — higher than pressure pump capabilities.

8437. Answer B. AC 65-12A

The purpose of an oil pressure relief valve is to maintain the correct system pressure. On most engines, the desired maximum oil pressure is reached before the engine reaches cruise rpm. Therefore, the relief valve is typically set at a pressure that is lower than the oil pump's maximum capabilities. This means that when an engine reaches cruise rpm, the relief valve must open slightly to maintain the correct oil pressure. Answer (A) is wrong because a relief valve set at a pressure lower than pump inlet pressure would never allow oil to flow through the pump. Answer (C) is incorrect because a relief valve set higher than the pressure pump's capabilities could damage system components by exposing them to excessive pressures.

8438. K02

(1) Fuel may be used to cool oil in gas turbine engines.
(2) Ram air may be used to cool oil in gas turbine engines.

Regarding the above statements,

A — only No. 1 is true.
B — only No. 2 is true.
C — both No. 1 and No. 2 are true.

8438. Answer C. AC 65-12A

Both statements (1) and (2) are correct. In gas turbine engines, fuel and ram air are both used to cool the oil. The fuel-cooled oil cooler acts as a fuel/oil heat exchanger in that the fuel cools the oil and the oil heats the fuel. The air-cooled oil cooler normally is installed at the front of the engine and is similar to those used on reciprocating engines.

8439. K02

In a reciprocating engine oil system, the temperature bulb senses oil temperature

A — at a point after the oil has passed through the oil cooler.
B — while the oil is in the hottest area of the engine.
C — immediately before the oil enters the oil cooler.

8439. Answer A. AC 65-12A

In wet sump engines, the oil temperature bulb is located after the oil cooler. This allows the sensing bulb to measure the temperature of the oil entering the engine. Both answers (B) and (C) are wrong because an indication of oil temperature before the oil is cooled is of little practical value.

8440. K02

The oil dampened main bearing utilized in some turbine engines is used to

A — provide lubrication of bearings from the beginning of starting rotation until normal oil pressure is established.
B — provide an oil film between the outer race and the bearing housing in order to reduce vibration tendencies in the rotor system, and to allow for slight misalignment.
C — dampen surges in oil pressure to the bearings.

8440. Answer B. TEP2

The oil dampened main bearings used in some turbine engines contain oil dampening compartments that provide space for an oil film to build between the outer race and the bearing housing. This oil film reduces vibration tendencies in the rotor system and allows for slight misalignment. Answer (A) is incorrect because during a start, residual oil on the bearing surfaces provides adequate lubrication until the oil pump develops sufficient pressure. Answer (C) is incorrect because an oil pressure relief valve, not dampened bearings, dampens pressure surges in the oil system.

8441. **K02**

What is the purpose of the last chance oil filters?

A — To prevent damage to the oil spray nozzle.
B — To filter the oil immediately before it enters the main bearings.
C — To assure a clean supply of oil to the lubrication system.

8441. Answer B. AC 65-12A

In addition to the main oil filters, turbine engine oil systems utilize multiple secondary filters located throughout the system. For example, fine mesh screens called last chance filters are often used to strain the oil just before it enters the main bearing compartment. Answer (A) is incorrect because, although a last change filter typically does filter the oil before it reaches the spray nozzle, the filter's primary function is to prevent foreign particles from entering the main bearings. Answer (C) is wrong because the main oil system filter, not the last chance filter, ensures a clean supply of oil.

8442. **K02**

In a jet engine which uses a fuel-oil heat exchanger, the oil temperature is controlled by a thermostatic valve that regulates the flow of

A — fuel through the heat exchanger.
B — both fuel and oil through the heat exchanger.
C — oil through the heat exchanger.

8442. Answer C. AC 65-12A

In oil systems using a fuel-oil heat exchanger, fuel flowing to the engine must pass through the heat exchanger. However, a thermostatic bypass valve controls the flow of oil through the heat exchanger to regulate the oil temperature. Answers (A) and (B) are incorrect because fuel flow through a fuel-oil heat exchanger is not regulated.

8443. **K02**

What prevents pressure within the lubricating oil tank from rising above or falling below ambient pressure (reciprocating engine)?

A — Oil tank check valve.
B — Oil pressure relief valve.
C — Oil tank vent.

8443. Answer C. AC 65-12A

To ensure proper tank ventilation at all flight attitudes reciprocating engine oil tanks are fitted with vent lines. These lines are usually connected to the engine crankcase and indirectly vent the oil tank to the atmosphere. This indirect venting prevents the tank pressure from rising above or falling below the outside ambient pressure. Answer (A) is incorrect because oil tanks typically do not have check valves while answer (B) is wrong because the oil pressure relief valve prevents oil system pressure from rising above a preset maximum value.

8444. **K02**

In an axial-flow turbine engine, compressor bleed air is sometimes used to aid in cooling the

A — fuel.
B — inlet guide vanes.
C — turbine, vanes, blades, and bearings.

8444. Answer C. AC 65-12A

In some axial-flow turbine engines, compressor bleed air is used to aid in cooling the turbine section, including the turbine vanes, blades, and bearings. Answers (A) and (B) are wrong because compressor bleed air is used to heat, not cool, fuel and inlet guide vanes to prevent ice formation.

8445. **K02**

Oil picks up the most heat from which of the following turbine engine components?

A — Rotor coupling.
B — Compressor bearing.
C — Turbine bearing.

8445. Answer C. AC 65-12A

The hottest section within a turbine engine where oil flows is the turbine section. Therefore, of the choices given, the oil will pick up the most amount of heat from the turbine bearing. In fact, the amount of heat absorbed by the turbine bearing is so great that the quantity of oil supplied to the bearing or bearings is often greater than to any of the other engine bearings. Answers (A) and (B) are incorrect because neither the rotor coupling nor the compressor bearing is exposed to potentially damaging temperatures.

8446.   K02

Which of the following is a function of the fuel-oil heat exchanger on a turbojet engine?

A — Aerates the fuel.
B — Emulsifies the oil.
C — Increases fuel temperature.

8446. Answer C. AC 65-12A

The fuel-oil heat exchanger is designed to exchange, or transfer heat from the engine oil to the fuel. This process warms the fuel sufficiently enough to prevent fuel icing. Answer (A) is incorrect because aerated fuel is undesirable and answer (B) is wrong because fuel and oil do not mix in a fuel-oil heat exchanger and, therefore, the emulsification qualities of the oil remain unchanged.

8447.   K02

According to Federal Aviation Regulations (FAR's), oil tank fillers on turbine engines must be marked with the word

A — "oil" and the type and grade of oil specified by the manufacturer.
B — "oil" and tank capacity.
C — "oil."

8447. Answer C. FAR 33.71

According to FAR 33.71, oil filler openings for turbine engines must be marked with the word "oil." Answers (A) and (B) are incorrect because neither the type and grade of oil nor the tank capacity must be indicated.

8448.   K02

After making a welded repair to a pressurized-type turbine engine oil tank, the tank should be pressure checked to

A — not less than 5 PSI plus the maximum operating pressure of the tank.
B — not less than 5 PSI plus the average operating pressure of the tank.
C — 5 PSI.

8448. Answer A. FAR 33.71

FAR 33.71 states that pressurized oil tanks may not leak when subjected to their maximum operating temperature and an internal pressure that is not less than 5 psi plus the maximum operating pressure of the tank.

8449.   K02

Why are fixed orifice nozzles used in the lubrication system of gas turbine engines?

A — To provide a relatively constant oil flow to the main bearings at all engine speeds.
B — To keep back pressure on the oil pump, thus preventing an air lock.
C — To protect the oil seals by preventing excessive pressure from entering the bearing cavities.

8449. Answer A. AC 65-12A

To lubricate a turbine engine's main bearings, pressurized oil is sprayed on the bearings through fixed orifice nozzles. These nozzles provide a relatively constant flow of oil at all engine operating speeds thereby ensuring adequate lubrication. Answer (B) is incorrect because the nozzles do not create back pressure on the oil pump and answer (C) is wrong because oil pressure is controlled by the oil pump and relief valve.

8450.   K02

Possible failure related ferrous-metal particles in turbine engine oil cause an (electrical) indicating-type magnetic chip detector to indicate their presence by

A — disturbing the magnetic lines of flux around the detector tip.
B — bridging the gap between the detector center (positive) electrode and the ground electrode.
C — generating a small electric current that is caused by the particles being in contact with the dissimilar metal of the detector tip.

8450. Answer B. TEP2

Chip detector systems warn of the presence of a substantial number of ferrous-metal particles in the engine oil. The warning feature on this type of system consists of an electrical circuit that is completed once debris bridges the gap between the magnetic positive electrode and the ground electrode (shell) of the chip detector probe. Answer (A) is wrong because a chip detector requires a conductive path between the electrode gap to provide a warning. Answer (C) is incorrect because a chip detector is basically a simple switch and does not generate an electric current.

8451.   K02

What would be the probable result if the oil system pressure relief valve should stick in the open position on a turbine engine?

A — Increased oil pressure.
B — Decreased oil temperature.
C — Insufficient lubrication.

8451. Answer C. AC 65-12A

If the oil system pressure should become excessive in a turbine engine, the pressure relief valve would open and direct oil back to the supply pump inlet before the oil reached any moving parts. Therefore, if the pressure relief valve should stick in the open position, system pressure would decrease below acceptable levels and insufficient lubrication be provided to moving parts. Answer (A) is incorrect because increased oil pressure would occur if the pressure relief valve stuck in the closed position, not the open position, and answer (B) is wrong because the oil system pressure relief valve has little effect on oil temperature.

8452.   K02

What is the primary purpose of the oil-to-fuel heat exchanger?

A — Cool the fuel.
B — Cool the oil.
C — De-aerate the oil.

8452. Answer B. AC 65-12A

The primary purpose of an oil-to-fuel heat exchanger in a turbine engine is to cool the engine oil. The heat exchanger does this by allowing the warm engine oil to transfer excess heat energy to the fuel. Answer (A) is wrong because the fuel is heated, not cooled, as it passes through a fuel-oil heat exchanger. Answer (C) is incorrect because oil is de-aerated in a special dwell chamber within the engine oil tank.

8453.   K02

What unit in an aircraft engine lubrication system is adjusted to maintain the desired system pressure?

A — Oil pressure relief valve.
B — Oil viscisity valve.
C — Oil pump.

8453. Answer A. AC 65-12A

In most aircraft engine lubrication systems the oil pump typically supplies more pressure than the system can handle. Therefore, the appropriate system pressure must be maintained by the oil pressure relief valve. Answer (B) is incorrect because an oil viscosity valve is used to regulate oil temperature. Answer (C) is incorrect because oil pumps are positive displacement units that pump a fixed quantity based on their speed of rotation and provide no pressure regulation.

8454.   K02

Low oil pressure can be detrimental to the internal engine components. However, high oil pressure

A — should be limited to the engine manufacturer's recommendations.
B — has a negligible effect.
C — will not occur because of pressure losses around the bearings.

8454. Answer A. AC 65-12A

An oil pressure relief valve limits oil pressure to a value specified by the engine manufacturer. If the relief valve should stick closed and allow the oil pressure to become excessive, leakage and damage to the oil system could result. Therefore, high oil pressure should always be limited to the engine manufacturer's recommendations (answer A). Since the damage that can be caused by excessive oil pressure is not negligible, answer (B) is incorrect. Answer (C) is wrong because, even if pressure losses around the bearings reduced oil pressure, excessive oil pressure would still exist at all points prior to the bearings.

8455.   K02
What is the primary purpose of the oil breather pressurization system that is used on turbine engines?

A — Prevents foaming of the oil.
B — Allows aeration of the oil for better lubrication because of the air/oil mist.
C — Provides a proper oil spray pattern from the main bearing oil jets.

8455. Answer C. AC 65-12A
The breather pressurizing system of a turbine engine ensures a proper spray pattern from the main bearing oil jets and furnishes a pressure head to the scavenge system. If the pressure within the bearing housings were allowed to drop as atmospheric pressure dropped with changes in altitude, the flow of oil from the oil jets would change. Therefore, to maintain a relatively constant flow rate the breather pressurizing system maintains a relatively constant pressure within the bearing compartments and oil tank as the aircraft climbs. Answer (A) is incorrect because an oil breather pressurization system does little to prevent oil foaming. Answer (B) is wrong because aerated oil provides inferior lubrication. For this reason, turbine engine oil tanks use air-oil separators to remove air from oil entering the tank.

8456.   K02
The purpose of directing bleed air to the outer turbine case on some engines is to

A — provide optimum turbine blade tip clearance by controlling thermal expansion.
B — provide up to 100 percent kinetic energy extraction from the flowing gases.
C — allow operation in a thermal environment 600 to 800 °F above the temperature limits of turbine blade and vane alloys.

8456. Answer A. TEP2
Active turbine blade tip clearance control is accomplished by varying the amount of bleed air that is let into the turbine case to control the thermal expansion of the outer turbine case. This, in turn, keeps efficiency losses at the blade tips to a minimum at all power settings. Answer (B) is incorrect because the degree to which kinetic energy is extracted relies primarily on the design of the turbine blades. Answer (C) is wrong because compressor bleed air is routed directly through turbine blades and stator vanes, not to the outer turbine case, to allow operation in the conditions specified.

8457.   K03
Some larger reciprocating engines use a compensating oil pressure relief valve to

A — provide a high engine oil pressure when the oil is cold and automatically lower the oil pressure when the oil warms up.
B — compensate for changes in atmospheric pressure that accompany altitude changes.
C — automatically keep oil pressure nearly the same whether the oil is warm or cold.

8457. Answer A. DSA-25
Some larger reciprocating engines require high oil pressure to force cold oil through the bearings during starting and warm-up. However, after the oil has warmed up, lower oil system pressure is preferred to minimize oil consumption. One way of providing varying oil pressures is with a compensating oil pressure relief valve. Answer (B) is incorrect because reciprocating engines typically do not have an altitude compensating oil system. Answer (C) is wrong because it is neither desirable nor possible to keep a constant oil pressure regardless of temperature.

8458.   K03
In order to relieve excessive pump pressure in an engine's internal oil system, most engines are equipped with a

A — vent.
B — bypass valve.
C — relief valve.

8458. Answer C. AC 65-12A
Almost all engine driven oil pumps provide excessive oil pressure at higher power settings. Therefore, most oil systems are equipped with a pressure relief valve that maintains the correct system pressure. Answer (A) is wrong because oil tank vents are connected to the engine crankcase to ventilate the oil tank, not regulate oil system pressure. Answer (B) is incorrect because a bypass valve only allows oil to bypass a failed or plugged component and does not relieve excessive system pressure.

8459.   **K03**

What is the source of most of the heat that is absorbed by the lubricating oil in a reciprocating engine?

A — Crankshaft main bearings.
B — Exhaust valves.
C — Pistons and cylinder walls.

8459. Answer C. AC 65-12A

As oil circulates through a reciprocating engine, it absorbs heat from the engine. Since the pistons and cylinder walls are exposed to the highest temperatures during the combustion process, they are the source of the greatest amount of heat that is absorbed by the oil. Crankshaft main bearings (answer A) are far from the heat of combustion and, therefore, operate at a comparatively cool temperature. Answer (B) is incorrect because even though exhaust valves become extremely hot during engine operation, little oil actually comes in contact with them.

8460.   **K03**

How are the teeth of the gears in the accessory section of an engine normally lubricated?

A — By splashed or sprayed oil.
B — By submerging the load-bearing portions in oil.
C — By surrounding the load-bearing portions with baffles or housings within which oil pressure can be maintained.

8460. Answer A. AC 65-12A

The gear teeth within an accessory section of a reciprocating engine are typically lubricated by oil that is sprayed by the accessory bearings and by oil that is splashed in the accessory case. Answer (B) is incorrect because submerging the load-bearing portions of the accessory section in oil is impractical since this would require a considerable amount of oil and a large sump area. Answer (C) is incorrect because surrounding the load-bearing portions with baffles or housings would add unnecessary weight and complexity.

8461.   **K03**

What is the purpose of the check valve generally used in a dry sump lubrication system?

A — To prevent the scavenger pump from losing its prime.
B — To prevent the oil from the supply tank from seeping into the crankcase during inoperative periods.
C — To prevent the oil from the pressure pump from entering the scavenger system.

8461. Answer B. AC 65-12A

Reciprocating engines using dry-sump oil systems often have a check valve installed in the oil filter. This check valve is held closed by a light spring load of one to three pounds when the engine is not operating and prevents oil from draining out of the supply tank and into the engine crankcase. Answer (A) is incorrect because scavenger pumps are located near the bottom of the engine where the oil collects and do not rely on oil draining back through the system to remain primed. Answer (C) is incorrect because lubrication systems are purposely designed to allow pressure pump oil to enter the scavenger system.

8462.   **K03**

From the following, identify the factor that has the least effect on the oil consumption of a specific engine.

A — Mechanical efficiency.
B — Engine RPM.
C — Lubricant characteristics.

8462. Answer A. AC 65-12A

The factors that affect oil consumption are engine speed, engine temperature, operating clearances, oil condition, and characteristics of the lubricant being used. An engine's mechanical efficiency has little effect on oil consumption. Therefore, answer (A) is correct.

8463.   **K03**

How is the oil collected by the piston oil ring returned to the crankcase?

A — Down vertical slots cut in the piston wall between the piston oil ring groove and the piston skirt.
B — Through holes drilled in the piston oil ring groove.
C — Through holes drilled in the piston pin recess.

8463. Answer B. AC 65-12A

Oil control rings regulate the oil film thickness on the cylinder wall. Excess oil that collects on oil control rings as a cylinder moves is routed back to the crankcase through holes that are drilled in the piston ring grooves or in the lands next to these grooves. Answers (A) and (C) are incorrect because vertical slots in the piston wall and holes in the piston pin recess would weaken the piston and eventually cause it to fail.

8464.   K03

Which of the following lubrication system components is never located between the pressure pump and the engine pressure system?

A — Oil temperature bulb.
B — Fuel line for oil dilution system.
C — Check valve.

8465.   K03

As an aid to cold-weather starting, the oil dilution system thins the oil with

A — kerosene.
B — alcohol.
C — gasoline.

8466.   K03

The basic oil pressure relief valve setting for a newly overhauled engine is made

A — within the first 30 seconds of engine operation.
B — when the oil is at a higher than normal temperature to assure high oil pressure at normal oil temperature.
C — in the overhaul shop.

8467.   K03

Where is the oil temperature bulb located on a dry sump reciprocating engine?

A — Oil inlet line.
B — Oil cooler.
C — Oil outlet line.

8468.   K03

Cylinder walls are usually lubricated by

A — splashed or sprayed oil.
B — a direct pressure system fed through the crankshaft, connecting rods, and the piston pins to the oil control ring groove in the piston.
C — oil that is picked up by the oil control ring when the piston is at bottom center.

8464. Answer B. AC 65-12A

The fuel line for an oil dilution system is never located between the pressure pump and the engine pressure system. The reason for this is that with an oil dilution system, the fuel must be introduced into unpressurized oil so there is almost no chance for oil to flow back through the dilution system and enter the fuel supply. Answer (A) is incorrect because oil temperature bulbs are often installed immediately after the pressure pump so the temperature of the oil entering the engine is known. Answer (B) is wrong because many radial engines use a check valve between the pressure pump and the engine pressure system to prevent oil from seeping into the engine when it is shut down.

8465. Answer C. AC 65-12A

Oil dilution systems thin engine oil for cold-weather starting by allowing the pilot to add fuel (gasoline) to the engine oil just prior to engine shut down. Although kerosene (answer A) and alcohol (answer B) can also be used to dilute engine oil, neither is typically carried on reciprocating engine aircraft.

8466. Answer C. AC 65-12A

Initial adjustment on the oil pressure relief valve for a newly overhauled engine is made in the overhaul shop. The adjustment is fine tuned after the engine is installed in a test stand and run. To help eliminate the risk of oil starvation, the initial adjustment should not wait until the engine is run. Answer (A) is incorrect because some sort of adjustment must be made before an engine is first started. Answer (B) is wrong because the relief valve is typically adjusted based on expected oil temperatures.

8467. Answer A. AC 65-12A

It is important for pilots to know the temperature of the oil just before it enters the engine. Therefore, in dry-sump lubricating systems, the oil temperature bulb may be located anywhere in the oil inlet line between the supply tank and the engine. Answers (B) and (C) are incorrect because placing the temperature bulb in either of these locations would not give the temperature of the oil entering the engine.

8468. Answer A. AC 65-12A

In most reciprocating engines, the cylinder walls receive oil spray from the crankshaft and crankpin bearings. Some of the oil coming from the crankshaft is also splashed onto the cylinder walls. Answer (B) is incorrect because no such lubrication system exists, and answer (C) is wrong because, although the oil control ring regulates the thickness of the lubricating film on the cylinder wall, it does not pick up any oil when the piston is at the bottom of a stroke.

8469.   K03

If a full-flow oil filter is used on an aircraft engine, and the filter becomes completely clogged, the

A — oil supply to the engine will be blocked.
B — oil will be bypassed back to the oil tank hopper where larger sediments and foreign matter will settle out prior to passage through the engine.
C — bypass valve will open and the oil pump will supply unfiltered oil to the engine.

8470.   K03

Oil accumulation in the cylinders of an inverted in-line engine and in the lower cylinders of a radial engine is normally reduced or prevented by

A — reversed oil control rings.
B — routing the valve-operating mechanism lubricating oil to a separate scavenger pump.
C — extended cylinder skirts.

8471.   K03

What is the primary purpose of changing aircraft engine lubricating oils at predetermined periods?

A — The oil becomes diluted with gasoline washing past the pistons into the crankcase.
B — The oil becomes contaminated with moisture, acids, and finely divided suspended solid particles.
C — Exposure to heat and oxygen causes a decreased ability to maintain a film under load.

8472.   K03

What determines the minimum particle size which will be excluded or filtered by a cuno-type (stacked disc, edge filtration) filter?

A — The disc thickness.
B — The spacer thickness.
C — Both the number and thickness of the discs in the assembly.

8469. Answer C. AC 65-12A

Full-flow oil filters used on aircraft engines are always equipped with a bypass valve which allows unfiltered oil to bypass the filter and enter the engine should the oil filter become clogged. Answer (A) is incorrect because the design of a full-flow filter prevents oil supply blockage, and answer (B) is wrong because oil is bypassed directly to the engine, not to the oil tank hopper.

8470. Answer C. AC 65-12A

Some radial engine cylinders and all cylinders in an inverted engine are located at the bottom of the engine. To prevent these cylinders from being flooded with oil and suffering hydraulic lock, extended cylinder skirts are often installed. With these extended skirts, oil that falls into the cylinders is immediately thrown back into the crankcase. Answer (A) is incorrect since oil control rings are nondirectional, and answer (B) is wrong because the oil that drains into inverted cylinders comes from the engine crankcase, not from the valve-operating mechanism.

8471. Answer B. AC 65-12A

Oil in an engine is constantly exposed to many harmful substances that reduce its ability to protect moving parts. These contaminants include moisture, acids, dirt, carbon, and metallic particles. Therefore, it is important that the oil be changed at regular intervals. Answer (A) is incorrect because the small amount of gasoline that washes past the pistons evaporates out of the engine oil at normal operating temperatures. Answer (C) is wrong because exposure to heat and oxygen typically does not affect the lubricant's ability to maintain a film.

8472. Answer B. DSA-25

A cuno-type oil filter consists of a cartridge consisting of disks, spacers, and a cleaner blade located between each pair of disks. As oil enters the filter it passes through the gaps between the closely spaced cartridge disks, then through the hollow center and on to the engine. The smaller the spacer thickness between the disks the smaller the particles that are filtered out of the oil. Answers (A) and (C) are incorrect because disk thickness does not determine the minimum particle size a cuno-type oil filter can screen.

8473.   **K03**

What is the primary purpose of the hopper located in the oil supply tank of some dry sump engine installations?

A — To reduce the time required to warm the oil to operating temperatures.

B — To reduce surface aeration of the hot oil and thus reduce oxidation and the formation of sludge and varnish.

C — To impart a centrifugal motion to the oil entering the tank so that the foreign particles in the oil will separate more readily.

8473. Answer A. AC 65-12A

Some oil tanks have a built-in hopper, or temperature accelerating well, that extends from the oil return fitting on top of the oil tank to the outlet fitting in the sump in the bottom of the oil tank. The primary purpose of the hopper is to separate the circulating oil from the surrounding oil in the tank so the circulating oil warms quickly after the engine is started (answer A). Answer (B) is incorrect because aeration occurs when the oil is agitated by an engine's moving parts, not by the oil entering the tank. Answer (C) is wrong because the centrifugal motion imparted on the oil as it enters the hopper is designed to reduce foaming, not to eliminate foreign particles.

8474.   **K03**

The purpose of the flow control valve in a reciprocating engine oil system is to

A — direct oil through or around the oil cooler.

B — deliver cold oil to the hopper tank.

C — compensate for volumetric increases due to foaming of the oil.

8474. Answer A. AC 65-12A

A flow control valve determines whether the oil passes through or around the oil cooler. When oil is cold, the flow control valve directs the oil around the cooler and back to the tank for circulation. However, when the oil is hot, the flow control valve directs the oil through the oil cooler. Answer (B) is wrong because the hopper tank receives cooled oil through an oil return fitting on top of the oil tank, while answer (C) is wrong because oil tanks have a built-in expansion space to compensate for volumetric changes.

8475.   **K03**

Where are sludge chambers, when used in aircraft engine lubrication systems, usually located?

A — In the crankshaft throws.

B — Adjacent to the scavenger pumps.

C — In the oil storage tank.

8475. Answer A. AC 65-12A

Some crankshafts are manufactured with hollow crankpins that serve as sludge removers, or chambers. On a crankshaft with sludge chambers, centrifugal motion forces sludge and other foreign material into the sludge chambers during engine operation. This sludge remains in the sludge chamber until the engine is overhauled.

8476.   **K03**

Why is an aircraft reciprocating engine oil tank on a dry sump lubrication system equipped with a vent line?

A — To prevent pressure buildup in the reciprocating engine crankcase.

B — To eliminate foaming in the oil tank.

C — To prevent pressure buildup in the oil tank.

8476. Answer C. AC 65-12A

Reciprocating engine oil tanks are equipped with vent lines to ensure proper tank ventilation in all flight attitudes and prevent pressure buildup in the oil tank. The vent line is usually connected to the engine crankcase which is vented to the atmosphere through the crankcase breather. Answer (A) is incorrect because the crankcase breather, not the oil tank vent line, prevents pressure buildup in the engine. Answer (B) is incorrect because oil foaming is a direct result of the oil being splashed around during circulation and has nothing to do with the oil tank vent lines.

8477.   **K03**

Excessive oil is prevented from accumulating on the cylinder walls of a reciprocating engine by

A — the design shape of the piston skirt.

B — internal engine pressure bleeding past the ring grooves.

C — oil control rings on the pistons.

8477. Answer C. AC 65-12A

Oil control rings regulate the oil film thickness on the cylinder wall by removing excess oil and allowing it to return to the crankcase. Although extended piston skirts can help keep oil from accumulating in the lower cylinders of radial engines, piston skirt shape (answer A) does not prevent excessive oil buildup on cylinder walls. Answer (B) is wrong because pressure bleeding past the ring grooves would reduce engine power output substantially.

8478.   **K03**

(1) Wet sump oil systems are most commonly used in gas turbine engines.
(2) In most turbine engine oil tanks, a slight pressurzation of the tank is desired to ensure a positive flow of oil.

Regarding the above statements,

A — both No. 1 and No. 2 are true.
B — only No. 2 is true.
C — neither No. 1 nor No. 2 is true.

8479.   **K03**

The pumping capacity of the scavenger pump in a dry sump aircraft engine's lubrication system

A — is greater than the capacity of the oil supply pump.
B — is less than the capacity of the oil supply pump.
C — is usually equal to the capacity of the oil supply pump in order to maintain constant oiling conditions.

8480.   **K03**

In which of the following situations will the oil cooler automatic bypass valve be open the greatest amount?

A — Engine oil above normal operating temperature.
B — Engine oil below normal operating temperature.
C — Engine stopped with no oil flowing after runup.

8481.   **K03**

In order to maintain a constant oil pressure as the clearances between the moving parts of an engine increase through normal wear, the supply pump output

A — increases as the resistance offered to the flow of oil increases.
B — remains relatively constant (at a given RPM) with less oil being returned to the pump inlet by the relief valve.
C — remains relatively constant (at a given RPM) with more oil being returned to the pump inlet by the relief valve.

8478. Answer B. AC 65-12A

Only statement number (2) is correct. Although wet sump oil systems were used on some early turbine engines, they are not commonly used today. However, most turbine engine oil tanks are pressurized slightly to ensure a positive flow of oil.

8479. Answer A. AC 65-12A

The scavenger pump in a dry sump lubrication system is responsible for pumping circulated oil from the sump back to the oil tank. However, because the oil thermally expands once it gets to the sump, scavenger pumps must have a greater capacity than the pressure pump to prevent oil from collecting in the sump. A scavenger pump with less capacity than the pressure pump (answer B) or an equal capacity (answer C) could not return enough oil to the oil tank which could lead to pressure pump cavitation.

8480. Answer B. AC 65-12A

The bypass valve on an oil cooler regulates the amount of oil that flows through the oil cooler. When the engine oil is below normal operating temperature the bypass valve is fully open so the oil can bypass the oil cooler. However, once the oil reaches its operating temperature, the bypass valve closes and allows the oil to pass through the oil cooler. Answers (A) and (C) are incorrect because at elevated temperatures during operation or just after engine shutdown, the bypass valve is partially closed.

8481. Answer B. AC 65-12A

Most oil pumps used in aircraft engines provide excessive oil pressure when run at a high rpm and, therefore, a relief valve must be used to maintain a constant pressure. When the relief valve opens, oil is directed back to the oil pump inlet for recirculation. With this type of system, as the clearances between moving parts increase, the pump output remains constant but less oil is returned to the pump inlet by the relief valve. Answer (A) is incorrect because resistance to oil flow drops as operating tolerances increase. Answer (C) is wrong because less oil is returned to the pump inlet, not more.

8482.   K03

The valve assemblies of opposed reciprocating engines are lubricated by means of a

A — gravity feed system.
B — splash and spray system.
C — pressure system.

8482. Answer C. AC 65-12A

The overhead valve assemblies of opposed engines used in helicopters and airplanes are lubricated by a pressure system. In this type of system, pressurized oil flows through the hydraulic tappet body and through hollow pushrods to the rocker arm where it lubricates the rocker arm bearing and the valve stem. Answer (A) is wrong because the valve train components are horizontal on an opposed engine and a gravity feed system would be ineffective. Answer (B) is incorrect because there would have to be a sump or reservoir of oil within each cylinder head for a splash system to work.

8483.   K03

What will result if an oil filter becomes completely blocked?

A — Oil will flow at a reduced rate through the system.
B — Oil flow to the engine will stop.
C — Oil will flow at the normal rate through the system.

8483. Answer C. AC 65-12A

Aircraft engine oil systems are equipped with a bypass valve that allows oil to flow at a normal rate around the filter in the event the filter should become clogged or the oil becomes too congealed to flow through it. Both answers (A) and (B) are wrong because, as long as there is a bypass valve, oil will continue to flow at a normal rate.

8484.   K03

A turbine engine dry sump lubrication system of the self-contained, high-pressure design

A — has no heat exchanger.
B — consists of pressure, breather, and scavenge subsystems.
C — stores oil in the engine crankcase.

8484. Answer B. AC 65-12A

The dry-sump lubrication system of a typical turbine engine consists of pressure, scavenge, and breather subsystems. The pressure system supplies oil to the main engine bearings and to the accessory drives, while the scavenge system returns the oil to the engine oil tank for recirculation. The breather system vents the individual bearing compartments and the oil tank to atmosphere through a breather pressurizing valve. Answer (A) is incorrect since all turbine engine lubrication systems contain a heat exchanger to cool the oil. Answer (C) is wrong because a turbine engine has no crankcase and, therefore, oil cannot be stored there.

8485.   K03

Lube system last chance filters in turbine engines are usually cleaned

A — during annual inspection.
B — during 100-hour inspections.
C — during overhaul.

8485. Answer C. AC 65-12A

Last chance filters in turbine engines are typically located at the oil jets within the bearing housing. Since bearing housings are not readily available for disassembly and inspection, last chance filters are typically cleaned when an engine is overhauled.

8486.   K03

How are the piston pins of most aircraft engines lubricated?

A — By pressure oil through a drilled passageway in the heavy web portion of the connecting rod.
B — By oil which is sprayed or thrown by the master or connecting rods.
C — By the action of the oil control ring and the series of holes drilled in the ring groove directing oil to the pin and piston pin boss.

8486. Answer B. AC 65-12A

The piston pins on most reciprocating engines are lubricated by oil which is sprayed or thrown from the master or connecting rod. Answer (A) is incorrect because connecting rods are highly stressed components and drilled passageways would weaken them substantially. Answer (C) is wrong because the oil control rings direct oil toward the crankcase, away from the piston pin and piston pin boss.

8487.   **K03**

The vent line connecting the oil supply tank and the engine in some dry sump engine installations permits

A — pressurization of the oil supply to prevent cavitation of the oil supply pump.
B — oil vapors from the engine to be condensed and drained into the oil supply tank.
C — the oil tank to be vented through the normal engine vent.

8488.   **K03**

An engine lubrication system pressure relief valve is usually located between the

A — oil cooler and the scavenger pump.
B — scavenger pump and the external oil system.
C — pump and the internal oil system.

8489.   **K03**

Where is the oil of a dry sump reciprocating engine exposed to the temperature control valve sensing unit?

A — Oil cooler inlet.
B — Engine outlet.
C — Engine inlet.

8490.   **K03**

Under which of the following conditions is the oil cooler flow control valve open on a reciprocating engine?

A — When the temperature of the oil returning from the engine is too high.
B — When the temperature of the oil returning from the engine is too low.
C — When the scavenger pump output volume exceeds the engine pump input volume.

8487. Answer C. AC 65-12A

Oil tanks are equipped with vent lines to ensure proper tank ventilation in all flight attitudes. These lines are usually connected to the engine crankcase which is vented to the atmosphere through the crankcase breather. Therefore, the oil tank is indirectly vented through the engine vent (answer C). Answer (A) is incorrect because oil tanks are typically not pressurized, and answer (B) is wrong because, although some engine oil vapors condense in the oil tank, this is a secondary function of the vent line.

8488. Answer C. AC 65-12A

To prevent internal engine damage caused by excessive oil pressure, an oil pressure relief valve is typically installed between the pressure pump and the internal oil system. This way, if the pump output pressure exceeds the recommended system pressure, the relief valve can relieve the excess pressure before the oil enters the engine. Answers (A) and (B) are incorrect since placing the relief valve downstream from where the oil enters the engine could result in substantial internal engine damage.

8489. Answer A. AC 65-12A

The temperature control valve, sometimes called the flow control valve, is located at the oil cooler inlet and determines whether or not the oil passes through the oil cooler. When the oil is cold, the flow control valve directs oil around the jacket surrounding the cooler to allow the oil to warm quickly. However, when the oil reaches its operating temperature, the flow control valve closes and directs oil through the oil cooler core. Since the flow control valve controls oil cooler operation, it cannot be located at the engine outlet (answer B) or inlet (answer C).

8490. Answer B. AC 65-12A

The temperature control valve, or flow control valve, is located at the oil cooler inlet and determines whether or not the oil passes through the oil cooler. When the oil is cold, the flow control valve is open and directs oil around the jacket surrounding the cooler to allow the oil to warm quickly. However, when the oil reaches its operating temperature, the flow control valve closes and directs oil through the oil cooler core. Answer (A) is incorrect because the flow control valve is closed, not open, when the oil temperature is too high. Furthermore, since flow control valve operation depends on temperature, scavenger pump output volume (answer C) has no bearing on the valve's function.

8491. K03
The purpose of a relief valve installed in the tank venting system of a turbine engine oil tank is to

A — prevent oil pump cavitation by maintaining a constant pressure on the oil pump inlet.
B — maintain internal tank air pressure at the ambient atmospheric level regardless of altitude or rate of change in altitude.
C — maintain a positive internal pressure in the oil tank after shutdown to prevent oil pump cavitation on engine start.

8492. K03
In a reciprocating engine, oil is directed from the pressure relief valve to the inlet side of the

A — scavenger pump.
B — oil temperature regulator.
C — pressure pump.

8493. K03
If the oil in the oil cooler core and annular jacket becomes congealed, what unit prevents damage to the cooler?

A — Oil pressure relief valve.
B — Airflow control valve.
C — Surge protection valve.

8494. K03
The primary source of oil contamination in a normally operating reciprocating engine is

A — metallic deposits as a result of engine wear.
B — atmospheric dust and pollution.
C — combustion deposits due to combustion chamber blow-by and oil migration on the cylinder walls.

8491. Answer A. AC 65-12A
In most turbine engine oil tanks, a slight pressure buildup is desired to ensure a positive flow of oil to the oil pump inlet. This pressure buildup is accomplished by installing an adjustable check relief valve in the tank overboard vent line. This check valve is set between three to six psig to maintain positive pressure within the oil tank. Answer (B) is wrong because the purpose of the relief valve is to maintain a tank pressure above that of the ambient pressure. Answer (C) is incorrect because the relief valve does not maintain system pressure after engine shutdown.

8492. Answer C. AC 65-12A
To avoid damage to an engine's internal lubrication system, an oil pressure relief valve is installed after the oil pressure pump outlet that relieves excess pressure by directing some of the excess oil back to the inlet side of the pressure pump.

8493. Answer C. AC 65-12A
If the oil in an oil cooler becomes congealed, the scavenge pump could build up enough pressure in the system to cause damage. To prevent this high pressure from damaging the oil cooler, some engines are equipped with a surge protection valve in either the oil cooler or the oil return line. Answer (A) is incorrect because the oil pressure relief valve is installed on the main pressure pump and is not able to relieve excess pressure created by the scavenge pump on the return side of the system. Answer (B) is wrong because an airflow control valve regulates cooling air that flows to the oil cooler and cannot relieve excessive oil pressures.

8494. Answer C. AC 65-12A
The primary source of oil contamination in a reciprocating engine is combustion by-products that escape past the piston rings (blow-by), and oil carbonizing that occurs when oil becomes trapped in the pores of the cylinder walls and is burned. Answer (A) is incorrect because an engine's oil filtration system eliminates most metallic particles, and answer (B) is wrong because most oil systems are fairly well sealed, making it extremely difficult for atmospheric dust and pollution to enter the oil.

8495.   **K03**

A drop in oil pressure may be caused by

A — the temperature regulator sticking open.
B — the bypass valve sticking open.
C — foreign material under the relief valve.

8496.   **K03**

The main oil filters strain the oil at which point in the system?

A — Immediately after it leaves the scavenger pump.
B — Immediately before it enters the pressure pump.
C — Just as it leaves the pressure pump.

8497.   **K03**

Which type valve prevents oil from entering the main accessory case when the engine is not running?

A — Bypass.
B — Relief.
C — Check.

8498.   **K03**

An oil tank having a capacity of 5 gallons must have an expansion space of

A — 2 quarts.
B — 4 quarts.
C — 5 quarts.

8499.   **K03**

As a general rule, a small amount of small fuzzy particles or gray metallic paste on a turbine engine magnetic chip detector

A — is considered to be the result of normal wear.
B — indicates an imminent component failure.
C — indicates accelerated generalized wear.

8495. Answer C. AC 65-12A

When oil pressure in an engine becomes excessive, the pressure relief valve unseats and excess oil is directed back to the inlet of the pressure pump. If foreign matter causes the relief valve to stick open, oil would continue to be bypassed even when the pressure was not excessive. This would cause a reduced amount of oil to flow to the engine which, in turn, would cause a low oil pressure. Answer (A) is incorrect because if a temperature regulator sticks open, oil temperature rises but oil pressure remains constant. Answer (B) is incorrect because if a bypass valve sticks open, the oil would simply bypass the oil filter with no change in pressure.

8496. Answer C. AC 65-12A

In most aircraft oil systems, the main oil filter is located immediately downstream of the pressure pump to ensure clean oil enters the engine. Answers (A) and (B) are incorrect because locating the main filter after the scavenge pump or just upstream of the pressure pump increases the chance of contamination being introduced into the engine.

8497. Answer C. AC 65-12A

In both reciprocating and turbine dry-sump lubrication systems, check valves are installed between the oil tank and the engine. These valves are set at two to five psi, and their purpose is to prevent oil from draining into the engine when the engine is not operating. Answers (A) and (B) are incorrect because bypass and relief valves open at pressure values considerably higher than a simple check valve requires.

8498. Answer A. FAR 23.1013

According to the FAR 23.1013, an oil tank must have an expansion space of 10 percent or 0.5 gallon, whichever is greater. In this example, 10 percent of 5 gallons is 2 quarts which is equivalent to 0.5 gallon. Therefore, answer (A) is correct.

8499. Answer A. ITP-P2

Normal turbine engine operation results in small fuzzy particles or a gray metallic paste accumulating on the chip detector. Imminent component failure (answer B) and accelerated generalized wear (answer C) are typically identified by larger particles of different metals.

8500.   **K03**

Why is expansion space required in an engine oil supply tank?

A — To eliminate oil foaming.
B — For oil enlargement and collection of foam.
C — For proper oil tank ventilation.

8501.   **K03**

The purpose of a dwell chamber in a turbine engine oil tank is to provide

A — a collection point for sediments.
B — for a pressurized oil supply to the oil pump inlet.
C — separation of entrained air from scavenged oil.

8502.   **K03**

Which of the following bearing types must be continuously lubricated by pressure oil?

A — Ball.
B — Roller.
C — Plain.

8500. Answer B. AC 65-12A

All oil tanks are provided with expansion space that allows for thermal expansion and foaming. The complete elimination of oil foaming (answer A) is impossible and proper tank ventilation (answer C) is provided by a vent line to the engine crankcase which, in turn, is vented to the atmosphere.

8501. Answer C. AC 65-12A

A dwell chamber, sometimes referred to as a deaerator, provides a means of separating entrained air from scavenge oil. Turbine engine oil tanks do not have separate collection points for sediments (answer A). Answer (B) is incorrect because in most turbine engine oil tanks, the tank vent line employs an adjustable check relief valve to maintain positive pressure.

8502. Answer C. AC 65-12A

All bearings require lubrication. However, plain bearings must have oil supplied to them under pressure to prevent metal-to-metal contact. Answers (A) and (B) are wrong because ball and roller bearings do not require oil supplied under pressure to prevent metal-to-metal contact.

IGNITION AND STARTING SYSTEMS

CHAPTER

8

This chapter provides information on reciprocating and turbine engine ignition and starting systems. For reciprocating engines, you must be familiar with the principles and proper maintenance practices used to inspect, service, troubleshoot, and repair both high and low tension magneto systems while for turbine engines you must understand the operation of a capacitance-type ignition system. The following FAA exam questions are taken from this chapter:

8503, 8504, 8505, 8506, 8507, 8508, 8509, 8510, 8511, 8512, 8513, 8514, 8515, 8516, 8517, 8518, 8519, 8520, 8521, 8522, 8523, 8524, 8525, 8526, 8527, 8528, 8529, 8530, 8531, 8532, 8533, 8534, 8535, 8536, 8537, 8538, 8539, 8540, 8541, 8542, 8543, 8544, 8545, 8546, 8547, 8548, 8549, 8550, 8551, 8552, 8553, 8554, 8555, 8556, 8557, 8558, 8559, 8560, 8561, 8562, 8563, 8564, 8565, 8566, 8567, 8568, 8569, 8570, 8571, 8572, 8573, 8574, 8575, 8576, 8577, 8578, 8579, 8580, 8581, 8582, 8583, 8584, 8585, 8586, 8587, 8588, 8589, 8590, 8591, 8592, 8593, 8594, 8595, 8596, 8597, 8598, 8599, 8600, 8601, 8602, 8603, 8604, 8605, 8606, 8607, 8608, 8609, 8610, 8611, 8612, 8613, 8614, 8615, 8616, 8617, 8618, 8619, 8620, 8621, 8622, 8623, 8624, 8625, 8626, 8627, 8628, 8629, 8630, 8631, 8632, 8633.

8503.   L01

When a magneto is disassembled, keepers are usually placed across the poles of the rotating magnet to reduce the loss of magnetism. These keepers are usually made of

A — chrome magnet steel.
B — soft iron.
C — cobalt steel.

8503. Answer B. AC 65-9A

Almost all magnets, regardless of their retentivity, lose some of their magnetic strength when their lines of flux pass through the air. Therefore, during the overhaul of a magneto, when the rotating magnet is removed, it should be placed in a soft iron keeper to prevent loss of magnetism. A "keeper" is a piece of soft iron that is used to link the magnetic poles and provide a highly permeable path for the flux. "Chrome magnet steel" (answer A) is not a commonly used term and does not describe an actual alloy. Answer (C) is incorrect because cobalt is rarely alloyed with steel.

8504.   L01

How is the strength of a magneto magnet checked?

A — Hold the points open and check the output of the primary coil with an ac ammeter while operating the magneto at a specified speed.
B — Check the ac voltage reading at the breaker points.
C — Check the output of the secondary coil with an ac ammeter while operating the magneto at a specified speed.

8504. Answer A.

There are two common methods for checking the strength of a magneto magnet. If the magnet is removed from the magneto, it is checked with a magnetometer. However, if the magneto is assembled, the magnet's strength is checked by holding the points open and then checking the output of the primary with an AC ammeter as the magneto is rotated at a specified speed. Answer (B) is incorrect because the breaker points only trigger the collapse of the primary field and cannot indicate its strength. Answer (C) is incorrect because the output of the secondary coil relates to factors other than the strength of the rotating magnet and, therefore, is not a reliable indicator of a magnet's strength.

8505.   L01

The E-gap angle is usually defined as the number of degrees between the neutral position of the rotating magnet and the position

A — where the contact points close.
B — where the contact points open.
C — of greatest magnetic flux density.

8505. Answer B. AC 65-12A

The number of degrees between the neutral position of the rotating magnet and the position where the contact points open is called the E-gap angle. When the rotor is at the E-gap angle the cam opens the breaker points and current stops flowing through the primary coil. This sudden stoppage of current flow causes the magnetic field in the coil core to collapse and induce a voltage into the secondary winding. Answer (A) is incorrect because the E-gap angle identifies the point where the contact points open, not where they close. Answer (C) is wrong because the flux density at the E-gap position is low.

8506.   L01

The greatest density of flux lines in the magnetic circuit of a rotating magnet-type magneto occurs when the magnet is in what position?

A — Full alignment with the field shoe faces.
B — A certain angular displacement beyond the neutral position, referred to as E-gap angle or position.
C — The position where the contact points open.

8506. Answer A. AC 65-12A

The greatest flux density within a rotating magnet-type magneto occurs when the poles of the magnet are fully aligned with the field shoe faces. This position is known as the full register position. Answer (B) is incorrect because the E-gap position identifies the point where the flux density is least dense, and answer (C) is wrong because the points open at the E-gap position which, as stated above, is the point where flux density is the least.

8507.   L01

Magneto breaker point opening relative to the position of the rotating magnet and distributor rotor (internal timing) can be set most accurately

A — during the magneto-to-engine timing operation.
B — during assembly of the magneto before installation on the engine.
C — by setting the points roughly at the required clearance before installing the magneto and then making the fine breaker point adjustment after installation to compensate for wear in the magneto drive train.

8507. Answer B. AC 65-12A

The internal timing of a magneto is most easily set when the magneto is being assembled prior to installation. Both answers (A) and (C) are wrong because both answers require the magneto to be installed and it is nearly impossible to internally time a magneto when it is installed on an engine.

8508.   L01

Why are high-tension ignition cables frequently routed from the distributors to the spark plugs in flexible metallic conduits?

A — To eliminate high altitude flashover.
B — To reduce the formation of corona and nitric oxide on the cable insulation.
C — To reduce the effect of the high-frequency electromagnetic waves emanated during operation.

8508. Answer C. AC 65-12A

The ignition harness on reciprocating engines serve several purposes. It supports the wires going from the magneto to each spark plug and protects them from engine heat, vibration, and weather. Ignition harnesses also serve as a conductor for the stray magnetic fields that surround the wires as they momentarily carry high-voltage current. Therefore, by routing the ignition leads through metallic conduits, the stray magnetic fields are easily conducted to ground, thereby reducing electrical interference with aircraft radio equipment. Answer (A) is wrong because flashover occurs in a distributor when high voltage current flashes across a wet insulating surface to ground. Answer (B) is incorrect because a corona occurs when a high voltage breaks down a conductor's insulation and discharges to the atmosphere or to some adjacent conductor. Since flexible metal conduits do not provide any additional insulation they do not prevent corona discharge.

8509. **L01**
What will be the results of increasing the gap of the breaker points in a magneto?

A — Retard the spark and increase its intensity.
B — Advance the spark and decrease its intensity.
C — Retard the spark and decrease its intensity.

8510. **L01**
What is the purpose of a safety gap in some magnetos?

A — To discharge the secondary coil's voltage if an open occurs in the secondary circuit.
B — To ground the magneto when the ignition switch is off.
C — To prevent flashover in the distributor.

8511. **L01**
When timing a magneto internally, the alignment of the timing marks indicates that the

A — breaker points are just closing.
B — magnets are in the neutral position.
C — magnets are in the E-gap position.

8512. **L01**
When internally timing a magneto, the breaker points begin to open when the rotating magnet is

A — fully aligned with the pole shoes.
B — a few degrees past full alignment with the pole shoes.
C — a few degrees past the neutral position.

8513. **L01**
What is the electrical location of the primary capacitor in a high-tension magneto?

A — In parallel with the breaker points.
B — In series with the breaker points.
C — In a series with the primary and secondary winding.

8509. Answer B. AC 65-12A
Any time the gap between the breaker points in a magneto is increased, the points will open early. When the points open early, the spark within the cylinder occurs in advance of when it is supposed to. Furthermore, early opening points also cause a decrease in spark intensity. Answers (A) and (C) are incorrect because the breaker point gap must be decreased to retard the spark.

8510. Answer A.
Some magnetos contain a safety gap that protects the secondary coil. The safety gap is connected in series with the secondary circuit by two electrodes. One electrode is attached to the high tension brush holder and the other electrode is grounded to the ground plate. With this configuration, if excessive voltage builds in the secondary circuit due to an open that does not allow the spark to jump the spark plug electrodes, the excessive voltage jumps the safety gap to the ground connection. This helps ensure that the voltage cannot rise high enough to damage the insulation within the secondary coil. Answer (B) is incorrect because the ignition switch, not the safety gap, grounds the magneto. Answer (C) is incorrect because flashover is prevented by ventilating the magneto to reduce moisture accumulation and by insulating coils, condensers, distributors, and distributor rotors with wax.

8511. Answer C. AC 65-12A
When the timing marks within a magneto are aligned, the magnets are in the E-gap position and the breaker points are just beginning to open. Answer (A) is wrong because alignment of the timing marks indicates that the breaker points are opening, not closing. Furthermore, since the magnets are several degrees past the neutral position when the timing marks are aligned, answer (B) is incorrect.

8512. Answer C. AC 65-12A
When internally timing a magneto, the breaker points should begin to open when the rotating magnet is a few degrees past the neutral position. The neutral position is defined as the point where the rotating magnet is 45 degrees past full alignment with the pole shoes.

8513. Answer A. AC 65-12A
The primary electrical circuit in a magneto consists of a set of breaker contact points, a capacitor, and an insulated coil. The capacitor is wired in parallel with the breaker points to prevent arcing between the points when they open, and to hasten the collapse of the magnetic field around the primary coil. If a capacitor were connected in series with the breaker points (answer B) the magneto would not operate. Answer (C) is wrong because a capacitor is only installed between the ignition switch and the breaker points of a low-tension magneto, and this question refers to a high-tension system.

8514. **L01**

In a high-tension ignition system, the current in the magneto secondary winding is

A — conducted from the primary winding via the discharge of the capacitor.
B — induced when the primary circuit is interrupted.
C — induced when the primary circuit discharges via the breaker points.

8515. **L01**

When a "Shower of Sparks" ignition system is activated at an engine start, a spark plug fires

A — as soon as the advance breaker points open.
B — only while both the retard and advance breaker points are closed.
C — only while both the retard and advance breaker points are open.

8516. **L01**

What is the radial location of the two north poles of a four-pole rotating magnet in a high-tension magneto?

A — 180° apart.
B — 270° apart.
C — 90° apart.

8517. **L01**

Magneto pole shoes are generally made of

A — laminations of high-grade soft iron.
B — laminations of high-grade Alnico.
C — pieces of high-carbon iron.

8514. Answer B. AC 65-12A

Current is induced into a magneto's secondary winding when the current within the primary winding is interrupted suddenly, causing a high rate of flux change. Current is interrupted by opening the primary breaker points when the rotating magnet is in the E-gap position. Answer (A) is wrong because the primary purpose of the capacitor is to prevent arcing between the points and have little to do with current in the secondary winding. Answer (C) is incorrect because the primary circuit does not discharge, it is only interrupted.

8515. Answer C. AC 65-12A

With a "shower of sparks" ignition system, an electrically operated vibrator rapidly opens and closes both the retard and advance breaker points. This action causes the current flowing through the primary coil to be interrupted several times per second which, in turn, causes the magnetic field surrounding the primary coil to build and collapse at the same rate. The rapid successions of separate voltages that are induced into the secondary coil by the pulsating magnetic field around the primary coil produce a "shower of sparks" across the selected spark plug when both of the breaker points are open (answer C). Answer (A) is wrong because both breaker points must be open to cause a spark plug to fire, and answer (B) is wrong because both the breaker points must be open to induce a spark, not closed.

8516. Answer A. AC 65-12A

In a four-pole rotating magnet, the two north poles are located 180 degrees apart. Answer (B) is wrong because it is impossible for the north poles of a rotating magnet with an even number of poles to be 270 degrees apart. Answer (C) is incorrect because the north poles would be 90 degrees apart on an eight-pole magnet, not a four-pole magnet.

8517. Answer A. AC 65-9A

Magneto pole shoes and their extensions must be extremely permeable to allow the rotating magnet's flux lines to easily pass from the magnet's north pole, through the primary coil, and back to the magnet's south pole. Therefore, magneto pole shoes are generally made of soft iron laminations. Answer (B) is wrong because Alnico is used in the magneto's rotating magnets but not in the pole shoes. Answer (C) is incorrect because high-carbon iron is not as permeable as soft iron.

8518.   **L01**
Capacitance afterfiring in most modern spark plugs is reduced by the use of

A — fine wire electrodes.
B — a built-in resistor in each plug.
C — aluminum oxide insulation.

8518. Answer B. ITP-P2
The shielding used on ignition leads to protect against radio interference can act as a capacitor and store electrical energy that is released when the spark jumps the spark plug gap. When this happens, the energy that is stored in the capacitance of the ignition harness is returned to the spark plug, and afterfiring occurs. To minimize this problem, spark plugs have a resistor installed inside the spark plug insulator that prevents the electrical energy stored in the harness from reaching the spark plug gap. Answer (A) simply lists a type of spark plug and has nothing to do with afterfiring. Answer (C) is wrong because aluminum oxide is not used as insulation.

8519.   **L01**
What components make up the magnetic system of a magneto?

A — Pole shoes, the pole shoe extensions, and the primary coil.
B — Primary and secondary coils.
C — Rotating magnet, the pole shoes, the pole shoe extensions, and the coil core.

8519. Answer C. AC 65-12A
The magnetic circuit of a magneto consists of a permanent rotating magnet, a pair of soft iron pole shoes and pole shoe extensions, and a coil core. Answers (A) and (B) are incorrect because the primary and secondary coils are part of the primary and secondary electrical circuits, not the magnetic system.

8520.   **L01**
In an aircraft ignition system, one of the functions of the capacitor is to

A — regulate the flow of current between the primary and secondary coil.
B — facilitate a more rapid collapse of the magnetic field in the primary coil.
C — stop the flow of magnetic lines of force when the points open.

8520. Answer B. AC 65-12A
The purpose of the capacitor in the primary electrical circuit is to prevent arcing between the points when they are opened, and to hasten the collapse of the magnetic field surrounding the primary coil. Answer (A) is incorrect because there is no flow of current between the primary and secondary coils. Answer (C) is wrong because opening the points stops current flow in the primary circuit, not the flow of magnetic lines of force.

8521.   **L01**
When will the voltage in the secondary winding of a magneto, installed on a normally operating engine, be at its highest value?

A — Just prior to spark plug firing.
B — Toward the latter part of the spark duration when the flame front reaches its maximum velocity.
C — Immediately after the breaker points close.

8521. Answer A. AC 65-12A
A high voltage is induced into the secondary winding when there is a rapid change in the magnetic field surrounding the primary coil. The amount of voltage within the secondary winding builds from its lowest value immediately before the breaker points close to a maximum value just prior to the spark plug firing. Answer (B) is incorrect because the voltage within the secondary winding approaches its lowest value toward the latter part of the spark duration. Answer (C) is wrong because when the breaker points are closed, there is little current induced in the secondary coil.

8522.   **L01**
When the switch is off in a battery ignition system, the primary circuit is

A — grounded.
B — opened.
C — shorted.

8522. Answer B. AC 65-12A
In a battery ignition system, when the ignition switch is on, current is supplied to the primary coil. However, when the switch is off, the primary circuit opens and current cannot flow to the primary coil. Answer (A) is wrong because it describes what happens to the primary circuit in a magneto system when the ignition switch is off.

8523.   L01

As an aircraft engine's speed is increased, the voltage induced in the primary coil of the magneto

A — remains constant.
B — increases.
C — varies with the setting of the voltage regulator.

8524.   L01

When internally timing a magneto, the breaker points begin to open when

A — the piston has just passed TDC at the end of the compression stroke.
B — the magnet poles are a few degrees beyond the neutral position.
C — the magnet poles are fully aligned with the pole shoes.

8525.   L01

The purpose of a safety gap in a magneto is to

A — prevent burning out the primary winding.
B — protect the high-voltage winding from damage.
C — prevent burning of contact points.

8526.   L01

A defective primary capacitor in a magneto is indicated by

A — a fine-grained frosted appearance of the breaker points.
B — burned and pitted breaker points.
C — a weak spark.

8523. Answer B. AC 65-12A

The amount of voltage induced in the primary coil of a magneto varies with the rate at which the magnet's lines of flux are cut. Therefore, the faster an engine runs, the faster the flux lines are cut and the greater the induced voltage (answer B). Answer (A) is incorrect because the amount of induced voltage does not remain constant, and answer (C) is incorrect because magneto ignition systems contain no voltage regulator.

8524. Answer B. AC 65-12A

When internally timing a magneto, the breaker points should begin to open when the rotating magnet is a few degrees past the neutral position. The neutral position is defined as the point where the rotating magnet is 45 degrees past full alignment with the pole shoes. Answer (A) is wrong because piston position relates to the timing of the magneto to the engine, not to the magneto's internal timing. Answer (C) is incorrect because when the poles are aligned with the pole shoes at the "full register" position, the breaker points are closed, not open.

8525. Answer B.

Some magnetos contain a safety gap that protects the secondary coil. The safety gap is connected in series with the secondary circuit by two electrodes. One electrode is attached to the high tension brush holder while the other electrode is grounded to the ground plate. With this configuration, if excessive voltage builds in the secondary circuit due to an open that does not allow the spark to jump the spark plug electrodes, the excessive voltage jumps the safety gap to the ground connection. This helps ensure that the voltage cannot rise high enough to damage insulation within the secondary coil. Answer (A) is wrong because a safety gap prevents the secondary winding from burning out, not the primary. Answer (C) is incorrect because a capacitor, not a safety gap, prevents contact points from becoming burned or pitted.

8526. Answer B. AC 65-12A

One of the purposes of a capacitor in a magneto is to prevent arcing across the breaker points once the points open. Therefore, a good indication of a defective capacitor is breaker points that are burned or pitted from arcing. Answer (A) is incorrect because a dull gray or sandblasted appearance indicates a properly functioning capacitor, and answer (C) is incorrect because a defective condenser will not have an appreciable affect on the strength of the spark.

8527.   L01
How many secondary coils are required in a low-tension ignition system on an 18-cylinder engine?

A — 36.
B — 18.
C — 9.

8527. Answer A. AC 65-12A
In a low-tension ignition system, a primary and secondary coil are located near each of the spark plugs. Therefore, a standard 18-cylinder engine with two spark plugs per cylinder utilizes 36 secondary coils.

8528.   L01
A magneto ignition switch is connected

A — in series with the breaker points.
B — parallel to the breaker points.
C — in series with the primary capacitor and parallel to the breaker points.

8528. Answer B. AC 65-12A
The ignition switch in a magneto circuit is wired in parallel with the breaker points and the primary capacitor. In other words, from the ignition switch, there are two possible paths current can flow; either through the breaker points or through the primary of the coil. Answer (A) is incorrect because the ignition switch is connected in parallel with the breaker points in a magneto system, not in series. Answer (C) is wrong because the primary capacitor is connected in parallel with the breaker points and, therefore, is in parallel with the ignition switch.

8529.   L01
The spark is produced in a magneto ignition system when the breaker points are

A — fully open.
B — beginning to open.
C — fully closed.

8529. Answer B. AC 65-12A
Current is induced into the secondary winding to produce a spark when the breaker points begin to open, causing the magnetic field surrounding the primary coil to collapse. The spark has subsided by the time the points are fully open (answer A), and when the points are fully closed (answer C) no spark is produced because there is no collapsing field to induce current in the secondary coil.

8530.   L01
Shielding is used on spark plug and ignition wires to

A — protect the wires from short circuits as a result of chafing and rubbing.
B — prevent outside electromagnetic emissions from disrupting the operation of the ignition system.
C — prevent interference with radio reception.

8530. Answer C. AC 65-12A
The shielding used on spark plug and ignition wires serves to prevent or reduce interference with radio reception. Without this shielding, the stray magnetic fields that surround the wires when they momentarily carry the high-voltage current could make radio communication virtually impossible. Protecting the wires from physical wear such as chafing and abrasion (answer A) is the job of the ignition wire's insulation and other protective sleeves. Answer (B) is wrong because, typically, there are no electromagnetic emissions produced in an aircraft that can disrupt the operation of the ignition system.

8531.   L01
What is the purpose of using an impulse coupling with a magneto?

A — To absorb impulse vibrations between the magneto and the engine.
B — To compensate for backlash in the magneto and the engine gears.
C — To produce a momentary high rotational speed of the magneto.

8531. Answer C. AC 65-12A
An impulse coupling is designed to induce a momentary high rotational speed which increases the rate at which the lines of flux in the primary coil are cut. This produces a more intense spark that aids in starting. Answers (A) and (B) are wrong because an impulse coupling does nothing to absorb vibrations between the magneto and the engine, or compensate for backlash in the magneto and engine gears.

8532.　　　L01

The purpose of staggered ignition is to compensate for

A — short ignition harness.
B — rich fuel/air mixture around exhaust valve.
C — diluted fuel/air mixture around exhaust valve.

8532. Answer C.

In a dual-ignition system, the spark plugs may be set to fire at the same instant (synchronized) or at slightly different intervals (staggered). When a staggered ignition is used, the spark plug in the exhaust side of the cylinder is always fired first to compensate for the slower burn rate of the diluted fuel/air mixture in this portion of the cylinder. Answer (A) is wrong because the only way to compensate for a short ignition harness is to install one of the correct size. Answer (B) is incorrect because heat from the exhaust valve expands and dilutes the fuel/air mixture, producing a lean mixture, not a rich mixture.

8533.　　　L01

Aircraft magneto housings are usually ventilated in order to

A — prevent the entrance of outside air which may contain moisture.
B — allow heated air from the accessory compartment to keep the internal parts of the magneto dry.
C — provide cooling and remove corrosive gases produced by normal arcing.

8533. Answer C. AC 65-12A

Magnetos require adequate drains and proper ventilation to provide cooling and prevent moisture from building inside a magneto and shorting across the internal components. In addition, good magneto ventilation helps ensure that the corrosive gases produced by normal arcing across the distributor air gap are carried away. Answer (A) is incorrect since outside air is intentionally admitted into the magneto to facilitate ventilation. Although heated air (answer B) helps remove moisture, operating magnetos require cooling air to prevent overheating.

8534.　　　L01

Failure of an engine to cease firing after turning the magneto switch off is an indication of

A — an open high tension lead.
B — an open P-lead to ground.
C — a grounded magneto switch.

8534. Answer B. AC 65-12A

In a magneto ignition system, if the engine does not stop firing when the ignition switch is turned off, there is an open P-lead to ground (answer B). Answer (A) is incorrect because an open high tension lead would only prevent voltage from reaching one spark plug and would not allow an engine to continue firing after the magneto switch is turned off. Answer (C) is wrong because, if a magneto switch is properly grounded, the engine will not fire when the switch is off.

8535.　　　L01

Alignment of the marks provided for internal timing of a magneto indicates that the

A — breaker points are just beginning to close for No.1 cylinder.
B — magneto is in E-gap position.
C — No.1 cylinder is on TDC of compression stroke.

8535. Answer B. AC 65-12A

When the timing marks within a magneto are aligned, the magnets are in the E-gap position and the breaker points are just beginning to open. Answer (A) is wrong because when the timing marks are aligned, the points are just beginning to open, not close. Answer (C) is incorrect because the timing marks within a magneto do not indicate the position of the number one piston.

8536.　　　L01

When using a timing light to time a magneto to an aircraft engine, the magneto switch should be placed in the

A — BOTH position.
B — OFF position.
C — LEFT or RIGHT position (either one).

8536. Answer A. AC 65-12A

When using a timing light to time a magneto to an engine, the master switch must be turned on and the ignition switch placed in the BOTH position. If the magneto switch is in the OFF position (answer B), the timing light will not indicate when the breaker points open, and if the magneto switch is in either the LEFT or RIGHT position (answer C), you could only time one of the magnetos.

8537.   L01

What is the difference between a low-tension and a high-tension engine ignition system?

A — A low-tension system produces relatively low voltage at the spark plug as compared to a high-tension system.
B — A high-tension system is designed for high-altitude aircraft, while a low-tension system is for low- to medium-altitude aircraft.
C — A low-tension system uses a transformer coil near the spark plugs to boost voltage, while the high-tension system voltage is constant from the magneto to the spark plugs.

8538.   L01

What test instrument could be used to test an ignition harness for suspected leakage?

A — A high-tension lead tester.
B — A high voltage dc voltmeter.
C — A high amperage dc ammeter.

8539.   L01

The amount of voltage generated in any magneto secondary coil is determined by the number of windings and by the

A — rate of buildup of the magnetic field around the primary coil.
B — rate of collapse of the magnetic field around the primary coil.
C — amount of charge released by the capacitor.

8540.   L01

Magneto breaker points must be timed to open when the

A — rotating magnet is positioned a few degrees before neutral.
B — greatest magnetic field stress exists in the magnetic circuit.
C — rotating magnet is in the full register position.

8537. Answer C. AC 65-12A

In a low-tension ignition system, the magneto generates a low voltage that flows to the primary winding of a transformer coil located near the spark plug. This differs from a high-tension ignition system which produces a high voltage at the magneto that travels through high-tension leads to fire the spark plug. Answer (A) is incorrect since both systems use the same high voltage to fire the spark plugs. Answer (B) is incorrect because the low-tension system is superior for high-altitude aircraft since it eliminates the problems of arcing at the points and corona discharge at high altitudes.

8538. Answer A. AC 65-12A

Several different types of test devices are used for determining the serviceability of a high-tension ignition harness. One common type of tester is capable of applying a direct current voltage up to 15,000 volts. Once voltage is applied to an ignition harness, a high-tension lead tester is used to measure any current that leaks through the insulation. Neither a high voltage DC voltmeter (answer B) nor a high amperage DC ammeter (answer C) is sensitive enough to detect leakage current from a high-tension harness.

8539. Answer B.

The amount of voltage induced into the secondary coil of a magneto is determined by the ratio of the number of turns of wire in the two coils and the speed at which the magnetic field around the primary coil collapses. The faster the magnetic coil collapses the greater the induced voltage. Answer (A) is incorrect because the rate of buildup of the magnetic field in the primary has little effect on the amount of current induced in the secondary coil. Answer (C) is wrong because the capacitor absorbs rather than releases current as the points open.

8540. Answer B. AC 65-21A

With the primary breaker points closed, the rotating magnet's flux generates an opposing magnetic field in the magneto coil. This opposing force is the source of magnetic field stress, and the point where this stress is highest is a few degrees beyond the neutral position or the E-gap position. It is here that the points open to induce the highest possible voltage into the secondary coil. Answer (A) is wrong because the voltage within the primary circuit is below its maximum prior to the neutral position and, if the breaker points were to open at this point, maximum voltage would not be induced into the secondary coil. Answer (C) is wrong because at the full register position, little current is induced in the primary.

8541.   L02

In reference to a "Shower of Sparks" ignition system,

(1) the retard breaker points are designed to keep the affected ignition system operating if the advance breaker points should fail during normal engine operation (after start).

(2) the timed opening of the retard breaker points is designed to prevent engine "kickback" during start. Regarding the above statements,

A — only No. 1 is true.
B — only No. 2 is true.
C — both No. 1 and No. 2 are true.

8542.   L02

The capacitor-type ignition system is used almost universally on turbine engines primarily because of its high voltage and

A — low amperage.
B — long life.
C — high-heat intensity.

8543.   L02

In a low-tension ignition system, each spark plug requires an individual

A — capacitor.
B — breaker assembly.
C — secondary coil.

8544.   L02

A certain nine-cylinder radial engine used a noncompensated single-unit, dual-type magneto with a four-pole rotating magnet and separately mounted distributors. Which of the following will have the lowest RPM at any given engine speed?

A — Breaker cam.
B — Engine crankshaft.
C — Distributors.

8545.   L02

What will be the effect if the spark plugs are gapped too wide?

A — Insulation failure.
B — Hard starting.
C — Lead damage.

8541. Answer B. AC 65-12A

Only statement number (2) is correct. The retard points are timed so that they open later than the normal points. This retarded timing ensures that the engine will not kick-back when it fires. Both sets of points must be open for the Shower of Sparks system to operate. After the starter switch is released, the retard points have no function.

8542. Answer C. AC 65-12A

Turbine engine ignition systems must deliver a high-heat intense spark to ignite fuel at low temperatures or high altitudes. To accomplish this, turbine engines employ a capacitor-ignition system that delivers a high amperage spark. Answer (A) is incorrect because a capacitor-type ignition system delivers a high amperage at the igniter plug while answer (B) is wrong because, although the capacitor ignition system has long life, this is not the primary reason for its use.

8543. Answer C. AC 65-12A

In a low-tension ignition system, the magneto produces a low voltage which is fed to an individual secondary coil located near each spark plug (answer C). Answers (A) and (B) are incorrect because each magneto, not sparkplug, in a low-tension ignition system requires only one capacitor and one breaker assembly.

8544. Answer C. AC 65-12A

A distributor used with any four-cycle engine must rotate at one-half the engine's speed to fire each spark plug in every two crankshaft revolutions. However, the speed of a magneto with an uncompensated cam is calculated by dividing the number of cylinders by twice the number of poles on the magnet. In this case, magneto speed is 1.125 times the crankshaft speed $(9 \div (4 \times 2) = 1.125)$. Based on this, the distributor rotates at the slowest speed.

8545. Answer B. AC 65-12A

Spark plugs that are gapped too wide generally lead to hard starting. The reason for this is that the wider gap requires a higher voltage to produce a spark that will jump the gap. Since the production of a higher voltage requires the magneto to rotate faster, starting becomes more difficult. Excessive spark plug gaps can cause insulation damage (answer A) and ignition lead damage (answer C) over time, but hard starting is much more immediate.

8546.   L02

When removing a shielded spark plug, which of the following is most likely to be damaged?

A — Center electrode.
B — Shell section.
C — Core insulator.

8547.   L02

What likely effect would a cracked distributor rotor have on a magneto?

A — Ground the secondary circuit through the crack.
B — Fire two cylinders simultaneously.
C — Ground the primary circuit through the crack.

8548.   L02

How does the ignition system of a gas turbine engine differ from that of a reciprocating engine?

A — One igniter plug is used in each combustion chamber.
B — Magneto-to-engine timing is not critical.
C — A high-energy spark is required for ignition.

8549.   L02

In a turbine engine dc capacitor discharge ignition system, where are the high-voltage pulses formed?

A — At the breaker.
B — At the triggering transformer.
C — At the rectifier.

8550.   L02

Which of the following breaker point characteristics is associated with a faulty capacitor?

A — Crowned.
B — Fine grained.
C — Coarse grained.

8546. Answer C. AC 65-12A

Before a spark plug is removed, its ignition harness lead must be disconnected. If the lead is not pulled straight out of the plug barrel, damage to the core insulator and the ceramic lead terminal may result. The center electrode (answer A) and shell section (answer B) are unlikely to be damaged unless the spark plug is dropped.

8547. Answer A. AC 65-12A

One end of a magneto secondary coil is grounded to the primary coil or the coil core while the other end is connected to the distributor rotor. Therefore, if the distributor rotor in a magneto is cracked, the current in the secondary coil has a less resistive path to ground through the crack to the metal shaft of the magneto (answer A). Answer (B) is incorrect because a cracked distributor rotor will not cause two cylinders to fire simultaneously. Answer (C) is wrong because the primary circuit is not electrically connected to the distributor and, therefore, cannot be grounded through a crack in a rotor.

8548. Answer C. AC 65-12A

Unlike the ignition system for a reciprocating engine that produces a high voltage, low amperage spark, turbine engine ignition systems deliver a high-energy spark with a substantially higher amperage. This high-energy spark is needed to ignite the fuel/air mixture in low temperatures and at high altitudes. Answer (A) is incorrect because most turbine engines utilize two igniter plugs in the entire engine while answer (B) is wrong because turbine engines do not use magneto ignition systems.

8549. Answer B. AC 65-12A

A high-voltage capacitor discharge ignition system in a turbine engine produces high voltage pulses at what is called a trigger transformer. Current is supplied to the trigger transformer through a contactor and large storage capacitor. When the storage capacitor becomes fully charged, the conductor is closed by the mechanical action of a single-lobe cam. With the contactor closed, the energy in the storage capacitor is allowed to flow to the trigger transformer where a high-voltage pulse is formed and sent to the igniter. Answers (A) and (C) are incorrect because relatively low voltage energy exists at the breaker assembly and rectifier.

8550. Answer C. AC 65-12A

One purpose of the capacitor in a magneto ignition system is to prevent arcing between the breaker points. Therefore, a faulty capacitor can be suspected if the breaker points take on a coarse-grained or sooty appearance (answer C). Crowned points (answer A) have a concave center and a convex rim and are the result of improper dressing, not a faulty capacitor, and points having a fine-grained appearance (answer B) indicates normal capacitor operation.

8551.   L02
How are most radial engine spark plug wires connected to the distributor block?

A — By use of cable-piercing screws.
B — By use of self-locking cable ferrules.
C — By use of terminal sleeves and retaining nuts.

8552.   L02
Thermocouples are usually inserted or installed on the

A — front cylinder of the engine.
B — rear cylinder of the engine.
C — hottest cylinder of the engine.

8553.   L02
Capacitance afterfiring of a spark plug is caused by

A — the stored energy in the ignition shielded lead unloading after normal timed ignition.
B — excessive center electrode erosion.
C — constant polarity firing.

8554.   L02
If it is found that a shielded ignition system does not adequately reduce ignition noise, it may be necessary to install

A — a second layer of shielding.
B — a filter between the magneto and magneto switch.
C — bonding wires from the shielding to ground.

8555.   L02
When a magneto is operating, what is the probable cause for a shift in internal timing?

A — The rotating magnet looses its magnetism.
B — The distributor gear teeth are wearing on the rotor gear teeth.
C — The cam follower wears and/or the breaker points wear.

8551. Answer A. AC 65-12A
Spark plug wires on most radial engines are normally connected to the distributor block with cable-piercing screws. Neither self-locking cable ferrules (answer B) nor terminal sleeves and retaining nuts (answer C) are used to attach spark plug wires to a distributor block.

8552. Answer C. AC 65-12A
A thermocouple-type indicating device is typically used to indicate the cylinder head temperature on a reciprocating engine. To help ensure that none of the cylinders are hotter than the temperature indicated in the cockpit, cylinder head temperature readings are usually taken from the hottest cylinder. Temperature readings are not taken at the front cylinder of an engine (answer A) because these cylinders receive a direct blast of cooling air and, therefore, are not representative of actual operating conditions. Although a rear cylinder (answer B) is typically the hottest cylinder on most four cylinder engines, this may not be the case with a six or eight cylinder engine.

8553. Answer A. ITP-P2
The shielding used on ignition leads to protect against radio interference can sometimes act as a capacitor and store residual electrical energy as the high voltage charge flows through the lead to the spark plug. When this happens, the energy stored in the ignition harness is returned to the spark plug after the primary spark has occurred. Although center electrode erosion (answer B) is not the cause of capacitance afterfiring, it is a typical consequence. Constant polarity firing (answer C), on the other hand, does not occur in magneto ignition systems.

8554. Answer A. AC 65-12A
If a typical shielded ignition system does not adequately reduce ignition noise, a second layer of shielding is typically installed. Answer (B) is incorrect because installing a filter between the magneto and magneto switch would do little to reduce ignition noise and answer (C) is wrong because shielding is grounded through the spark plugs and does not require bonding wires.

8555. Answer C. AC 65-12A
A magneto is internally timed to ensure that the breaker points open at the E-gap position to produce the greatest flux change around the primary coil. Since the breaker points are opened by a cam, wear to either the cam or the breaker points themselves could cause a magneto's internal timing to shift. Answer (A) is wrong because the strength of the permanent magnet has no effect on the E-gap position and answer (B) is incorrect because wear on the distributor gear teeth or rotor teeth would change the magneto-to-engine timing, not the magneto's internal timing.

8556. **L02**
Why are turbine engine igniters less susceptible to fouling than reciprocating engine spark plugs?

A — The high-intensity spark cleans the igniter.
B — The frequency of the spark is less for igniters.
C — Turbine igniters operate at cooler temperatures.

8556. Answer A. AC 65-12A
Turbine engine igniters are far less susceptible to electrode fouling than reciprocating engine spark plugs because the heat of the high-intensity spark produced tends to clean the igniter electrodes. Although the frequency of the spark is lower for igniters (answer B), this has little bearing on plug fouling characteristics. Answer (C) is incorrect because turbine engine igniters operate at much higher temperatures than spark plugs do.

8557. **L02**
The constrained-gap igniter plug used in some gas turbine engines operates at a cooler temperature because

A — it projects into the combustion chamber.
B — the applied voltage is less.
C — the construction is such that the spark occurs beyond the face of the combustion chamber liner.

8557. Answer C. AC 65-12A
In a constrained-gap igniter plug, the center electrode is recessed into the body of the plug. Therefore, in order for the high-intensity spark to get from the electrode to ground, it must jump out away from the plug's tip. Because of this, constrained-gap igniter plugs do not have to project into the combustion chamber liner which allows them to operate at a cooler temperature. Answer (A) is wrong because constrained-gap igniter plugs do not project into the combustion chamber, and answer (B) is incorrect because the applied voltage is the same for a given ignition system.

558. **L02**
What should be used to clean grease or carbon tracks from capacitors or coils that are used in magnetos?

A — Solvent.
B — Acetone.
C — Naphtha.

8558. Answer B. AC 65-12A
When inspecting a magneto, all accessible condensers should be cleaned with a lint-free cloth moistened with acetone. However, you should always observe the magneto manufacturer's recommendations since some cleaners can damage the protective coating on some components.

8559. **L02**
Generally, when removing a turbine engine igniter plug, in order to eliminate the possibility of the technician receiving a lethal shock, the ignition switch is turned off and

A — disconnected from the power supply circuit.
B — the igniter lead is disconnected from the plug and the center electrode grounded to the engine after disconnecting the transformer-exciter input lead and waiting the prescribed time.
C — the transformer-exciter input lead is disconnected and the center electrode grounded to the engine after disconnecting the igniter lead from the plug and waiting the prescribed time.

8559. Answer B. AC 65-12A
To minimize the risk of shock when removing an igniter plug, it is important that you take all necessary precautions. As a general rule, you should begin removing an igniter plug by disconnecting the transformer exciter input lead and waiting the time prescribed by the manufacturer. Once this is complete, disconnect the igniter lead and ground the center electrode to the engine. When these steps are followed, the chances of receiving a shock are nearly eliminated.

8560.   L02

Great caution should be exercised in handling damaged hermetically sealed turbine engine igniter transformer units because

A — compounds in the unit may become a fire or explosion hazard when exposed to the air.
B — some contain radioactive material.
C — some contain toxic chemicals.

8561.   L02

Igniter plugs used in turbine engines are subjected to high intensity spark discharges and yet they have a long service life because they

A — operate at much lower temperatures.
B — are not placed directly into the combustion chamber.
C — do not require continuous operation.

8562.   L02

The electrical circuit from the spark plug back to the magneto is completed by grounding through the

A — engine structure.
B — P-lead.
C — cockpit switch.

8563.   L02

Spark plugs are considered worn out when the

A — electrodes have worn away to about one-half of their original dimensions.
B — center electrode edges have become rounded.
C — electrodes have worn away to about two-thirds of their original dimensions.

8564.   L03

Which of the following could cause damage to the nose ceramic or to the electrode of an aircraft sparkplug?

A — Plug installed without a copper gasket.
B — Improper gapping procedures.
C — Excessive magneto voltage.

8560. Answer B. TEP2

Great caution should be exercised in handling damaged transformer units from turbine engine ignition systems since some units may have radioactive material on the air gap points. This material is used to calibrate the discharge points to a preset voltage. No igniter transformer units contain compounds that present fire or explosion hazards (answer A). Although the radioactive compounds present in these units do present a toxicity hazard (answer (C), their radioactivity is the primary concern.

8561. Answer C. AC 65-12A

The high-energy current used to fire turbine engine igniters, if used continuously, would quickly cause electrode erosion. However, since combustion in a turbine engine is self-supporting, igniter plugs are only used for short periods and, therefore, they maintain a relatively long service life (answer C). The ignition system is used primarily to start an engine and ensure ignition during takeoff, icing conditions, landing, and moderate to severe turbulence. Answer (A) is incorrect because turbine engine igniters operate at much higher temperatures than spark plugs while answer (B) is wrong because igniters are placed directly into the combustion chamber.

8562. Answer A. ITP-P2

In a typical magneto-type ignition system, the magneto produces a high voltage charge that flows through the distributor to the ignition leads and spark plugs. To complete the circuit, the electrical charge jumps the gap in the spark plug which is grounded through the engine structure. Answers (B) and (C) are incorrect because neither the P-lead wire nor the cockpit (ignition) switch are part of the electrical circuit from the sparkplug to the magneto.

8563. Answer A. ITP-P2

Any spark plug whose electrodes have worn to approximately one-half their original dimension should be replaced. Spark plug electrodes become rounded fairly quickly (answer B), and replacing them at this point would be wasteful and expensive. However, waiting until the electrodes are two-thirds worn (answer C) brings a greater risk of plug malfunction.

8564. Answer B. AC 65-12A

When gapping spark plugs, you typically decrease the clearance between the center electrode and the ground electrode. However, it is not recommended that a gap be widened after it has been inadvertently decreased too much since damage to the center electrode insulator typically results. Neither the lack of a copper gasket (answer A) nor excessive magneto voltage (answer C) will damage the nose ceramic or electrode.

8565.   L03
Sharp bends should be avoided in ignition leads primarily because

A — weak points may develop in the insulation through which high tension current can leak.
B — ignition lead wire conductor material is brittle and may break.
C — ignition lead shielding effectiveness will be reduced.

8566.   L03
In a high-tension ignition system, a primary capacitor of too low a capacity will cause

A — excessive primary voltage.
B — excessively high secondary voltage.
C — the breaker contacts to burn.

8567.   L03
Which of the following, obtained during magneto check at 1,700 RPM, indicates a short (grounded) circuit between the right magneto primary and the ignition switch?

A — BOTH-1,700 RPM, R-1,625 RPM, L-1,700 RPM, OFF-1,625 RPM.
B — BOTH-1,700 RPM, R-0 RPM, L-1,700 RPM, OFF-0 RPM.
C — BOTH-1,700 RPM, R-0 RPM, L-1,675 RPM, OFF-0 RPM.

8568.   L03
If an aircraft ignition switch is turned off and the engine continues to run normally, the trouble is probably caused by

A — an open ground lead in the magneto.
B — arcing magneto breaker points.
C — primary lead grounding.

8565. Answer A.
Although newer ignition harnesses are flexible and can be installed with smaller bend radii, older ignition cables have a low tolerance for sharp bends. Over time, the stress imposed by sharp bends on an ignition lead's insulation can cause the insulation to break down and allow current to leak. Answer (B) is wrong because conductor wire is not brittle and will not break because of occasional bending. Answer (C) is incorrect because the effectiveness of the shielding is not appreciably affected by sharp bends.

8566. Answer C. AC 65-12A
One of the purposes of the capacitor in a magneto is to prevent arcing and burning of the breaker points. Therefore, if the capacitor lacks sufficient capacity, arcing will occur and the points will burn. Answer (A) is wrong because primary voltage is not affected by the capacitor. Answer (B) is incorrect because a capacitor with a low capacity will cause the secondary voltage to drop, not increase excessively.

8567. Answer B. AC 65-12A
The ignition switch for a magneto ignition system removes current from the primary circuit by grounding the magneto primary leads. Therefore, if the primary lead to the right magneto is grounded, no current flows from the magneto to the spark plug. A grounded right magneto is identified during a magneto check by the engine quitting when the ignition switch is moved to the RIGHT position. However, in the BOTH position and in the LEFT position, the engine will run at the established rpm setting (1,700 rpm). Answer (A) is wrong because it indicates an improperly grounded P-lead for the right magneto. Answer (C) indicates a defective ignition switch since both magnetos operate in the BOTH position but the right magneto does not supply current in the RIGHT position.

8568. Answer A. AC 65-12A
The ignition switch for a magneto ignition system shuts an engine down by supplying a path to ground through the ignition switch. If the engine does not shut down when the ignition switch is turned to the OFF position, there is either an open ground lead in the magneto or a faulty ignition switch. Arcing magneto breaker points (answer B) will not cause an engine to continue to run when the ignition switch is turned off. Answer (C) is incorrect because if both primary leads are grounded the engine will shut down, not continue to run.

8569.   L03

Which statement is correct regarding the ignition system of a turbine engine?

A — The system is normally de-energized as soon as the engine starts.
B — It is energized during the starting and warmup periods only.
C — The system generally includes a polar inductor-type magneto.

8570.   L03

When the ignition switch of a single (reciprocating) engine aircraft is turned to the OFF position,

A — the primary circuits of both magnetos are grounded.
B — the secondary circuits of both magnetos are opened.
C — all circuits are automatically opened.

8571.   L03

A spark plug's heat range is the result of

A — the area of the plug exposed to the cooling airstream.
B — its ability to transfer heat from the firing end of the spark plug to the cylinder head.
C — the heat intensity of the spark.

8572.   L03

If staggered ignition timing is used, the

A — spark plug nearest the exhaust valve will fire first.
B — spark will be automatically advanced as engine speed increases.
C — spark plug nearest the intake valve will fire first.

8573.   L03

The term "reach," as applied to spark plug design and/or type, indicates the

A — linear distance from the shell gasket seat to the end of the threads on the shell skirt.
B — length of center electrode exposed to the flame of combustion.
C — length of the shielded barrel.

8569. Answer A. AC 65-12A

The high-energy current used to fire the turbine engine igniter, if used continuously, would quickly cause electrode erosion. However, since combustion is continuous once a turbine engine is started, the ignition system is typically de-energized soon after the engine starts. Answer (B) is incorrect because there is no need to leave the ignition system on during warmup periods. Answer (C) is wrong because there is no such thing as a polar inductor-type magneto.

8570. Answer A. AC 65-12A

The ignition switch for a magneto ignition system shuts an engine down by supplying a path to ground for both magnetos through the ignition switch. The ignition switch neither opens the secondary circuits (answer B) nor automatically opens all circuits (answer C) when it is placed in the OFF position.

8571. Answer B. AC 65-12A

The heat range of a spark plug refers to the ability of the insulator and center electrode to conduct heat away from the plug tip and transfer it to the cylinder head (answer B). "Hot" plugs have a long insulator that creates a long heat transfer path while "cold" plugs have a short insulator that rapidly transfers heat to the cylinder head. Answer (A) is wrong because spark plugs are cooled more by conduction to the cylinder head than by the airstream. The heat intensity of the spark (answer C) has nothing to do with a spark plug's heat range.

8572. Answer A.

When staggered ignition timing is used, the spark plug nearest the exhaust valve fires first. This is done because the fuel/air mixture nearest the exhaust valve is diluted and burns more slowly. Answer (B) is incorrect because aircraft ignition systems do not employ spark advance. Answer (C) is wrong because the fuel/air mixture is richer near the intake valve and does not require an early spark.

8573. Answer A. AC 65-12A

The reach of a spark plug is the linear distance from the shell gasket to the end of the threads on the plug skirt. This does not include any space taken up by the gasket. In simple terms, it is how far a plug extends into the cylinder head. Reach does not refer to either the length of the center electrode exposed to the combustion flame (answer B) or the length of the shielded barrel (answer C).

8574.   L03

The numbers appearing on the ignition distributor block indicate the

A — sparking order of the distributor.
B — relation between distributor terminal numbers and cylinder numbers.
C — firing order of the engine.

8575.   L03

When testing a magneto distributor block for electrical leakage, which of the following pieces of test equipment should be used?

A — A high-tension harness tester.
B — A continuity tester.
C — A high-range ammeter.

8576.   L03

(1) The platinum and iridium ground electrodes used on fine wire spark plugs are extremely brittle and can be broken if they are improperly handled or adjusted.
(2) When gapping massive-electrode spark plugs, a wire gauge should be inserted between the center and ground electrodes while moving the ground electrode in order to avoid setting the gap too close.

Regarding the above statements,

A — only No. 1 is true.
B — only No. 2 is true.
C — both No. 1 and No. 2 are true.

8577.   L03

Hot spark plugs are generally used in aircraft power-plants

A — with comparatively high compression or high operating temperatures.
B — with comparatively low operating temperatures.
C — which produce high power per cubic inch displacement.

8574. Answer A. AC 65-12A

The numbers on a distributor block always indicate the sparking order of the distributor (answer A). These numbers do not indicate the relationship between the distributor terminals and the cylinder numbers (answer B) nor do they indicate the engine's firing order (answer C).

8575. Answer A. AC 65-12A

In addition to being able to check ignition leads, a high-tension harness tester (answer A) can also be used to indicate the condition of the distributor block. If the majority of ignition leads being tested show excessive leakage, there is a good possibility that the distributor block is at fault. Answer (B) is wrong because a distributor block can have continuity and still have electrical leakage, and answer (C), a high-range ammeter, is incorrect because any leakage at the distributor block would possess such a low amperage that it would be nearly impossible to detect with a high-range ammeter.

8576. Answer A. ITP-P2

Only statement (1) is true. Although fine wire electrodes are easier to gap than massive electrode plugs, extreme care must be taken because both platinum and iridium are extremely brittle and can break if improperly handled. For massive electrode spark plugs, the wire gauge must not be between the electrodes when you move the ground electrode over since this will place a side load on the center electrode which could crack the ceramic.

8577. Answer B. AC 65-12A

The heat range of a spark plug refers to the ability of the insulator and the center electrode to conduct heat away from the plug tip. Hot spark plugs, or plugs that have a long insulator, slowly transfer heat and are typically used in engines whose cylinder temperatures are relatively low. Cold spark plugs, on the other hand, have a short insulator that rapidly transfers heat which makes them appropriate for hot running, high-compression engines. Using a hot plug in a hot-running engine (answer A) typically causes plugs to overheat and cause preignition. An engine's power output per cubic inch displacement (answer C) is a function of its design and is not affected by a spark plug's heat range.

8578.   L03
If a spark plug lead becomes grounded, the

A — magneto will not be affected.
B — distributor rotor finger will discharge to the next closest electrode within the distributor.
C — capacitor will break down.

8578. Answer A.
In a normally operating ignition system, when a spark plug fires, current from the magneto passes to ground by jumping the spark plug's air gap. Therefore, if a spark plug lead becomes grounded, current would simply flow through the lead to ground with no effect on the magneto. Answer (B) is wrong because the distributor rotor finger will discharge normally through the adjacent electrode when a lead becomes grounded. Answer (C) is incorrect because a grounded magneto will operate normally and the capacitor will be unaffected by the short.

8579.   L03
Which of the following statements regarding magneto switch circuits is NOT true?

A — In the BOTH position, the right and left magneto circuits are grounded.
B — In the OFF position, neither the right nor left magneto circuits are open.
C — In the RIGHT position, the right magneto circuit is open and the left magneto circuit is grounded.

8579. Answer A. AC 65-12A
When the ignition switch for a magneto is in the BOTH position, the primary leads to the magnetos are open, or ungrounded. On the other hand, the primary leads are grounded when the ignition switch is turned to the OFF position. In the RIGHT position the right magneto is open and the left magneto is grounded. Based on this information, answer (A) is the only statement that is not true.

8580.   L03
Which of the following statements most accurately describes spark plug heat range?

A — The length of the threaded portion of the shell usually denotes the spark plug heat range.
B — A hot plug is designed so that the insulator tip is reasonably short to hasten the rate of heat transfer from the tip through the spark plug shell to the cylinder head.
C — A cold plug is designed so that the insulator tip is reasonably short to hasten the rate of heat transfer from the tip through the spark plug shell to the cylinder head.

8580. Answer C. AC 65-12A
The heat range of a spark plug is a measure of a spark plug's ability to transfer heat to the cylinder head. The primary factor in determining the heat range of a plug is the length of the nose core. For example, cold plugs have a relatively short insulator to provide a rapid transfer of heat to the cylinder head while hot plugs have a long insulator nose that creates a long heat transfer path. Answer (A) is wrong because the length of the threaded portion of the shell denotes reach, not heat range. Answer (B) is incorrect because a hot plug has a long insulator to create a long heat transfer path, not a short insulator.

8581.   L03
When does battery current flow through the primary circuit of a battery ignition coil?

A — Only when the breaker points are open.
B — At all times when the ignition switch is on.
C — When the breaker points are closed and the ignition switch is on.

8581. Answer C. AC 65-12A
In a battery ignition system, current is supplied by the battery through the ignition switch with a return to ground through the breaker points. Therefore, in order for current to flow, the ignition switch must be on and the breaker points closed. Answer (A) is incorrect because when the breaker points are open there is no path to ground and current cannot flow. Answer (B) is wrong because just having the ignition switch on does not allow current to flow.

8582.   L03
In order to turn a magneto off, the primary circuit must be

A — grounded.
B — opened.
C — shorted.

8582. Answer A. AC 65-12A
In a magneto ignition system, the purpose of the ignition switch is to ground out the primary of the magneto when the switch is OFF. Once grounded, the breaker points are effectively shorted making the magneto inoperative. Answers (B) and (C) are incorrect because either an open primary circuit or a shorted primary circuit will prevent the magneto from operating at all.

8583.   L03
When performing a magneto ground check on an engine, correct operation is indicated by

A — a slight increase in RPM.
B — no drop in RPM.
C — a slight drop in RPM.

8583. Answer C. AC 65-12A
When performing a magneto ground check, the engine is operated at a specified rpm and the ignition switch is moved from BOTH to LEFT and back to BOTH; then from BOTH to RIGHT and back to BOTH. When this check is performed there should be a small drop in rpm at the LEFT and the RIGHT positions. This occurs because with only one magneto selected, only one spark plug fires in each cylinder thereby causing a slight decrease in power output. Answer (A) is incorrect because correct magneto operation is indicated by a slight decrease in rpm, not an increase. Answer (B) is wrong because no drop in rpm indicates that one of the magnetos is not operating.

8584.   L03
Defective spark plugs will cause intermittent missing of the engine at

A — high speeds only.
B — low speeds only.
C — all speeds.

8584. Answer C. AC 65-12A
A defective spark plug, meaning a plug which is not firing or is firing intermittently, will cause the engine to miss at all engine speeds. Answers (A) and (B) are wrong because defective spark plugs will cause an engine to miss at any speed.

8585.   L03
A spark plug is fouled when

A — its spark grounds by jumping electrodes.
B — it causes preignition.
C — its spark grounds without jumping electrodes.

8585. Answer C. AC 65-12A
A spark plug is fouled when it becomes contaminated with foreign matter to the point that the spark flows through the foreign matter to ground rather than jumping the air gap at the electrode. Answer (A) is incorrect because a normally operating spark plug grounds by jumping electrodes. Answer (B) is wrong because preignition occurs when an isolated hot spot in the cylinder ignites the fuel/air mixture before the time of normal ignition.

8586.   L03
Which of the following would be cause for rejection of a spark plug?

A — Carbon fouling of the electrode and insulator.
B — Insulator tip cracked.
C — Lead fouling of the electrode and insulator.

8586. Answer B. AC 65-12A
A spark plug whose insulator tip is cracked should be replaced. This condition can affect the firing of the plug as well as its ability to transfer heat. Carbon fouling (answer A) and lead fouling (answer C) happens during the combustion process and can be removed from a spark plug in the shop. Therefore, neither of these conditions would be cause for rejection.

8587.   L03
What will be the result of using too hot a spark plug?

A — Fouling of plug.
B — Preignition.
C — Burned capacitor.

8587. Answer B. AC 65-12A
The heat range of a spark plug refers to the ability of the insulator and the center electrode to conduct heat away from the plug tip. Hot spark plugs, or plugs that have a long insulator, slowly transfer heat and are typically used in an engine whose cylinder temperatures are relatively low. Cold spark plugs, on the other hand, have a short insulator that rapidly transfers heat which makes them appropriate for hot running, high-compression engines. An engine which runs hot requires a relatively cold spark plug, whereas an engine which runs cool requires a relatively hot spark plug. If a hot spark plug is installed in an engine which runs hot, the tip of the plug could overheat and cause pre-ignition. Plug fouling (answer A) is caused by an excessively rich mixture or by an intermittently firing spark plug, but not by a hot spark plug. Using a hot spark plug will not cause a burned capacitor (answer C).

8588.   L03
Upon inspection of the spark plugs in an aircraft engine, the plugs were found caked with a heavy black soot. This indicates

A — worn oil seal rings.
B — a rich mixture.
C — a lean mixture.

8588. Answer B. AC 65-12A
Carbon fouling of spark plugs appears as a heavy black soot on the plug tip. The most common cause of carbon fouling is running an engine with an excessively rich fuel/air mixture. Answer (A) is wrong because worn oil seals will cause the spark plug to be wet with oil, and answer (C) is incorrect because an excessively lean mixture would cause carbon to burn from the plug surface leaving a gray or tan color.

8589.   L03
Spark plug heat range is determined by

A — the reach of the spark plug.
B — its ability to transfer heat to the cylinder head.
C — the number of ground electrodes.

8589. Answer B. AC 65-12A
The heat range of a spark plug is a measure of a plug's ability to transfer heat to the cylinder head. The primary factor in determining the heat range of a plug is the length of the nose core. For example, cold plugs have a relatively short insulator to provide a rapid transfer of heat to the cylinder head while hot plugs have a long insulator nose that creates a long heat transfer path. A spark plug's reach (answer A) is the threaded portion of the spark plug and does not affect the plug's ability to transfer heat. The number of ground electrodes (answer C) also has no affect on heat range.

8590.   L03
Ignition check during engine runup indicates excessive RPM drop during operation on the right magneto. The major portion of the RPM loss occurs rapidly after switching to the right magneto position (fast drop). The most likely cause is

A — faulty or fouled spark plugs.
B — incorrect ignition timing on both magnetos.
C — one or more dead cylinders.

8590. Answer A. AC 65-12A
When performing a magneto check on an engine, an excessive and rapid rpm drop is usually the result of faulty or failed spark plugs or a faulty ignition harness. Answer (B) is incorrect because incorrect ignition timing is made apparent by a slow rpm drop, and a dead cylinder (answer C) may not be detected during a magneto check.

8591. **L03**

If new breaker points are installed in a magneto on an engine, it will be necessary to time the

A — magneto internally and the magneto to the engine.
B — breaker points to the No.1 cylinder.
C — magneto drive to the engine.

8591. Answer A. AC 65-12A

When installing new breaker points in a magneto, the internal timing of the magneto must be checked to ensure that the point opening coincides with the E-gap position of the rotor. The timing of the magneto to the engine must also be checked to ensure that the firing of the spark plugs occurs at the proper time in relation to piston position. Answer (B) is incorrect because the breaker points are timed to open at the E-gap, not to the No. 1 cylinder. Answer (C) is wrong because the magneto, not its drive, is timed to the engine.

8592. **L03**

Using a cold spark plug in a high-compression aircraft engine would probably result in

A — normal operation.
B — a fouled plug.
C — detonation.

8592. Answer A. AC 65-12A

The heat range of a spark plug refers to the ability of the plug's insulator and center electrode to conduct heat away from the tip. Hot spark plugs, or plugs that have a long insulator, slowly transfer heat and are typically used in an engine whose cylinder temperatures are relatively low. Cold spark plugs, on the other hand, have a short insulator that rapidly transfers heat which makes them appropriate for hot running, high-compression engines. Therefore, when a cold spark plug is used in a high-compression engine the engine will run normally. A fouled plug (answer B) and/or preignition would result from using a hot plug in a high-compression engine. Detonation (answer C) is the explosive burning of the fuel/air charge and is a function of an engine's compression, the fuel grade used, and the fuel/air ratio, not the spark plug.

8593. **L03**

Spark plug fouling caused by lead deposits occurs most often

A — during cruise with rich mixture.
B — when cylinder head temperatures are relatively low.
C — when cylinder head temperatures are high.

8593. Answer B. AC 65-12A

Lead fouling can occur at any power setting, however, it is most frequently associated with cruising power settings with lean mixtures. At these power settings, the cylinder head temperature is relatively low and there is an excess of oxygen above that needed to consume all the fuel in the fuel/air mixture. The excess oxygen ends up combining with lead and builds up in layers on the cool cylinder walls and the spark plugs. A rich mixture (answer A) combines with most of the oxygen to reduce lead deposits, although a too-rich mixture can lead to carbon fouling. At high cylinder head temperatures (answer C) the lead vapors cannot easily solidify on the cylinder walls, so lead buildup is minimized.

8594. **L03**

In a four-stroke cycle aircraft engine, when does the ignition event take place?

A — Before the piston reaches TDC on compression stroke.
B — After the piston reaches TDC on power stroke.
C — After the piston reaches TDC on compression stroke.

8594. Answer A. AC 65-12A

The ignition event in a four-stroke engine occurs before the piston reaches top dead center on the compression stroke. This ensures complete combustion of the fuel/air charge by the time the piston is slightly past top dead center. If the fuel/air charge were ignited after TDC, power output would decrease substantially.

8595.   L03

When installing a magneto on an engine, the

A — piston in the No.1 cylinder must be a prescribed number of degrees before top center on the compression stroke.
B — magneto breaker points must be just closing.
C — piston in the No.1 cylinder must be a prescribed number of degrees after top center on the intake stroke.

8596.   L03

The spark occurs at the spark plug when the ignition's

A — secondary circuit is completed.
B — primary circuit is completed.
C — primary circuit is broken.

8597.   L03

The type of ignition system used on most turbine aircraft engines is

A — high resistance.
B — low tension.
C — capacitor discharge.

8598.   L03

Ignition check during engine runup indicates a slow drop in RPM. This is usually caused by

A — defective spark plugs.
B — a defective high-tension lead.
C — incorrect ignition timing or valve adjustment.

8599.   L03

If the ground wire of a magneto is disconnected at the ignition switch, the result will be the

A — affected magneto will be isolated and the engine will run on the opposite magneto.
B — engine will stop running.
C — engine will not stop running when the ignition switch is turned off.

8595. Answer A. AC 65-12A

Magneto to engine timing is based on having the magneto in the E-gap, or firing position and the number one cylinder a prescribed number of degrees before top dead center on the compression stroke. This position represents the point in which the fuel/air mixture ignites. Answer (B) is wrong since the breaker points are just opening when a magneto is in the E-gap position, and answer (C) is incorrect because the magneto does not fire on the intake stroke.

8596. Answer C. AC 65-12A

In both a battery and magneto ignition system, the spark occurs at the spark plug when voltage is induced into the secondary winding. Voltage is induced when the primary circuit is opened at the breaker points. Answer (A) is incorrect because voltage must be induced into the secondary circuit before a spark plug can fire. Answer (B) is wrong because when the primary circuit is completed, its magnetic flux does not change rapidly enough to induce a high voltage into the secondary coil.

8597. Answer C. AC 65-12A

Because of the high-energy spark required to ignite a turbine engine, the capacitor discharge type ignition system is most often used on turbine engines. Answer (A) is wrong because "high resistance" does not really designate a type of ignition system. Answer (B) is incorrect because all turbine engine ignition systems operate at high voltages and thus are high tension systems.

8598. Answer C. AC 65-12A

When performing a magneto check, a slow drop in rpm is usually caused by incorrect ignition timing or faulty valve adjustment. With late ignition timing, the fuel/air charge is ignited late in relation to piston travel and maximum combustion pressures are not obtained. The result is a gradual power loss when checking a single magneto. Defective spark plugs (answer A) or a defective high-tension lead (answer B) cause an abrupt drop in rpm during a magneto check and, therefore, are incorrect.

8599. Answer C. AC 65-12A

In a magneto ignition system, the purpose of the ignition switch is to ground out the primary circuit when the switch is OFF. By grounding out the primary circuit continuously, insufficient voltage is induced into the secondary coil to produce a spark. Therefore, if the ground wire to the ignition switch is disconnected, the engine will continue running when the ignition is turned to the OFF position (answer C). Answer (A) is wrong because a disconnected ground wire will not isolate a magneto but will cause it to operate continuously. Answer (B) is incorrect because there will be no way to shut off one magneto and, therefore, the engine will keep running.

8600.   **L03**

Which of the following are advantages of dual ignition in aircraft engines?

1. Gives a more complete and quick combustion of the fuel.
2. Provides a backup magneto system.
3. Increases the output power of the engine.
4. Permits the use of lower grade fuels.
5. Increases the intensity of the spark at the spark plugs.

A — 2, 3, 4.
B — 2, 3, 5.
C — 1, 2, 3.

8600. Answer C. DSA-25

The principal advantages of a dual magneto-ignition system are that if any part of one magneto should fail to operate, the other magneto will continue to furnish ignition. Furthermore, a dual ignition system firing two spark plugs ignites the fuel/air mixture in each cylinder simultaneously at two different places, resulting in more complete and quick combustion and increased engine power. Based on this, choices 1, 2, and 3 are correct (answer C). Answer (A) is wrong because the fuel grade used in an engine depends more on the engine's compression ratio than it does on the ignition system. Answer (B) is incorrect because spark intensity depends on the speed of the collapsing primary filed in the magneto and the integrity of the ignition system components.

8601.   **L03**

How does high-tension ignition shielding tend to reduce radio interference?

A — Prevents ignition flashover at high altitudes.
B — Reduces voltage drop in the transmission of high-tension current.
C — Receives and grounds high-frequency waves coming from the magneto and high-tension ignition leads.

8601. Answer C. AC 65-12A

The shielding used on an ignition harness serves as a conductor to receive and ground stray magnetic fields that are produced when high-voltage current passes through the leads. By conducting these magnetic lines of force to ground, the ignition harness cuts down electrical interference with the aircraft radio and other electrically sensitive equipment. Answer (A) is incorrect because flashover is prevented by waxing the coils, condensers, distributors, and distributor rotors in magnetos. Answer (B) is incorrect because an ignition lead's voltage drop depends on its resistance, not the characteristics of its shielding.

8602.   **L03**

Which of the following are distinct circuits of a high-tension magneto?

1. Magnetic.
2. Primary.
3. E-gap.
4. P-lead.
5. Secondary.

A — 1, 2, 5.
B — 1, 3, 4.
C — 2, 4, 5.

8602. Answer A. AC 65-12A

A high-tension magneto system is divided into three distinct circuits: the magnetic, the primary, and the secondary. Therefore, answer (A) is correct. The E-gap represents a specific position of a magneto's rotating magnet just before the breaker points open. The P-lead, on the other hand, identifies the wire that is used to ground a magneto.

8603.   **L03**
What are two parts of a distributor in an aircraft engine ignition system?

1. Coil.
2. Block.
3. Stator.
4. Rotor.
5. Transformer.

A — 2 and 4.
B — 3 and 4.
C — 2 and 5.

8604.   **L03**
What is a result of "flashover" in a distributor?

A — Intense voltage at the spark plug.
B — Reversal of current flow.
C — Conductive carbon trail.

8605.   **L03**
What is the relationship between distributor and crankshaft speed of aircraft reciprocating engines?

A — The distributor turns at one-half crankshaft speed.
B — The distributor turns at one and one-half crankshaft speed.
C — The crankshaft turns at one-half distributor speed.

8606.   **L03**
Why do turbine engine ignition systems require high energy?

A — To ignite the fuel under conditions of high altitude and high temperatures.
B — Because the applied voltage is much greater.
C — To ignite the fuel under conditions of high altitude and low temperatures.

8603. Answer A. AC 65-12A
The distributor in a magneto ignition system consists of two parts. The revolving part is called a distributor rotor and the stationary part is called a distributor block. Therefore, answer (A) is correct.

8604. Answer C. AC 65-12A
Flashover in a distributor can lead to carbon tracking, which appears as a fine pencil-like carbon trail where the flashover occurred. This carbon trail typically collects on the distributor and forms a conductive path to ground which increases the potential for additional flashover to occur. Answer (A) is incorrect because flashover actually discharges the high-voltage charge before it reaches the spark plug and, therefore, results in a less intense spark at the spark plug. Answer (B) is incorrect because a magneto produces direct current that can only flow from source to ground and cannot reverse.

8605. Answer A. AC 65-12A
In order for a magneto to provide a spark at the appropriate time in the four-stroke process, the distributor must turn at one-half the crankshaft speed. Another way to look at this is that it takes two revolutions of the crankshaft to fire all the cylinders and, therefore, the distributor only needs to rotate at half the crankshaft speed.

8606. Answer C. AC 65-12A
The fuel/air mixture in turbine engines can be ignited readily in standard atmospheric conditions. However, since turbine engines often operate in the low temperatures of high altitudes, it is imperative that their ignition systems be capable of supplying the high-intensity spark needed to ignite the mixture under these conditions. Answer (A) is wrong because it is fairly easy to ignite a turbine engine's fuel/air mixture at high temperatures, and answer (B) is wrong because turbine engines typically use a standard 24-volt DC power source for their ignition systems.

8607.   L03

Which of the following are included in a typical turbine engine ignition system?

1. Two igniter units.
2. Two transformers.
3. One exciter unit.
4. Two intermediate ignition leads.
5. Two low-tension igniter leads.
6. Two high-tension igniter leads.

A — 2, 3, 4.
B — 1, 4, 5.
C — 1, 3, 6.

8608.   L03

At what RPM is a reciprocating engine ignition switch check made?

A — 1,500 RPM.
B — The slowest possible RPM.
C — Full throttle RPM.

8609.   L03

What is the approximate position of the rotating magnet in a high-tension magneto when the points first close?

A — Full register.
B — Neutral.
C — A few degrees after neutral.

8610.   L03

What component of a dual magneto is shared by both ignition systems?

A — High-tension coil.
B — Rotating magnet.
C — Capacitor.

8611.   L03

What would be the result if a magneto breaker point mainspring did not have sufficient tension?

A — The points will stick.
B — The points will not open to the specified gap.
C — The points will float or bounce.

8607. Answer C. TEP2

A typical turbine engine ignition system includes 2 igniter units (igniter plugs), 2 exciter units, and 2 high-tension leads. However, in some aircraft the exciter units may be contained in a single housing. Based on this, the best possible answer is (C). Answers (A) and (B) are wrong because a typical ignition system does not include two intermediate or low-tension igniter leads.

8608. Answer B. AC 65-12A

An ignition switch check requires that the ignition be momentarily turned to the OFF position and then back to BOTH while the engine is running to see if all magneto ground leads are electrically grounded. To prevent backfiring when the ignition switch is returned to the BOTH position, an ignition switch check is usually made at the slowest possible rpm setting, typically between 500 and 700 rpm. Both answers (A) and (C) are incorrect because conducting an ignition switch test at either 1,500 rpm or full throttle will almost always load up the cylinders and cause the engine to backfire.

8609. Answer A. AC 65-12A

The primary breaker points in a magneto close at approximately the full register position. In this position, the poles of the magnet are perfectly aligned with the pole shoes and the maximum number of flux lines flow through the magnetic circuit. Answers (B) and (C) are incorrect because in both the neutral and a few degrees after neutral the breaker points have been closed for a while and are actually preparing to open.

8610. Answer B. AC 65-12A

A dual magneto incorporates two magnetos in one housing. This configuration allows somewhat of a weight savings because one rotating magnet and one cam can be used for both magnetos. Answers (A) and (C) are wrong because each ignition system requires its own high-tension coil and capacitor.

8611. Answer C. AC 65-12A

If a breaker point mainspring does not apply sufficient tension to the breaker points, the points could bounce or float at higher speeds. A bouncing or floating point would prevent the normal induction buildup within the magneto thereby reducing the magneto output. Both answers (A) and (B) are incorrect because sticking or slowly opening magneto points and points not opening to the specified gap are caused by excessive mainspring tension.

8612.   L03

The secondary coil of a magneto is grounded through the

A — ignition switch.
B — primary coil.
C — grounded side of the breaker points.

8613.   L03

In the aircraft magneto system, if the P-lead is disconnected, the magneto will be

A — on regardless of ignition switch position.
B — grounded regardless of ignition switch position.
C — open regardless of ignition switch position.

8614.   L03

(Refer to figure 5.) Placing the engine master and battery switch in the on position, and advancing the power lever allows current to flow from the bus to the

A — fuel valve, external power receptacles, undercurrent solenoid contacts, starter solenoid coil, and ignition solenoid contacts.
B — fuel valve, external power receptacles, power lever switch, power lever relay coil, and ignition solenoid contactor.
C — fuel valve, power lever switch, power lever relay coil, fuel pumps, and one ignition solenoid coil.

8615.   L03

(Refer to figure 5.) With power applied to the bus bar, what switch changes will allow the ignition exciters test switch to function?

A — Engine master switch, battery switch, and power lever switch.
B — Engine master switch, start switch, and test switch.
C — Engine master switch, power lever switch.

8612. Answer B. AC 65-12A

The secondary coil of a magneto is made up of a winding containing approximately 13,000 turns of fine, insulated wire. One end of the wire is electrically grounded to the primary coil or coil core, while the other end is connected to the distributor rotor. Answer (A) is wrong because the primary coil, not the secondary coil, is grounded through the ignition switch. Answer (C) is wrong because the primary coil is grounded through the breaker points when the points are closed.

8613. Answer A. AC 65-12A

The magneto ground lead, or P-lead, grounds the primary side of the magneto coil when the magneto switch is in the OFF position. This effectively shorts the breaker points, rendering the magneto inoperable. Therefore, if the P-lead should become disconnected or broken, the magneto will be on all the time regardless of the ignition switch position. Answer (B) is incorrect because the P-lead cannot ground the magneto if it is disconnected, and answer (C) is wrong because a magneto is not "open" if the P-lead is disconnected.

8614. Answer C. ITP-P2

Closing the battery switch energizes the battery solenoid coil which closes the battery solenoid and allows power to flow to the bus. Closing the engine master switch allows current to flow to the fuel valve and to the power lever switch. Once the power lever is advanced, the power lever switch moves to the advance position and current flows to the power lever relay coil, causing the power lever relay to close and allow power to flow to the fuel pumps and one side of the ignition solenoid. Therefore, answer (C) is correct. Answer (A) is wrong because only one ignition solenoid contact is powered when the master and battery switches are on and the power lever is advanced. Answer (B) is incorrect because the start switch must be in the start position to supply power to the ignition solenoid coil.

8615. Answer C. ITP-P2

If power is already applied to the bus, current will flow to the ignition exciter test switch when the engine master switch and power lever switch (throttle), move from the positions indicated (answer C). With power at the bus, once the engine master switch is closed, current flows to the power lever switch (throttle). When this switch is advanced, the power lever relay coil will receive current and pull the power lever relay down to supply power to one end of the ignition solenoid. To get power from one side of the solenoid to the other and on to the ignition exciters, the test switch must be closed.

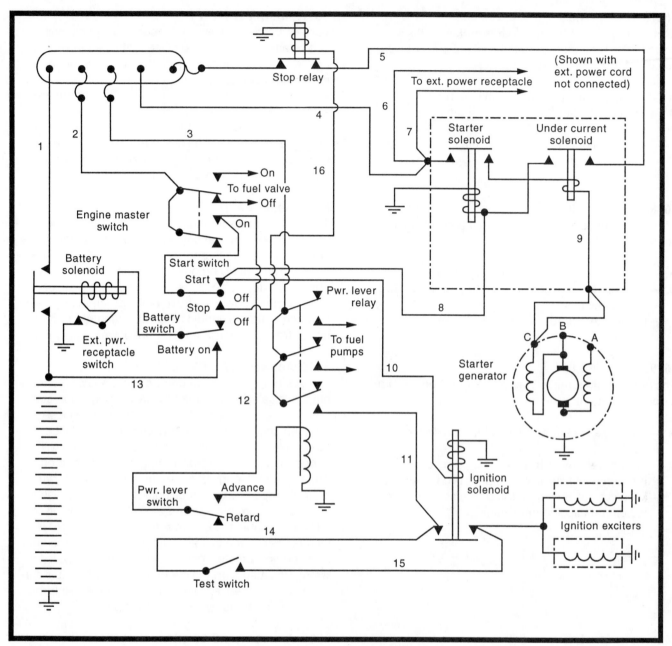

Figure 5.— Starter-Generator Circuit.

8616.   L03

(Refer to figure 5.) The type of system depicted is capable of operating with

A — external power only.
B — either battery or external power.
C — battery power and external power simultaneously.

8616. Answer B. ITP-P2

The system illustrated may be operated with either battery power or external power, but not both at the same time. To prevent both an external power source and the battery from operating simultaneously, an external power receptacle switch is placed just after the battery solenoid coil that removes power from the battery solenoid coil and, ultimately, battery power from the bus when external power is plugged in.

8617.   L03

(Refer to figure 5.) If wire No.8 is broken or disconnected after rotation is initiated, and the power lever is advanced, the

A — starting sequence will continue normally.
B — starter will shut down, but the igniters will continue to fire.
C — starting sequence will discontinue.

8618.   L03

(Refer to figure 5.) When an external power source is connected to the aircraft,

A — the battery cannot be connected to the bus.
B — both battery power and external power are available to the bus.
C — the start solenoid coil has a path to ground.

8619.   L03

The purpose of an under current relay (or solenoid) in a starter-generator system is to

A — provide a backup for the motor relay (or solenoid).
B — disconnect power from the starter-generator and ignition when sufficient engine speed is reached.
C — keep current flow to the starter-generator under the circuit capacity maximum.

8620.   L03

In a typical starter-generator system, under which of the following starting circumstances may it be necessary to use the start stop switch?

A — Hung start.
B — Hot start.
C — Contacts stick open.

8617. Answer A. ITP-P2

Wire 8 supplies current to the starter solenoid coil which makes the solenoid close. With the starter solenoid closed, power flows from the bus, through the undercurrent solenoid coil and on to the starter generator. Since current is flowing through the undercurrent solenoid coil, the solenoid will close and provide a secondary power source to keep the starter solenoid engaged and, as long as the start switch is closed, the start sequence progressing normally if wire 8 should break or become disconnected.

8618. Answer A. ITP-P2

The system illustrated may be operated with either battery power or external power, but not both at the same time. To prevent both an external power source and the battery from supplying power to the system simultaneously, an external power receptacle switch is placed just after the battery solenoid coil that removes power from the battery solenoid coil and, ultimately, battery power from the bus when external power is plugged in.

8619. Answer B. AC 65-12A

In a system that uses an undercurrent relay, an engine start is initiated by placing the start switch in the start position for a few seconds to allow current to close both the starter and undercurrent solenoids. Once these solenoids are closed, the start sequence will support itself and the start switch can be turned off. Then, once the engine speed increases and starter current drops, the undercurrent relay opens to disconnect power from the starter-generator and ignition circuits and enable the generator circuit. Answer (A) is incorrect since the systems that use starter-generators do not employ motor relay backups. Answer (C) is wrong because current flow to a starter-generator during a start sequence is limited by the starter's internal characteristics and by circuit breakers.

8620. Answer A. AC 65-12A

When a hung start occurs, the engine fails to reach a self-sustaining speed and the starter continues to crank the engine. To abort a hung start, the start/stop switch must be pressed or toggled manually to de-energize the starter generator. Answer (B) is wrong because during a hot start you want to shut off the fuel and continue cranking the engine to remove the excess fuel for the engine. Answer (C) is incorrect because if a start circuit's contacts stick open, no current flows to the starter generator and the engine cannot be started.

8621.   L03

(Refer to figure 5.) Which malfunctions will allow the igniters to operate when tested but be inoperative during a start attempt?

1. Conductor No.10 broken.
2. Conductor No.11 broken.
3. Ignition solenoid inoperative.
4. Conductor No.12 broken.

A — 1 or 4.
B — 2 or 3.
C — 1 or 3.

8621. Answer C. ITP-P2

Neither a break in conductor No. 10 nor an inoperative ignition solenoid would prevent current from being supplied to the ignition test switch. However, both of these malfunctions would prevent the ignition exciters from being operated during a start attempt. Therefore, answer (C) is correct.

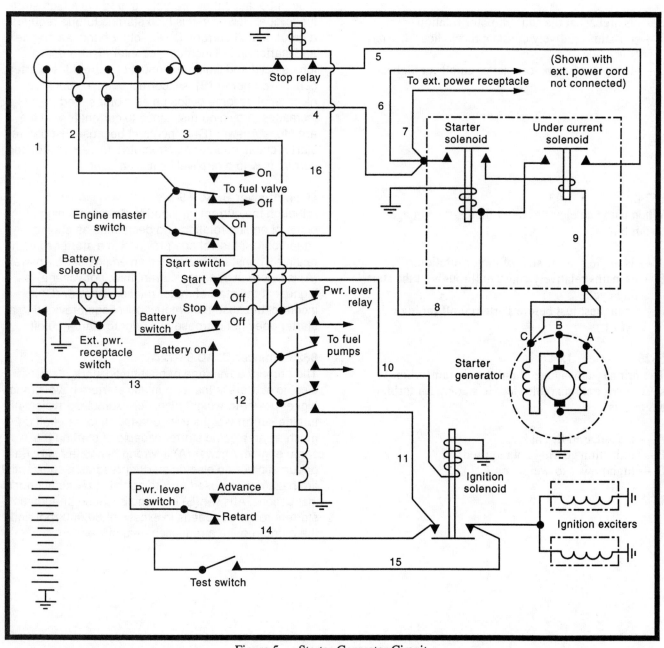

Figure 5.— Starter-Generator Circuit.

8622.   L03

(Refer to figure 5.) Which malfunctions will allow the igniters to operate normally during start but be inoperative when tested?

1. Conductor No.14 broken.
2. Conductor No.10 broken.
3. Conductor No.15 broken.
4. Conductor No.12 broken.

A — 2 or 4.
B — 1 or 3.
C — 3 or 4.

8623.   L03

When using an electric starter motor, current usage

A — is highest at the start of motor rotation.
B — remains relatively constant throughout the starting cycle.
C — is highest just before starter cutoff (at highest RPM).

8624.   L03

When using an electric starter motor, the voltage through it

A — is highest at the start of motor rotation.
B — remains relatively constant throughout the starting cycle.
C — is highest just before starter cutoff (at highest RPM.).

8625.   L04

The primary advantage of pneumatic (air turbine) starters over comparable electric starters for turbine engines is

A — a decreased fire hazard.
B — reduction gearing not required.
C — high power-to-weight ratio.

8622. Answer B. ITP-P2

The igniter test circuit consists primarily of two conductors (14 and 15) and a test switch. Therefore, if any of these three components should fail, the igniters could not be tested but would operate normally during a start. Based on this, answer (B) is correct.

8623. Answer A. AC 65-12A

Series-wound motors are typically used for starter motors because they are able to produce a high starting torque. However, this high starting torque requires a great deal of current. On the other hand, as engine and starter speed increase, counter electromotive forces build and limit the amount of current the starter can draw. Answer (B) is incorrect because counter electromotive force builds up as motor speed increases, providing resistance to current flow in the armature. Answer (C) is incorrect because just before starter cutoff, counter electromotive force has reduced current flow to a relatively small amount.

8624. Answer B. AC 65-9A

Although the current provided to a starter is high at the onset of engine rotation and decreases as engine speed builds, the voltage provided to a starter remains relatively constant throughout an engine start. Answer (A) is incorrect because current flow, not voltage, is highest at the start of motor rotation. Answer (C) is incorrect because the amount of voltage provided to a starter does not increase just prior to starter cutoff.

8625. Answer C. AC 65-12A

The primary advantage of pneumatic starters over electric starters is that pneumatic starters have a much higher power-to-weight ratio. For example, a typical air turbine starter weighs from one-fourth to one-half as much as an electric starter capable of starting the same engine. Answer (A) is wrong because neither a pneumatic nor an electric starter presents a substantial fire hazard when used according to the manufacturer's instructions. Answer (B) is wrong because pneumatic starters rotate at speeds in excess of 60,000 rpm and, therefore, require a reduction gear system.

8626. L04

A clicking sound heard at engine coast-down in a pneumatic starter incorporating a sprag clutch ratchet assembly is an indication of

A — gear tooth and/or pawl damage.
B — one or more broken pawl springs.
C — the pawls re-contacting and riding on the ratchet gear.

8627. L04

Pneumatic starters are usually designed with what types of airflow impingement systems?

A — Radial inward flow turbine and axial-flow turbine.
B — Centrifugal compressor and axial-flow compressor.
C — Double entry centrifugal outward flow and axial-flow turbines.

8628. L04

Inspection of pneumatic starters by maintenance technicians usually includes checking the

A — oil level and magnetic drain plug condition.
B — stator and rotor blades for FOD.
C — rotor alignment.

8629. L04

Air turbine starters are generally designed so that reduction gear distress or damage may be detected by

A — characteristic sounds from the starter assembly during engine start.
B — breakage of a shear section on the starter drive shaft.
C — inspection of a magnetic chip detector.

8630. L04

Airflow to the pneumatic starter from a ground unit is normally prevented from causing starter overspeed during engine start by

A — stator nozzle design that chokes airflow and stabilizes turbine wheel speed.
B — activation of a flyweight cutout switch.
C — a preset timed cutoff of the airflow at the source.

8626. Answer C. AC 65-12A

In a pneumatic starter that incorporates a sprag clutch ratchet assembly, the pawls are forced inward by small leaf springs to engage the sprag clutch ratchet when the engine is at rest. However, once the engine reaches a given rpm during a start, centrifugal force pulls the pawls outward, disengaging them from the sprag clutch ratchet. On coastdown the springs force the pawls to ride the ratchet gear until the engine comes to a stop. Answers (A) and (B) are wrong because the clicking sound indicates normal operation.

8627. Answer A. ITP-P2

Pneumatic starters that utilize a low pressure, high volume air supply typically employ a radial inward flow turbine or an axial-flow turbine. Answer (B) is incorrect because pneumatic starters receive compressed air from an outside source and, therefore, do not incorporate a compressor as a component. Answer (C) is wrong because there is no such thing as a double entry centrifugal outward flow turbine.

8628. Answer A. ITP-P2

Because of their high rotational speed, pneumatic starters require frequent inspection of their oil level and the condition of their magnetic drain plugs. Answer (B) is wrong because pneumatic starters rarely sustain damage from foreign objects, and answer (C) is wrong because a pneumatic starter's rotor alignment is typically checked at overhaul.

8629. Answer C. ITP-P2

Most air turbine starters utilize a self-contained lubrication system that incorporates a magnetic chip detector. When inspecting a chip detector, if metallic particles are found, it may indicate internal stress or damage to the starter's reduction gearing (answer C). Answer (A) is incorrect because starters are not designed to make a specific sound to indicate reduction gear damage. Answer (B) is wrong because the purpose of the shear shaft is to prevent the engine from over speeding the starter, not to indicate reduction gear damage.

8630. Answer B. ITP-P2

In the normal operation of a pneumatic starter, once the starter reaches a predetermined drive speed, the starter's air supply is cut off by a centrifugal cutout flyweight switch (answer B). If the cutout switch should fail, most pneumatic starters incorporate a stator nozzle that chokes the incoming airflow supply to stabilize the turbine wheel speed below the burst speed (answer A). Answer (C) is wrong because a timed cutoff cannot take into account varying air supply pressure, changing ambient conditions, or other factors that can affect a turbine engine start sequence.

8631.   L04

A safety feature usually employed in pneumatic starters that is used if the clutch does not release from the engine drive at the proper time during start is the

A — flyweight cutout switch.
B — spring coupling release.
C — drive shaft shear point.

8632.   L04

A safety feature usually employed in pneumatic starters that is used to prevent the starter from reaching burst speed if inlet air does not terminate on schedule is the

A — drive shaft shear point.
B — stator nozzle design that chokes airflow and stabilizes turbine wheel speed.
C — spring coupling release.

8633.   L04

In the event a pneumatic start valve will not operate and the manual override must be used, the starter T handle must be closed at scheduled starter drop out because

A — the starter will overheat.
B — the starter will overspeed at a given N2.
C — the starter oil will be blown over board.

8631. Answer C. AC 65-12A

To help protect pneumatic starters from being damaged if the clutch does not release from the engine drive at the proper speed, a drive shaft shear point is typically incorporated. Answers (A) and (B) are incorrect because neither a flyweight switch nor a spring coupling release would operate at the speeds used in pneumatic starters.

8632. Answer B. ITP-P2

To protect against damage in the event of an overspeed, many pneumatic starters employ a stator nozzle design that chokes the incoming airflow and stabilizes turbine wheel speed. A drive shaft shear point (answer A) keeps an engine from driving a starter but will not protect the starter if inlet air flow continues. Answer (C) is wrong because a spring coupling release will not operate at the high shaft speeds encountered by pneumatic starters.

8633. Answer B. TEP2

If the pneumatic starter on a turbine engine is inoperative, the engine can be started by manually actuating the start valve. This is typically done by pulling a T-handle on the start valve, turning the T-handle to the OPEN position, and holding it in this position until the start is self-sustaining. If the T-handle is not returned to the CLOSED position after a successful start, the starter will overspeed and fail. Answer (A) is incorrect because overspeed, not overheat, causes the starter to fail. Answer (C) is wrong because, as opposed to a starter overspeed, oil loss is a minor consideration when conducting a manual start.

FUEL METERING SYSTEM

The chapter on fuel metering systems describes methods used to inspect, check, service, troubleshoot, and repair fuel metering systems and components. Included is a discussion on both float-type and pressure-type carburetors as well as fuel injection systems. In addition, information regarding turbine engine fuel control units is also presented. The following FAA exam questions are taken from this chapter:

8634, 8635, 8636, 8637, 8638, 8639, 8640, 8641, 8642, 8643, 8644, 8645, 8646, 8647, 8648, 8649, 8650, 8651, 8652, 8653, 8654, 8655, 8656, 8657, 8658, 8659, 8660, 8661, 8662, 8663, 8664, 8665, 8666, 8667, 8668, 8669, 8670, 8671, 8672, 8673, 8674, 8675, 8676, 8677, 8678, 8679, 8680, 8681, 8682, 8683, 8684, 8685, 8686, 8687, 8688, 8689, 8690, 8691, 8692, 8693, 8694, 8695, 8696, 8697, 8698, 8699, 8700, 8701, 8702, 8703, 8704, 8705, 8706, 8707, 8708, 8709, 8710, 8711, 8712, 8713, 8714, 8715, 8716, 8717, 8718, 8719, 8720, 8721, 8722, 8723, 8724, 8725, 8726, 8727, 8728, 8729, 8730, 8731.

8634.   M01

What factor is not used in the operation of an aircraft gas turbine engine fuel control unit?

A — Compressor inlet air temperature.
B — Mixture control position.
C — Power lever position.

8635.   M01

In order to stabilize cams, springs, and linkages within the fuel control, manufacturers generally recommend that all final turbine engine trim adjustments be made in the

A — increase direction.
B — decrease direction.
C — decrease direction after over-adjustment.

8636.   M01

When trimming a turbine engine, the fuel control is adjusted to

A — produce as much power as the engine is capable of producing.
B — set idle RPM and maximum speed or EPR.
C — allow the engine to produce maximum RPM without regard to power output.

8634. Answer B. AC 65-12A

Automatic fuel control units sense power lever position, engine rpm, compressor inlet air temperature and density, and burner pressure or discharge pressure. Since turbine engine aircraft do not utilize a mixture control, it is not a factor in the operation of the fuel control unit.

8635. Answer A. ITP-P2

In order to stabilize internal components and ensure consistent results, most engine manufacturers specify that all trim adjustments be made in the increase direction. In other words, the engine will idle at a value just above the minimum idle speed and maximum thrust will be obtained slightly before the power levers reach the full forward position. Trim adjustments are not made in the decrease direction (answers B and C) because this could lead to slack in the fuel control and incorrect settings at high power levels.

8636. Answer B. AC 65-12A

Field adjustments, or trimming adjustments made to turbine engine fuel controls are limited to idle rpm and maximum speed adjustments. Answers (A) and (C) are incorrect because engines are never trimmed to produce maximum power or maximum rpm with no regard to other limiting factors such as EGT, fuel flow, or EPR.

8637.   M01

A supervisory electronic engine control (EEC) is a system that receives engine operating information and

A — adjusts a standard hydromechanical fuel control unit to obtain the most effective engine operation.
B — develops the commands to various actuators to control engine parameters.
C — controls engine operation according to ambient temperature, pressure, and humidity.

8637. Answer A.

A supervisory electronic engine control (EEC) includes a computer that monitors several engine operating criteria and uses this information to adjust a standard hydromechanical fuel control unit (FCU) to obtain a constant thrust for a given power lever position. Answer (B) is incorrect because a full-authority EEC develops commands to various actuators that control the engine parameters, whereas a supervisory EEC commands only the hydromechanical FCU. Answer (C) is wrong because a typical supervisory EEC senses pressure and temperature, but not humidity.

8638.   M01

A full-authority electronic engine control (EEC) is a system that receives all the necessary data for engine operation and

A — adjusts a standard hydromechanical fuel control unit to obtain the most effective engine operation.
B — develops the commands to various actuators to control engine parameters.
C — controls engine operation according to ambient temperature, pressure, and humidity.

8638. Answer B.

A full-authority electronic engine control (EEC) performs all of the functions required to operate an engine. In other words, it receives data from the aircraft and engine systems and then issues commands to various actuators that control engine operating parameters. Answer (A) is incorrect because a supervisory EEC, not a full-authority EEC, adjusts a standard hydromechanical fuel control unit. Answer (C) is wrong because a full authority EEC does not monitor humidity.

8639.   M01

In a supervisory EEC system, any fault in the EEC that adversely affects engine operation

A — causes redundant or backup units to take over and continue normal operation.
B — usually degrades performance to the extent that continued operation can cause damage to the engine.
C — causes an immediate reversion to control by the hydromechanical fuel control unit.

8639. Answer C.

Any fault in a supervisory electronic engine control (EEC) automatically causes the EEC to relinquish engine control to the hydromechanical control unit. At the same time, the EEC sends a signal to the cockpit that illuminates an annunciator light to inform the flight crew of the change in operating mode. Answer (A) is incorrect because systems that use supervisory EECs do not utilize backups. Answer (B) is wrong because a supervisory EEC automatically disengages itself before it can harm an engine.

8640.   M01

The active clearance control (ACC) portion of an EEC system aids turbine engine efficiency by

A — adjusting stator vane position according to operating conditions and power requirements.
B — ensuring compressor and turbine blade to engine case clearances are kept to a minimum by controlling case temperatures.
C — automatically adjusting engine speed to maintain a desired EPR.

8640. Answer B.

The active clearance control (ACC) portion of an electronic engine control (EEC) system controls compressor and turbine blade-to-engine case clearances by controlling the amount of air that is directed through the engine case. By keeping clearances to a minimum, pressure losses caused by air leakage at the blade tips is minimized. Answer (A) is incorrect because the variable stator vane (VSV) portion of the EEC controls stator vane position. Answer (C) is wrong because the thrust management computer adjusts engine speed to maintain a desired EPR.

8641.   M01

What should be checked/changed to ensure the validity of a turbine engine performance check if an alternate fuel is to be used?

A — Fuel specific gravity setting.
B — Maximum RPM adjustment.
C — EPR gauge calibration.

8642.   M01

The generally acceptable way to obtain accurate on-site temperature prior to performing engine trimming is to

A — call the control tower to obtain field temperature.
B — observe the reading on the aircraft Outside Air Temperature (OAT) gauge.
C — hang a thermometer in the shade of the nose wheel-well until the temperature reading stabilizes.

8643.   M01

An aircraft should be facing into the wind when trimming an engine. However, if the velocity of the wind blowing into the intake is excessive, it is likely to cause a

A — false low exhaust gas temperature reading.
B — trim setting resulting in engine overspeed.
C — false high compression and turbine discharge pressure, and a subsequent low trim.

8644.   M01

Generally, the practice when trimming an engine is to

A — turn all accessory bleed air off.
B — turn all accessory bleed air on.
C — make adjustments (as necessary) for all engines on the same aircraft with accessory bleed air settings the same—either on or off.

8645.   M02

A reciprocating engine automatic mixture control responds to changes in air density caused by changes in

A — altitude or humidity.
B — altitude only.
C — altitude or temperature.

8641. Answer A. AC 65-9A

Turbine engines are designed to operate using a specific type of fuel with a given BTU value and specific gravity. Therefore, if a performance check is made on an engine using an alternate fuel, the specific gravity setting should be checked and changed as necessary on the fuel control unit to ensure proper performance. Although an alternate fuel is likely to cause an engine to perform differently, neither maximum rpm (answer B) nor EPR calibration (answer C) is normally checked or changed when an alternate fuel is used.

8642. Answer C. TEP2

Part of the procedure used for trimming an engine includes measuring engine inlet barometric pressure and ambient temperature. To ensure a temperature value that is accurate, it is common practice to hang a thermometer in the shade of the nose wheel-well. Answer (A) is wrong because the control tower reading could be measurably different from the temperature where an aircraft is located. Answer (B) is incorrect because outside air temperature gauge probes can become heat soaked from exposure to the sun or proximity to hot pavement and give incorrect readings.

8643. Answer C. TEP2

Facing an engine into a strong wind produces the same effect as improving the efficiency of the engine's compressor. Therefore, if an engine is trimmed while facing into an excessive wind, a false high compression and turbine discharge pressure, as well as a subsequent low trim are likely to occur. Answer (A) is incorrect because exhaust gas temperature (EGT) is primarily a function of turbine efficiency and fuel flow, and a direct headwind will have no effect on EGT readings. Answer (B) is wrong because a low, not high, trim will result.

8644. Answer A. AC 65-12A

When high-pressure air is bled from the compressor for various aircraft functions, it has the same effect as decreasing the compressor's efficiency. Therefore, if a trim adjustment is made with the bleeds on, an inaccurate or overtrimmed condition will result. Because of this, most engine manufacturers require that an engine be trimmed with the engine bleeds off.

8645. Answer C. AC 65-12A

An automatic mixture control utilizes a sealed, helium-filled bellows that fluctuates with changes in air density. As air density decreases due to an increase in altitude or temperature (answer C), the helium pressure inside the bellows causes the bellows to expand and move a poppet valve that adjusts the fuel/air mixture. Answer (A) is wrong because an automatic mixture control does not sense humidity, and answer (B) is wrong because an automatic mixture control senses temperature in addition to altitude.

8646.   M02

On a float-type carburetor, the purpose of the economizer valve is to

A — provide extra fuel for sudden acceleration of the engine.
B — maintain the leanest mixture possible during cruising best power.
C — provide a richer mixture and cooling at maximum power output.

8646. Answer C. AC 65-12A

For an engine to develop maximum power at full throttle, the fuel mixture must be richer than that used at cruise power settings. The additional fuel is used to cool the engine and prevent detonation. One way to make sure the engine gets this additional fuel is with an economizer valve which automatically enriches the fuel/air mixture at throttle settings above 60 to 70 percent power. Answer (A) is wrong because a separate accelerating system enriches the mixture during abrupt engine acceleration, and answer (B) is wrong because an economizer valve does not lean the mixture, it enriches it.

8647.   M02

The fuel metering force of a conventional float-type carburetor in its normal operating range is the difference between the pressure acting on the discharge nozzle located within the venturi and the pressure

A — acting on the fuel in the float chamber.
B — of the fuel as it enters the carburetor.
C — of the air as it enters the venturi (impact pressure).

8647. Answer A. AC 65-12A

The force that is responsible for discharging fuel into the throat of a float-type carburetor is a result of the differential pressure between the fuel discharge nozzle within the venturi and the pressure exerted on the fuel within the float chamber. As engine speed increases the amount of air flowing past the venturi increases causing a greater pressure differential and corresponding increase in fuel flow. Answer (B) is incorrect because the needle valve regulates fuel flow into the float chamber and, in effect, isolates the float chamber from fuel pump pressure. Answer (C) is wrong because impact pressure is not a fuel metering force.

8648.   M02

If the main air bleed of a float-type carburetor becomes clogged, the engine will run

A — lean at rated power.
B — rich at rated power.
C — rich at idling.

8648. Answer B. AC 65-12A

The main air bleed in a float-type carburetor allows air to be drawn into the carburetor venturi along with the fuel. The additional air helps decrease the fuel density and destroy surface tension, resulting in better vaporization and control of fuel discharge at lower engine speeds. If the main air bleed becomes clogged, it stands to reason that less air will be drawn into the engine and the fuel/air mixture will become excessively rich at high power settings. Answer (A) is wrong since a clogged air bleed results in more fuel flow. Answer (C) is incorrect because a clogged air bleed will deliver less fuel at lower power settings, resulting in a lean mixture.

8649.   M02

Which method is commonly used to adjust the level of a float in a float-type carburetor?

A — Lengthening or shortening the float shaft.
B — Add or remove shims under the needle-valve seat.
C — Change the angle of the float arm pivot.

8649. Answer B. ITP-P2

Most carburetor floats are adjusted by adding or removing shims between the needle seat and the throttle body. This method of adjustment is much more convenient and precise than adjusting the length of the float shaft (answer A) or changing the angle of the float arm pivot (answer C).

8650. M02

What is the possible cause of an engine running rich at full throttle if it is equipped with a float-type carburetor?

A — Float level too low.
B — Clogged main air bleed.
C — Clogged atmospheric vent.

8651. M02

One of the things a calibrated orifice in a main air bleed helps to accomplish (at a given altitude) in a carburetor is

A — pressure in the float chamber to increase as airflow through the carburetor increases.
B — a progressively richer mixture as airflow through the carburetor increases.
C — better fuel vaporization and control of fuel discharge, especially at lower engine speeds.

8652. M02

A punctured float in a float-type carburetor will cause the fuel level to

A — lower, and enrich the mixture.
B — rise, and enrich the mixture.
C — rise, and lean the mixture.

8653. M02

The back-suction mixture control system operates by

A — varying the pressure within the venturi section.
B — varying the pressure acting on the fuel in the float chamber.
C — changing the effective cross-sectional area of the main metering orifice (jet).

8650. Answer B. AC 65-12A

The main air bleed in a float-type carburetor allows air to be drawn into the carburetor venturi along with the fuel. Therefore, if the air bleed becomes clogged, less air will be drawn into the engine and the fuel/air mixture will become excessively rich at high power settings. A low float level (answer A) allows less fuel into the bowl, but has no effect on mixture, and a clogged atmospheric vent (answer C) will decrease the pressure differential between the float bowl and the venturi thereby reducing the fuel metering force and causing a leaning of the mixture.

8651. Answer C. AC 65-12A

One way to help promote better fuel vaporization within the throat of a carburetor is to allow a calibrated amount of air from an air bleed to be mixed with the fuel as the fuel enters the carburetor throat. Mixing fuel and air also allows better control of the fuel discharge rate, especially at low engine speeds. Answer (A) is incorrect because most float chambers are vented directly to the atmosphere and, therefore, the pressure within them is the same as atmospheric pressure. Answer (B) is wrong because the main air bleed actually helps maintain the desired fuel/air mixture rather than allow the mixture to become progressively richer as airflow increases.

8652. Answer B. AC 65-12A

During engine operation, the carburetor float is responsible for maintaining the appropriate amount of fuel within the float bowl. When fuel is drawn from the bowl, the float lowers and fuel is allowed into the bowl. By the same token, if a float should become punctured, it would fill with fuel and sink. With the float resting on the bottom of the bowl, fuel would be allowed to continually enter the bowl and eventually enrich the fuel/air mixture.

8653. Answer B. AC 65-12A

The back-suction type mixture control system used on some float-type carburetors utilizes low pressure from the venturi to control the amount of air pressure within the float chamber. By varying the pressure acting on the fuel in the float chamber, the pressure differential between the carburetor throat and float bowl can be controlled which, in turn, provides control of the mixture being supplied to the engine. Answer (A) is incorrect because a back-suction mixture control system controls the amount of fuel allowed to enter the carburetor throat and does nothing to vary pressure within the venturi. Answer (C) is incorrect because it is impractical to change the main metering jet's cross-sectional area to control the mixture.

8654.   M02
If an aircraft engine is equipped with a carburetor that is not compensated for altitude and temperature variations, the fuel/air mixture will become

A — leaner as either the altitude or temperature increases.
B — richer as the altitude increases and leaner as the temperature increases.
C — richer as either the altitude or temperature increases.

8655.   M02
Float-type carburetors which are equipped with economizers are normally set for

A — their richest mixture delivery and leaned by means of the economizer system.
B — the economizer system to supplement the main system supply at all engine speeds above idling.
C — their leanest practical mixture delivery at cruising speeds and enriched by means of the economizer system at higher power settings.

8656.   M02
If a float-type carburetor becomes flooded, the condition is most likely caused by

A — a leaking needle valve and seat assembly.
B — the accelerating pump shaft being stuck.
C — a clogged back-suction line.

8657.   M02
If an engine is equipped with a float-type carburetor and the engine runs excessively rich at full throttle, a possible cause of the trouble is a clogged

A — main air bleed.
B — back-suction line.
C — atmospheric vent line.

8654. Answer C. AC 65-12A
As both altitude and temperature increase, the air becomes less dense. Therefore, as an airplane climbs or as the air temperature increases, the amount of oxygen drawn into an engine decreases. In either of these situations if an engine is not equipped with a carburetor that can be adjusted for increases in altitude and temperature, the fuel/air mixture will become excessively rich. Answers (A) and (B) are incorrect because there is less air in the fuel/air mixture at elevated altitudes and temperatures, so the mixture becomes richer.

8655. Answer C. AC 65-12A
For an engine to develop maximum power at full throttle, the fuel mixture must be richer than that used at cruise power. The additional fuel is used to cool the engine and prevent detonation. One way to make sure the engine gets this additional fuel is with an economizer valve which is set to the leanest practical mixture at cruise power settings, then automatically enriches the fuel/air mixture at throttle settings above 60 to 70 percent power. Answer (A) is incorrect because carburetors are rarely set to deliver the richest possible mixture. Answer (B) is wrong because an economizer system typically operates above 60 to 70 percent of rated power and not at every power setting.

8656. Answer A.
A likely cause of float-type carburetor flooding is an improperly set float level or a leak at the needle valve and seat assembly. A stuck accelerating pump shaft (answer B) is unlikely to flood an engine since it sprays a charge of fuel into the carburetor throat only when the shaft and pump are advanced rapidly. Answer (C) is wrong because, although a clogged back-suction line will result in a rich mixture at altitude, it will not flood the engine.

8657. Answer A. AC 65-12A
The main air bleed in a float-type carburetor allows air to be drawn into a carburetor's venturi along with the fuel to improve vaporization. Therefore, if the air bleed becomes clogged, the engine will draw too much fuel and the fuel/air mixture will become excessively rich. Answer (B) is incorrect because a clogged back-suction line will cause a lean fuel/air mixture, and answer (C) is wrong because a clogged atmospheric vent line will prevent the flow of fuel to the engine.

8658.   M02

What occurs when a back-suction type mixture control is placed in IDLE CUTOFF?

A — The fuel passages to the main and idle jets will be closed by a valve.
B — The float chamber will be vented to a negative pressure area.
C — The fuel passage to the idle jet will be closed by a valve.

8659.   M02

Which of the following best describes the function of an altitude mixture control?

A — Regulates the richness of the fuel/air charge entering the engine.
B — Regulates the air pressure above the fuel in the float chamber.
C — Regulates the air pressure in the venturi.

8660.   M02

Select the correct statement concerning the idle system of a conventional float-type carburetor.

A — The low-pressure area created in the throat of the venturi pulls the fuel from the idle passage.
B — Climactic conditions have very little effect on idle mixture requirements.
C — The low pressure between the edges of the throttle valve and the throttle body pulls the fuel from the idle passage.

8661.   M02

On an engine equipped with a pressure-type carburetor, fuel supply in the idling range is ensured by the inclusion in the carburetor of

A — a spring in the unmetered fuel chamber to supplement the action of normal metering forces.
B — an idle metering jet that bypasses the carburetor in the idle range.
C — a separate boost venturi that is sensitive to the reduced airflow at start and idle speeds.

8658. Answer B. AC 65-12A

In a back-suction type mixture control system a certain amount of low pressure air from the venturi acts on the fuel in the float chamber. By controlling the amount of low pressure air that is vented to the float chamber you can control the pressure differential between the carburetor throat and float chamber which, in turn, dictates the amount of fuel that flows into the engine. With this type of system, when the mixture control is placed in idle cutoff position, all atmospheric pressure is removed from the float chamber and the fuel is placed under negative pressure. This stops fuel flow which, in turn, stops the engine. Answers (A) and (C) are wrong because no jets are closed by cockpit-actuated valves.

8659. Answer A. AC 65-12A

The function of a mixture control is to regulate the richness of the fuel/air mixture entering the engine. Answer (B) is incorrect because, although some mixture control systems do control the amount of fuel in the fuel/air mixture by varying the amount of air pressure in the float chamber, it does not represent the function of all mixture controls. Answer (C) is wrong because the throttle valve regulates the air pressure in the venturi by regulating the speed of airflow through it.

8660. Answer C. AC 65-12A

With the throttle valve closed at idling speed, air velocity through the venturi is so low that it cannot draw enough fuel from the main discharge nozzle to keep an engine running. Therefore, in order to allow the engine to idle, a fuel passageway called an idling jet is incorporated in the low pressure area between the throttle valve and throttle body that discharges fuel into the throttle body. Answer (A) is incorrect because with the throttle closed, there is not enough of a pressure drop within the throat to pull fuel from the idle passage. Answer (B) is wrong because climactic conditions such as temperature, pressure, and humidity have a substantial effect on mixture requirements.

8661. Answer A. AC 65-12A

In a pressure-type carburetor, fuel follows in the same path at idling as it does when the main metering system is in operation. However, because of the low air velocity through the venturi, insufficient differential pressure exists to displace the diaphragm that holds the poppet valve open and allows fuel to flow. Therefore, a spring is used to physically hold the poppet valve off its seat so fuel can flow while the engine is idling. Answer (B) is wrong because pressure-type carburetors do not use idle metering jets like float carburetors do. Answer (C) is wrong because, although pressure-type carburetors do use a boost venturi, it does not help supply fuel during idling operations.

8662.   M02

The economizer system of a float-type carburetor per-forms which of the following functions?

A — It supplies and regulates the fuel required for all engine speeds.
B — It supplies and regulates the additional fuel required for all engine speeds above cruising.
C — It regulates the fuel required for all engine speeds and all altitudes.

8663.   M02

How will the mixture of an engine be affected if the bellows of the automatic mixture control (AMC) in a pressure carburetor ruptures while the engine is operat-ing at altitude?

A — It will become leaner.
B — No change will occur until the altitude changes.
C — It will become richer.

8664.   M02

The fuel level within the float chamber of a properly adjusted float-type carburetor will be

A — slightly higher than the discharge nozzle outlet.
B — slightly lower than the discharge nozzle outlet.
C — at the same level as the discharge nozzle outlet.

8665.   M02

The metered fuel pressure (chamber C) in an injection-type carburetor

A — is held constant throughout the entire engine operating range.
B — varies according to the position of the poppet valve located between chamber D (unmetered fuel) and chamber E (engine-driven fuel pump pressure).
C — will be approximately equal to the pressure in chamber A (impact pressure).

8662. Answer B. AC 65-12A

In order for an engine to effectively develop maximum power at full throttle, the fuel/air mixture must be richer than that used for cruise power settings. The additional fuel is used for cooling the engine to prevent detona-tion. One way to make sure the engine gets this addi-tional fuel is with an economizer valve which automatically supplies and regulates the additional fuel needed at throttle settings above 60 to 70 percent power. Answers (A) and (C) are wrong because the economizer valve supplies and regulates fuel only at engine speeds above cruise.

8663. Answer C. AC 65-12A

The automatic mixture control on a pressure carburetor contains a tapered needle valve that is connected to a pressurized metallic bellows that expands and con-tracts with changes in air pressure. With this type of system, when the aircraft climbs and the atmospheric pressure decreases, the bellows expands and pushes the tapered needle valve into the atmospheric passage which restricts the flow of air to the regulator unit. With the flow of air to the regulator decreased, the amount of fuel allowed to flow to the engine is also decreased. Based on this, if the bellows in an automatic mixture control were to rupture, fuel flow would continue nor-mally and the engine would run rich.

8664. Answer B. AC 65-12A

In a float-type carburetor, a float chamber is provided between the fuel supply and the metering system to provide a nearly constant level of fuel to the main dis-charge nozzle. The fuel level in the float chamber is set slightly lower than the discharge nozzle outlet to allow differential pressure to draw the fuel into the carburetor throat. If the float chamber fuel level was higher (answer A) or at the same level as the nozzle outlet (answer C), fuel would run out of the carburetor when the engine was shut down.

8665. Answer A. AC 65-12A

The function of the metered fuel pressure chamber (chamber C) is to deliver fuel to the fuel control unit at a relatively constant pressure at all engine speeds. Therefore, the fuel pressure within chamber C must be held relatively constant. Answer (B) is incorrect because the fuel pressure in chamber C remains con-stant and does not vary according to the position of the poppet valve. Answer (C) is wrong because the metered fuel pressure in chamber C is under consider-ably more pressure than the impact air pressure in chamber A.

8666.   M02

Select the statement which is correct relating to a fuel level check of a float-type carburetor.

A — Use 5 pounds fuel pressure for the test if the carburetor is to be used in a gravity fuel feed system.
B — Block off the main and idle jets to prevent a continuous flow of fuel through the jets.
C — Do not measure the level at the edge of the float chamber.

8667.   M02

What carburetor component measures the amount of air delivered to the engine?

A — Economizer valve.
B — Automatic mixture control.
C — Venturi.

8668.   M02

If a float-type carburetor leaks fuel when the engine is stopped, a likely cause is that the

A — float needle valve is worn or otherwise not seated properly.
B — float level is adjusted too low.
C — main air bleed is clogged.

8669.   M02

Fuel is discharged for idling speeds on a float-type carburetor

A — from the idle discharge nozzle.
B — in the venturi.
C — through the idle discharge air bleed.

8666. Answer C. ITP-P2

The fuel level in the float chamber of a carburetor should be one-eighth inch below the main discharge outlet. When measuring this level, your measurements should be taken away from the edge of the float chamber since the fuel tends to cling to the walls of the chamber. If a measurement were taken at the edge, an inaccurate measurement may result. Therefore answer (C) is correct. Answer (A) is wrong because there is no specific requirement that fuel be pressurized to 5 pounds of pressure to set the float level. Answer (B) is incorrect because an insignificant amount of fuel will flow through the main or idle jets in the absence of suction from the venturi.

8667. Answer C. AC 65-12A

A carburetor measures airflow through its induction system using a venturi. As air passes through the venturi, its velocity increases and its pressure drops. The pressure drop is proportional to the velocity and, therefore, is a measure of the airflow. Answer (A) is incorrect because an economizer valve enrichens the fuel/air mixture at high power settings and is controlled by the throttle. Answer (B) is wrong because an automatic mixture control responds to changes in ambient temperature and pressure to adjust the fuel/air mixture.

8668. Answer A.

If a float type carburetor leaks when an engine is shut down, either the needle valve is not firmly seated or the float level is adjusted too high. Based on this, answer (A) is correct. Answer (B) is wrong because if the float level is adjusted to low, fuel will not reach the main discharge nozzle and the carburetor will not leak. Answer (C) is incorrect because a clogged main air bleed will cause an engine to run rich at high power settings, but will not cause fuel to leak.

8669. Answer A. AC 65-12A

The main discharge nozzle cannot be used at idle speeds because there is insufficient airflow through the venturi to create enough of a pressure differential to force fuel from the nozzle. Because of this, float-type carburetors employ an idle jet or idle discharge nozzle that takes advantage of the low pressure area between the throttle valve and throttle body. This idle jet provides sufficient fuel flow to allow an engine to run at low rpm. Answer (B) is incorrect because the idle discharge nozzle is located downstream of the venturi and answer (C) is wrong because the idle air bleed discharges air that mixes with the idle fuel but does not discharge fuel.

8670.   M02
When air passes through the venturi of a carburetor, what three changes occur?

A — Velocity increases, temperature increases, and pressure decreases.
B — Velocity decreases, temperature increases, and pressure increases.
C — Velocity increases, temperature decreases, and pressure decreases.

8671.   M02
Where is the throttle valve located on a float-type carburetor?

A — Between the venturi and the discharge nozzle.
B — After the main discharge nozzle and venturi.
C — After the venturi and just before the main discharge nozzle.

8672.   M02
An aircraft carburetor is equipped with a mixture control in order to prevent the mixture from becoming too

A — lean at high altitudes.
B — rich at high altitudes.
C — rich at high speeds.

8673.   M02
Which of the following is NOT a function of the carburetor venturi?

A — Proportions the air/fuel mixture.
B — Regulates the idle system.
C — Limits the airflow at full throttle.

8670. Answer C. AC 65-12A
To answer this question you must be familiar with Bernoulli's Principle and Charles' Gas Law. Bernoulli's Principle states that when air flows through a converging duct such as a carburetor venturi, its velocity rises and its pressure drops. Charles' Law, on the other hand, states that pressure and temperature are directly proportional. In other words, a decrease in pressure means a decrease in temperature. Therefore, when air passes through a carburetor venturi, air velocity decreases while air temperature and pressure decrease (answer C).

8671. Answer B. AC 65-12A
In a float-type carburetor, the throttle valve controls the mass airflow through the venturi and, therefore, must be located downstream of both the venturi and the main discharge nozzle. However, in pressure injection carburetors the throttle valve is located after the venturi and just before the main discharge nozzle (answers A and C).

8672. Answer B. AC 65-12A
Carburetors are calibrated at sea level, and the correct fuel/air mixture is established at that altitude with the mixture control set in the FULL RICH position. However, as altitude increases, the density of air entering the carburetor decreases while the density of the fuel remains the same. This means that at higher altitudes, the mixture becomes progressively richer (answer B). Therefore, the purpose of the mixture control is to allow the pilot to control the amount of fuel that is mixed with the incoming air.

8673. Answer B. AC 65-12A
The venturi in a carburetor performs three functions. It proportions the fuel/air mixture, it decreases pressure at the discharge nozzle, and it limits the airflow at full throttle. Based on this, the only choice that does not represent a function of the venturi is answer (B). The reason for this is that the idle system introduces fuel into the airflow downstream of the venturi at low throttle settings and, therefore, is not affected by the venturi.

8674.   **M02**

Idle cutoff is accomplished on a carburetor equipped with a back-suction mixture control by

A — introducing low pressure (intake manifold) air into the float chamber.
B — turning the fuel selector valve to OFF.
C — the positive closing of a needle and seat.

8674. Answer A. AC 65-12A

In float-type carburetors with a back-suction type mixture control system, a certain amount of low pressure air from the venturi is vented to the float chamber to control the pressure differential between the float chamber and venturi. By varying the pressure acting on the fuel in the float chamber, the system varies the amount of fuel being supplied to the engine. With this type of system, when the mixture is placed in the idle cutoff position, the float chamber is filled with low pressure air from the venturi eliminating the pressure differential. With no difference in air pressure, there is no force to pump fuel into the engine and, therefore, the engine quits running. Answer (B) is wrong because the fuel selector valve shuts off flow from the tank, not the carburetor, and answer (C) is wrong because a needle and seat are used to stop fuel flow to the float chamber, not to stop the flow of fuel to the engine.

8675.   **M02**

One purpose of an air bleed in a float-type carburetor is to

A — increase fuel flow at altitude.
B — meter air to adjust the mixture.
C — decrease fuel density and destroy surface tension.

8675. Answer C. AC 65-12A

The main air bleed on a float-type carburetor allows air to be mixed with the fuel being drawn out of the main discharge nozzle to decrease fuel density and decrease surface tension. This results in better fuel vaporization and allows better control of fuel discharge rates, especially at low engine speeds. Answer (A) is incorrect because fuel flow is a function of airflow through the venturi and is not affected by the air bleed. Answer (B) is wrong because an air bleed does not adjust the mixture, but instead helps produce a more uniform mixture.

8676.   **M02**

To determine the float level in a float-type carburetor, a measurement is usually made from the top of the fuel in the float chamber to the

A — parting surface of the carburetor.
B — top of the float.
C — centerline of the main discharge nozzle.

8676. Answer A. ITP-P2

The float level in a float-type carburetor is determined by measuring the distance from the top of the fuel to the parting surface of the carburetor body or the point where the float chamber separates. Answer (B) is wrong because the top of the float is a variable dimension and answer (C) is wrong because the main discharge nozzle centerline is not identified in most carburetors.

8677.   **M02**

The throttle valve of float-type aircraft carburetors is located

A — ahead of the venturi and main discharge nozzle.
B — after the main discharge nozzle and ahead of the venturi.
C — between the venturi and the engine.

8677. Answer C. AC 65-12A

In a float-type carburetor, the throttle valve controls the mass airflow through the venturi and, therefore, must be located downstream of the venturi and upstream of the engine (answer C). If the throttle valve were located ahead of the venturi (answers A and B) the fuel/air charge delivered to the engine would not be uniform.

8678. **M02**

Why must a float-type carburetor supply a rich mixture during idle?

A — Engine operation at idle results in higher than normal volumetric efficiency.
B — Because at idling speeds the engine may not have enough airflow around the cylinders to provide proper cooling.
C — Because of reduced mechanical efficiency during idle.

8679. **M02**

What component is used to ensure fuel delivery during periods of rapid engine acceleration?

A — Acceleration pump.
B — Water injection pump.
C — Power enrichment unit.

8680. **M02**

The device that controls the ratio of the fuel/air mixture to the cylinders is called a

A — throttle valve.
B — mixture control.
C — metering jet.

8681. **M02**

The device that controls the volume of the fuel/air mixture to the cylinders is called a

A — mixture control.
B — metering jet.
C — throttle valve.

8682. **M03**

Which statement is correct regarding a continuous-flow fuel injection system used on many reciprocating engines?

A — Fuel is injected directly into each cylinder.
B — Fuel is injected at each cylinder intake port.
C — Two injector nozzles are used in the injector fuel system for various speeds.

8678. Answer B.

When a reciprocating aircraft engine is idling, there is typically not enough air movement around the cylinders to provide sufficient cooling. Therefore, most float-type carburetors provide a rich mixture during idle to help cool the engine. Answer (A) is incorrect because volumetric efficiency is always lower, not higher, during part-throttle operations such as idling. Answer (C) is wrong because mechanical efficiency is reduced at low power settings regardless of the fuel/air mixture.

8679. Answer A. AC 65-12A

When the throttle valve is opened quickly, a large volume of air rushes through the carburetor. To ensure that enough fuel is mixed with the onrush of air, carburetors are equipped with a small fuel pump called an accelerator pump that provides a short burst of fuel when the throttle is advanced rapidly. Answer (B) is incorrect because a water injection pump injects a water-alcohol mixture into the carburetor during takeoff to produce more power. Answer (C) is wrong because a power enrichment unit automatically enriches the mixture at high power settings.

8680. Answer B. AC 65-12A

A mixture control on a carburetor controls the ratio of the fuel/air mixture by allowing a pilot to regulate the amount of fuel introduced into the mixture. Depending on the type of carburetor, the mixture control can be a manual or an automatic device. Answer (A) is incorrect because a throttle valve determines the volume of the fuel/air mixture that goes to the cylinders. Answer (C) is wrong because a metering jet dictates the rate of fuel discharge at a given differential pressure and does not directly effect the mixture.

8681. Answer C. AC 65-12A

The throttle valve controls the amount, or volume of fuel/air mixture that is allowed to pass through the carburetor to the cylinders. Answer (A) is wrong because a mixture control is used to control the amount of fuel that is added to the fuel/air mixture, and answer (B) is incorrect because the metering jet dictates the rate of fuel discharge, not its volume.

8682. Answer B. AC 65-12A

Some continuous-flow fuel injection systems used on aircraft engines have a fuel discharge nozzle located in each cylinder head. The nozzle outlet is directed into the intake port where fuel and air are mixed just prior to entering the cylinder. Although some systems inject fuel directly into each cylinder (answer A), this is not the case with continuous-flow systems. Answer (C) is incorrect because fuel injection systems rarely use two injector nozzles per cylinder.

8683.   M03
During the operation of an aircraft engine, the pressure drop in the carburetor venturi depends primarily upon the

A — air temperature.
B — barometric pressure.
C — air velocity.

8684.   M03
Which of the following causes a single diaphragm accelerator pump to discharge fuel?

A — An increase in venturi suction when the throttle valve is open.
B — An increase in manifold pressure that occurs when the throttle valve is opened.
C — A decrease in manifold pressure that occurs when the throttle valve is opened.

8685.   M03
At what engine speed does the main metering jet actually function as a metering jet in a float-type carburetor?

A — All RPM'S.
B — Cruising RPM only.
C — All RPM's above idle range.

8686.   M03
An aircraft engine continuous cylinder fuel injection system normally discharges fuel during which stroke(s)?

A — Intake.
B — Intake and compression.
C — All (continuously).

8687.   M03
What is the purpose of the carburetor accelerating system?

A — Supply and regulate the fuel required for engine speeds above idle.
B — Temporarily enrich the mixture when the throttle is suddenly opened.
C — Supply and regulate additional fuel required for engine speeds above cruising.

8683. Answer C. AC 65-12A
According to Bernoulli's Principle, when air flows at a continuous rate, its pressure is indirectly proportional to its velocity. Therefore, when air flow increases through the venturi of a carburetor, air pressure decreases. The faster the air flows through the venturi, the greater the pressure drop. Neither air temperature (answer A) nor barometric pressure (answer B) affect pressure drop in a carburetor venturi.

8684. Answer B. AC 65-12A
The accelerator pump in a pressure injection carburetor responds to changes in manifold pressure. For example, when the throttle valve is opened rapidly manifold pressure increases and causes the accelerator pump to inject additional fuel into the carburetor throat to maintain the proper fuel/air mixture. Answer (A) is incorrect because the accelerator pump is located downstream of the venturi and is not exposed to its suction. Answer (C) is wrong because manifold pressure increases when the throttle valve is opened.

8685. Answer C. AC 65-12A
Fuel metering in a float-type carburetor is accomplished with either an idle jet or a main metering jet. At idle speeds, airflow through the venturi is not great enough to draw fuel from the main discharge nozzle, so an idle jet located between the throttle valve and throttle body supplies fuel at low speeds when the throttle valve is closed. However, at all speeds above idle, the main metering jet supplies the necessary fuel to keep the engine running. Answer (A) is wrong because the main metering jet cannot meter fuel at idle speeds. Answer (B) is incorrect because the main metering jet operates from just above idle speed to full power and not just at cruising speeds.

8686. Answer C. AC 65-12A
This question is asking when the fuel injection system discharges fuel into the intake port, not when the fuel enters the cylinders. In a continuous cylinder fuel injection system, the injector pump is not timed to inject fuel into the intake port at a specific time. Instead, fuel is always available at all intake ports. Therefore, answer (C) is correct.

8687. Answer B. AC 65-12A
When the throttle valve is opened quickly, a large volume of air rushes through the carburetor. To ensure that enough fuel is mixed with the onrush of air, carburetors are equipped with a small fuel pump called an accelerator pump that provides a momentary burst of fuel that temporarily enriches the mixture when the throttle is opened rapidly. Answer (A) is incorrect because an accelerating system supplies fuel only during a rapid acceleration, not for sustained operation. Answer (C) is wrong because the main metering jet does not provide the additional fuel required during rapid acceleration.

8688.   M03
When troubleshooting an engine for too rich a mixture to allow the engine to idle, what would be a possible cause?

A — A primer line open.
B — Mixture setting too rich.
C — Air leak in the intake manifold.

8688. Answer B. AC 65-12A
A carburetor mixture set too rich is likely to cause the mixture to be too rich to allow the engine to idle properly. Answer (A) is wrong because an open primer line would supply less fuel for priming and could cause hard starting, but should not effect an engines ability to idle. Answer (C) is wrong because an air leak in the intake manifold will cause a lean mixture, not a rich mixture.

8689.   M03
What is the relationship between the accelerating pump and the enrichment valve in a pressure injection carburetor?

A — No relationship since they operate independently.
B — Fuel pressure affects both units.
C — The accelerating pump actuates the enrichment valve.

8689. Answer A. AC 65-12A
In a pressure injection carburetor, the accelerating pump and the enrichment valve operate independently of each other (answer A). The accelerating pump senses rapid changes in manifold pressure and injects fuel into the carburetor throat any time the throttle is opened rapidly. On the other hand, the enrichment valve responds to metered fuel pressure to increase fuel flow to the discharge nozzle when the engine runs at high power settings.

8690.   M03
What is the relationship between the pressure existing within the throat of a venturi and the velocity of the air passing through the venturi?

A — There is no direct relationship between the pressure and the velocity.
B — The pressure is directly proportional to the velocity.
C — The pressure is inversely proportional to the velocity.

8690. Answer C. AC 65-12A
According to Bernoulli's Principle, as the velocity of a fluid increases, its internal pressure decreases. In other words, pressure is inversely proportional to velocity. Answer (A) is wrong because, as Bernoulli's Principle states, pressure and velocity are inversely related. Answer (B) is incorrect because pressure is inversely proportional to velocity, not directly proportional.

8691.   M03
Which of the following is least likely to occur during operation of an engine equipped with a direct cylinder fuel injection system?

A — Afterfiring.
B — Kickback during start.
C — Backfiring.

8691. Answer C. AC 65-12A
Backfiring is a condition that occurs when the fuel/air mixture within the induction system ignites and explodes when the intake valve opens. In a direct cylinder fuel injection system, the intake valve only allows air to enter the cylinder, while the fuel is injected through a separate nozzle. This eliminates any mixing of fuel and air in the induction system which, in turn, prevents backfiring. Answer (A) is incorrect because a direct cylinder fuel injection system is susceptible to afterfiring when unburned fuel enters an engine's exhaust system and ignites. In addition, direct cylinder fuel injection systems can experience kickback during start (answer (B), which is a reverse rotation of the propeller during an engine start that is caused by premature ignition.

8692.   M03
What carburetor component actually limits the desired maximum airflow to the engine at full throttle?

A — Throttle valve.
B — Venturi.
C — Manifold intake.

8692. Answer B. AC 65-12A
The throttle valve limits the airflow through the carburetor at all throttle settings except full throttle. At full throttle, the throttle valve is opened all the way leaving only the venturi to limit the airflow. The manifold intake (answer C) is comparatively large in relation to the venturi and, therefore, does not limit maximum airflow.

8693. M03

On a carburetor without an automatic mixture control as you ascend to altitude, the mixture will

A — be enriched.
B — be leaned.
C — not be affected.

8694. M03

During engine operation, if carburetor heat is applied, it will

A — increase air-to-fuel ratio.
B — increase engine RPM.
C — decrease the air density to the carburetor.

8695. M03

The desired engine idle speed and mixture setting

A — is adjusted with engine warmed up and operating.
B — should give minimum RPM with maximum manifold pressure.
C — is usually adjusted in the following sequence; speed first, then mixture.

8696. M03

A nine-cylinder radial engine, using a multiple-point priming system with a central spider, will prime which cylinders?

A — One, two, three, eight, and nine.
B — All cylinders.
C — One, three, five, and seven.

8697. M03

What is a function of the idling air bleed in a float-type carburetor?

A — It provides a means for adjusting the mixture at idle speeds.
B — It vaporizes the fuel at idling speeds.
C — It aids in emulsifying/vaporizing the fuel at idle speeds.

8693. Answer A. AC 65-12A

As altitude increases, the air becomes less dense. Therefore, if the fuel/air mixture is not leaned as an aircraft ascends, the mixture will become excessively rich (answer A). Answer (B) is wrong because, at altitude, if the same amount of fuel is mixed with less air, a rich mixture will result. Answer (C) is incorrect because, if the carburetor does not compensate for the less dense air, the fuel/air mixture is affected.

8694. Answer C. AC 65-12A

When carburetor heat is applied, warm air is directed into the carburetor intake. Warm air is less dense than cool air and, therefore, the application of carburetor heat results in a richer fuel/air mixture. Answer (A) is incorrect because the air-to-fuel ratio actually decreases when carburetor heat is applied, and answer (B) is wrong because the application of carburetor heat causes engine rpm to decrease, not increase.

8695. Answer A. AC 65-12A

When adjusting a carburetor's idle speed or mixture, the engine should be warmed up and operating in its normal temperature range, since fuel vaporization qualities are different in an engine when it is cold. Therefore, any adjustment made on a cold engine will not be accurate. Answer (B) is wrong because a correctly adjusted carburetor should give maximum rpm with maximum manifold pressure. Answer (C) is incorrect because, in flight, you do not adjust the speed of the aircraft, you adjust the propeller rpm or the manifold pressure.

8696. Answer A.

On radial engines, fluids tend to seep into the lower cylinders and cause liquid lock. To prevent adding to this problem, the priming system on a radial engine only primes the cylinders that are horizontal or pointing upward. Therefore, on a nine-cylinder radial engine, only cylinders one, two, three, eight, and nine are primed. Answer (B) is incorrect because priming the lower cylinders on a radial engine could lead to liquid lock. Answer (C) is wrong because cylinders five and seven on a nine-cylinder radial engine are below the engine's horizontal axis and, therefore, are not typically primed.

8697. Answer C. AC 65-12A

The idle jet in a float-type carburetor utilizes an idle air bleed that allows air to be mixed with the fuel before it enters the carburetor throat. This aids in vaporizing fuel before it is drawn into the cylinder. The idle air bleed does not adjust the mixture at idle speeds (answer A) nor does it actually vaporize fuel at idle speeds (answer B).

8698.   M03

If the volume of air passing through a carburetor venturi is reduced, the pressure at the venturi throat will

A — decrease.
B — be equal to the pressure at the venturi outlet.
C — increase.

8699.   M04

(Refer to figure 6.) Which curve most nearly represents an aircraft engine's fuel/air ratio throughout its operating range?

A — 1.
B — 3.
C — 2.

8698. Answer C. AC 65-12A

According to Bernoulli's Principle, fluid pressure and velocity are inversely related. In other words, as the velocity of a fluid increases, its internal pressure decreases and when the velocity of a fluid decreases, its internal pressure increases. Therefore, if the volume of air flowing through a carburetor decreases, the pressure will increase.

8699. Answer C. AC 65-12A

At idle speeds, an engine requires a rich fuel/air mixture so there is additional fuel available for cooling. However, as engine speed is increased to a cruise setting, the additional ram airflow created by the propeller and forward section of the aircraft cool the engine sufficiently and fuel requirements decrease. Then, as power output approaches maximum, additional fuel is again required to aid in cooling and help prevent detonation. Based on this, curve number two (answer C) best represents an aircraft engine's fuel/air ratio throughout its operating range.

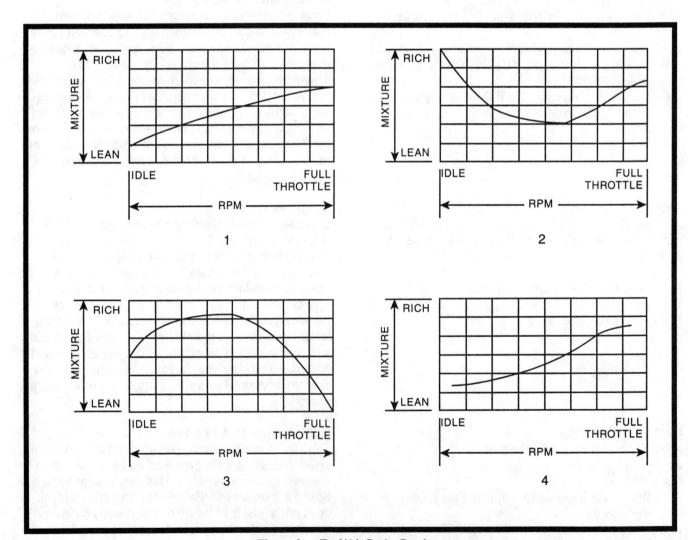

Figure 6.— Fuel/Air Ratio Graphs.

8700.   M04

What will occur if the vapor vent float in a pressure carburetor loses its buoyancy?

A — The amount of fuel returning to the fuel tank from the carburetor will be increased.
B — The engine will continue to run after the mixture control is placed in IDLE CUTOFF.
C — A rich mixture will occur at all engine speeds.

8700. Answer A. AC 65-12A

Pressure carburetors employ vapor venting systems that take the excess fuel vapor created in the fuel system and direct it back to the fuel tank. With this type of system, air enters the vented chamber and displaces the fuel thereby lowering the fuel level. When the fuel level reaches a predetermined level, the float pulls down on the vapor vent valve and allows fuel vapor to flow back to the fuel tank. Based on this, if the vapor vent valve should stick open or the float become filled with fuel and sink, fuel and fuel vapor continuously flow back to the fuel tank (answer A). Answer (B) is incorrect because an engine will shut down normally with a defective vapor vent valve or float. Answer (C) is wrong because the vapor vent valve only affects the fuel/air mixture when the valve sticks closed, not when it sticks open.

8701.   M04

What method is ordinarily used to make idle speed adjustments on a float-type carburetor?

A — An adjustable throttle stop or linkage.
B — An orifice and adjustable tapered needle.
C — An adjustable needle in the drilled passageway which connects the airspace of the float chamber and the carburetor venturi.

8701. Answer A. AC 65-12A

Idle speed on engines using a float-type carburetor is adjusted by limiting how far the throttle valve will close. This is usually accomplished with an adjustable throttle stop or linkage. Although an orifice and adjustable tapered needle (answers B and C) are often used on automobile engines, this arrangement is not used on aircraft engines.

8702.   M04

For what primary purpose is a turbine engine fuel control unit trimmed?

A — To obtain maximum thrust output when desired.
B — To properly position the power levers.
C — To adjust the idle RPM.

8702. Answer A. AC 65-12A

The primary reason for trimming a turbine engine is to ensure that the desired thrust is obtained when the power lever is in the full power position (answer A). Answer (B) is wrong because power levers are not typically adjusted when an engine is trimmed. Answer (C) is incorrect because, although idle speed is checked and adjusted on a trim run, the ability to obtain maximum thrust on demand is the primary purpose of trimming a fuel control unit.

8703.   M04

Which type of fuel control is used on most of today's turbine engines?

A — Electromechanical.
B — Mechanical.
C — Hydromechanical or electronic.

8703. Answer C. AC 65-12A

Most fuel controls in use today are hydromechanical or electronic. Answer (A) is incorrect because "electro-mechanical" fuel control units do not exist. Answer (B) is wrong because mechanical fuel controls are rarely, if ever, used on modern turbine engines.

8704.   M04

Under which of the following conditions will the trimming of a turbine engine be most accurate?

A — High wind and high moisture.
B — High moisture and low wind.
C — No wind and low moisture.

8704. Answer C. AC 65-12A

The ideal conditions for trimming a turbine engine are no wind, low humidity, and standard temperature and pressure. Because standard day conditions seldom exist, engine manufacturers produce trim charts to compensate for nonstandard conditions. Attempting to trim an engine in any wind (answers A and B) will result in an inaccurate trim.

8705. **M04**
(1) The mixture used at rated power in air cooled reciprocating engines is richer than the mixture used through the normal cruising range.
(2) The mixture used at idle in air cooled reciprocating engines is richer than the mixture used at rated power.
Regarding the above statements,

A — only No. 1 is true.
B — only No. 2 is true.
C — both No. 1 and No. 2 are true.

8705. Answer C. AC 65-12A
Both statements (1) and (2) are true. Rich mixtures are required at idle speeds and at full rated power to aid in engine cooling. However, since there is more airflow over the engine running at its rated power than when the engine is idling, the mixture used at idle is typically richer than the mixture used at rated power.

8706. **M04**
Under which of the following conditions would an engine run lean even though there is a normal amount of fuel present?

A — The use of too high an octane rating fuel.
B — Incomplete fuel vaporization.
C — The carburetor air heater valve in the HOT position.

8706. Answer B. AC 65-12A
To ensure efficient combustion, fuel must be properly mixed with air, or atomized, before it enters the cylinders. The more fully a mixture is vaporized, the greater the efficiency of the combustion process. On the other hand, if the fuel is not fully vaporized, less fuel mixes with the intake air and the mixture becomes lean even though there is an abundance of fuel present. Answer (A) is incorrect because the use of a fuel with an excessively high octane rating will have no effect on the fuel/air mixture. Answer (C) is wrong because the application of carburetor heat introduces less dense air into the engine which essentially enriches the mixture.

8707. **M04**
During idle mixture adjustments, which of the following is normally observed to determine when the correct mixture has been achieved?

A — Changes in fuel/air pressure ratio.
B — Fuel flowmeter.
C — Changes in RPM or manifold pressure.

8707. Answer C. AC 65-12A
When adjusting the mixture on an idling engine, you should observe the engine rpm gauge on aircraft with a fixed-pitch propeller and the manifold pressure gauge on aircraft equipped with constant-speed propellers. In either case, the power output will increase to a maximum when the mixture is set properly. Answer (A) is wrong because there is no practical way to determine a fuel/air pressure ratio. Answer (B) is wrong because a fuel flowmeter is not precise enough to determine the correct mixture at idle speeds.

8708. **M04**
An indication that the optimum idle mixture has been obtained occurs when the mixture control is moved to IDLE CUTOFF and manifold pressure

A — decreases momentarily and RPM drops slightly before the engine ceases to fire.
B — increases momentarily and RPM drops slightly before the engine ceases to fire.
C — decreases and RPM increases momentarily before the engine ceases to fire.

8708. Answer C. AC 65-12A
When the mixture is adjusted properly, engine power output will be at maximum as indicated by the manifold pressure gauge. Therefore, when the mixture is moved to the idle cutoff position, it will become excessively lean and engine power will decrease immediately, causing a decrease in manifold pressure. This drop in manifold pressure will allow the engine to momentarily rotate faster causing an increase in rpm before the engine ceases to fire.

8709. **M04**

The use of less than normal throttle opening during starting will cause

A — a rich mixture.
B — a lean mixture.
C — backfire due to lean fuel/air ratio.

8710. **M04**

When checking the idle mixture on a carburetor, the engine should be idling normally, then pull the mixture control toward the IDLE CUTOFF position. A correct idling mixture will be indicated by

A — an immediate decrease in RPM.
B — a decrease of 20 to 30 RPM before quitting.
C — an increase of 10 to 50 RPM before decreasing.

8711. **M04**

When a new carburetor is installed on an engine,

A — warm up the engine and adjust the float level.
B — do not adjust the idle mixture setting; this was accomplished on the flow bench.
C — and the engine is warmed up to normal temperatures, adjust the idle mixture, then the idle speed.

8712. **M04**

The purpose of the back-suction mixture control in a float-type carburetor is to adjust the mixture by

A — regulating the pressure drop at the venturi.
B — regulating the pressure on the fuel in the float chamber.
C — regulating the suction on the mixture from behind the throttle valve.

8713. **M04**

Reciprocating engine power will be decreased at all altitudes if the

A — air density is increased.
B — humidity is increased.
C — manifold pressure is increased.

8709. Answer A.

The position of the throttle valve determines the amount of air that flows into the engine. When an engine is started, a high vacuum is created on the engine side of the throttle. Therefore, if the throttle valve opening is less than normal at this time, the high vacuum will draw excessive fuel from the idle jet and create a richer than normal mixture. Both answers (B) and (C) are wrong because the resulting mixture will be rich, not lean.

8710. Answer C. AC 65-12A

On engines that do not use a manifold pressure gauge, you must observe the tachometer for an indication of correct idle mixture. In most cases, the idle mixture should be adjusted so that when the mixture control is pulled toward the idle cutoff position, a 10 to 50 rpm rise occurs prior to a rapid decrease as the engine ceases to fire. Answers (A) and (B) are incorrect because a correct idling mixture is indicated by an rpm increase, not a decrease.

8711. Answer C. AC 65-12A

When a new carburetor is installed on an engine, the idle speed and mixture must be set. These adjustments should be made after the engine has been operating long enough to achieve normal cylinder head temperatures. Answer (A) is incorrect because the float level is checked and adjusted during the assembly process when the carburetor is off engine. Answer (B) is wrong because a final idle adjustment must be performed after a new carburetor is installed on an engine.

8712. Answer B. AC 65-12A

The back-suction type mixture control system controls the amount of fuel injected into the carburetor throat by controlling pressure differential between the carburetor throat and float chamber. This is done by allowing a certain amount of venturi low pressure air to act on the fuel in the float chamber. Answer (A) is wrong because the throttle valve, not the back suction, regulates the pressure drop at the venturi. Answer (C) is incorrect because it is not possible to regulate the suction on the mixture from behind the throttle valve.

8713. Answer B. AC 65-9A

Water vapor is a non-combustible gas. Therefore, when humid air is drawn into an engine, the engine's volumetric efficiency decreases, causing a decrease in engine power. Answers (A) and (C) are incorrect because increasing either air density or manifold pressure will increase engine power at altitude.

8714.   M04

If the idling jet becomes clogged in a float-type carburetor, the

A — engine operation will not be affected at any RPM.
B — engine will not idle.
C — idle mixture becomes richer.

8714. Answer B. AC 65-12A

At low engine speeds there is insufficient airflow through the carburetor to allow the main discharge nozzle to operate properly; therefore, a separate idle jet is installed in the low pressure area between the throttle valve and throttle body to supply fuel for idling. If an idle jet should become clogged, the engine will not idle. Answer (A) is wrong because engine operation is seriously affected at idle rpm if the idling jet becomes clogged, and answer (C) is incorrect because a clogged idling jet reduces fuel flow to the carburetor and, therefore, results in a leaner mixture.

8715.   M04

An aircraft engine equipped with a pressure-type carburetor is started with the

A — primer while the mixture control is positioned at IDLE CUTOFF.
B — mixture control in the FULL-RICH position.
C — primer while the mixture control is positioned at the FULL-LEAN position.

8715. Answer A. AC 65-9A

Aircraft engines using pressure-type carburetors are generally started using the primer with the mixture control in the idle cutoff position. Then, as soon as the engine starts, the mixture control is moved to the full rich position while the primer is released as soon as the rpm indicates the engine is receiving fuel. Answer (B) is incorrect because float-type carburetors, not pressure-type carburetors, are started with the mixture control in the FULL-RICH position. Answer (C) is wrong because pressure-type carburetors do not have a FULL-LEAN mixture position.

8716.   M04

One of the best ways to increase engine power and control detonation and preignition is to

A — enrich the fuel/air mixture.
B — use water injection.
C — lean the fuel/air mixture.

8716. Answer B. AC 65-12A

A water injection system adds an alcohol-water compound to the fuel/air mixture to allow an engine to achieve higher manifold pressures and corresponding increase in power without promoting detonation. Answer (A) is incorrect because enriching the fuel/air mixture beyond a certain point does not increase engine power, and answer (C) is wrong because a lean fuel/air mixture increases the chances of experiencing detonation at high power settings.

8717.   M04

An excessively lean fuel/air mixture may cause

A — an increase in cylinder head temperature.
B — high oil pressure.
C — backfiring through the exhaust.

8717. Answer A. AC 65-12A

When an engine is operated on a lean mixture, all the fuel in the mixture is used to support combustion and there is no excess fuel left to aid in engine cooling. Therefore, lean fuel/air mixtures typically cause an increase in cylinder head temperatures. Answer (B) is incorrect because high cylinder head temperatures typically produce a lower oil pressure, not a high oil pressure. Answer (C) is wrong because backfiring occurs in the induction system, not through the exhaust.

8718.   M04

The density of air is very important when mixing fuel and air to obtain a correct fuel-to-air ratio. Which of the following weighs the most?

A — 75 parts of dry air and 25 parts of water vapor.
B — 100 parts of dry air.
C — 50 parts of dry air and 50 parts of water vapor.

8719.   M04

An air/fuel mixture ratio of 11:1 is

A — 1 part fuel to 11 parts air.
B — too rich to burn.
C — 1 part air to 11 parts fuel.

8720.   M04

The economizer system in a float-type carburetor

A — keeps the fuel/air ratio constant.
B — functions only at cruise and idle speeds.
C — increases the fuel/air ratio at high power settings.

8721.   M04

A carburetor is prevented from leaning out during quick acceleration by the

A — power enrichment system.
B — mixture control system.
C — accelerating system.

8718. Answer B. AC 65-9A

For a given volume, air containing water vapor weighs approximately five-eighths as much as dry air. Therefore, 100 percent dry air (answer B) weighs more than a mixture of dry air and water vapor.

8719. Answer A. AC 65-12A

In any air/fuel mixture ratio, the larger number always refers to the amount of air in the mixture. Therefore, an air/fuel mixture ratio of 11:1 is 1 part fuel to 11 parts air (answer A). Answer (B) is incorrect because air/fuel mixtures as rich as 8:1 or as lean as 16:1 will burn in an engine cylinder. Answer (C) is wrong because a mixture of 1 part air to 11 parts fuel will not burn in a reciprocating engine.

8720. Answer C. AC 65-12A

In order for an engine to effectively operate at high power settings, the fuel/air mixture must be rich so there is additional fuel available to aid in cylinder cooling. On engines equipped with an economizer system, when the throttle is advanced beyond approximately 70 percent power the economizer valve opens and automatically enriches the fuel/air mixture. Answer (A) is wrong because an economizer system automatically changes the fuel/air ratio. Answer (B) is incorrect because an economizer system only operates at power settings above cruise power.

8721. Answer C. AC 65-12A

When the throttle valve is opened quickly, a large volume of air rushes into the carburetor. To prevent the fuel/air mixture from becoming excessively lean when the additional air enters the engine, most carburetors are equipped with an accelerating system that provides a momentary burst of fuel to maintain the proper mixture. Answer (A) is incorrect because a power enrichment system enriches the mixture at high power settings to prevent detonation and does not help during periods of quick acceleration. Answer (B) is wrong because a mixture control system compensates for changes in air density encountered at high altitudes.

8722.   M04
In turbine engines that utilize a pressurization and dump valve, the dump portion of the valve

A — cuts off fuel flow to the engine fuel manifold and dumps the manifold fuel into the combustor to burn just before the engine shuts down.
B — drains the engine manifold lines to prevent fuel boiling and subsequent deposits in the lines as a result of residual engine heat (at engine shutdown).
C — dumps extra fuel into the engine in order to provide for quick engine acceleration during rapid throttle advancement.

8723.   M04
What effect does high atmospheric humidity have on the operation of a jet engine?

A — Decreases engine pressure ratio.
B — Decreases compressor and turbine RPM.
C — Has little or no effect.

8724.   M04
What are the positions of the pressurization valve and the dump valve in a jet engine fuel system when the engine is shut down?

A — Pressurization valve closed, dump valve open.
B — Pressurization valve open, dump valve open.
C — Pressurization valve closed, dump valve closed.

8725.   M04
In a float type carburetor, what could cause a lean mixture and high cylinder head temperature at sea level or low altitudes?

A — Economizer valve open.
B — Automatic mixture control sticks in the extended position.
C — Accelerator pump sticks in the extended position.

8722. Answer B. AC 65-12A
With aircraft that utilize a pressurization and dump valve the "dump" feature refers to the dumping of fuel from the fuel manifold after engine shutdown. Manifold dumping sharply cuts off combustion and drains the manifold lines of fuel to prevent fuel boiling and eliminate solid deposits in the manifold. Answers (A) and (C) are incorrect because a pressurization and dump valve does not dump any fuel into the engine on shutdown.

8723. Answer C. AC 65-12A
Of the air consumed by a turbine engine, only about 25 percent is used to support combustion. Because of this, high atmospheric humidity has very little effect on the thrust produced by a jet engine. Furthermore, neither engine pressure ratio (answer A) nor compressor and turbine rpm (answer B) decreases noticeably.

8724. Answer A. AC 65-12A
On an aircraft that utilizes a pressurization and dump valve, the pressurizing part of the valve separates the primary and secondary fuel flows. At all engine speeds below approximately 30 to 50 percent N_1, the pressurization valve is closed and fuel flows through the primary only. Therefore, when the engine is shut down, the pressurization valve is closed, and stays closed until the engine is running at a medium power setting. The dump part of the valve drains, or dumps the fuel manifold when the engine is shut down. Therefore, when an engine with a pressurization and dump valve is shut down, both valves are open (answer A).

8725. Answer B. AC 65-12A
To compensate for decreases in air density, an automatic mixture control decreases fuel flow from the carburetor as an aircraft climbs to higher altitudes. However, if the automatic mixture control were to malfunction and stick in the extended position, the fuel/air mixture would become progressively leaner as the aircraft descends to lower altitudes. With a lean mixture, there is little excess fuel available to aid in engine cooling, so engines that run on a lean mixture typically have high cylinder head temperatures. Answer (A) is wrong because an economizer valve enriches the mixture when the valve is open. Answer (C) is incorrect because an accelerator pump that is stuck in the extended position would result in sluggish acceleration but would have little effect on cylinder head temperature.

8726.   **M04**
Which of the following is NOT an input parameter for a turbine engine fuel control unit?

A — Compressor inlet pressure.
B — Compressor inlet temperature.
C — Ambient humidity.

8726. Answer C. AC 65-12A
A typical fuel control senses a number of engine variables, depending upon the installation. For example, a standard fuel control unit can sense engine speed, inlet pressure, compressor discharge pressure, burner can pressure, and compressor inlet temperature. Based on this, the only choice listed that is not an input parameter for a fuel control unit is ambient humidity (answer C).

8727.   **M04**
Detonation occurs when the air/fuel mixture

A — burns too fast.
B — ignites before the time of normal ignition.
C — is too rich.

8727. Answer A. AC 65-12A
Detonation is the explosive, or rapid combustion of unburned fuel in a cylinder that results in an extremely rapid pressure rise. Detonation can happen any time an engine overheats or if the improper fuel grade is used. Answer (B) is wrong because burning before the time of normal ignition is called preignition and is caused by residual hot spots in the combustion chamber. Answer (C) is incorrect because detonation typically occurs when the air/fuel mixture is too lean, not too rich.

8728.   **M04**
What corrective action should be taken when a carburetor is found to be leaking fuel from the discharge nozzle?

A — Replace the needle valve and seat.
B — Raise the float level.
C — Turn the fuel off each time the aircraft is parked.

8728. Answer A. AC 65-12A
If a carburetor leaks fuel from the discharge nozzle, it is an indication that the fuel level is too high in the float chamber. A high fuel level can be caused by a float that is adjusted too high, a leaking or saturated float, dirt trapped between the needle and seat, or a worn needle and seat. Based on this and the choices given, the only logical choice would be to replace the needle valve and seat (answer A). Answer (B) is wrong because raising the float level could increase the leakage. Answer (C) is incorrect because simply turning off the fuel does not fix the problem.

8729.   **M04**
A major difference between the Teledyne- Continental and RSA (Precision Airmotive or Bendix) continuous flow fuel injection systems in fuel metering is that the

A — RSA system uses fuel pressure only as a metering force.
B — Continental system utilizes airflow as a metering force.
C — Continental system uses fuel pressure only as a metering force.

8729. Answer C. ITP-P2
The RSA fuel injection system relies on both air and fuel forces to provide the correct pressure differential across the primary metering jet. The Teledyne-Continental injection system, on the other hand, uses a special fuel pump to produce the fuel metering pressure. Answer (A) is incorrect because an RSA system meters fuel based on a pressure drop that is proportional to airflow through the venturi. Answer (B) is wrong because the Continental system does not use airflow as a metering force.

8730.　　　**M04**
The function of the altitude compensating, or aneroid valve used with the Teledyne-Continental fuel injection system on many turbocharged engines is to

A — prevent an overly rich mixture during sudden acceleration.
B — prevent detonation at high altitudes.
C — provide a means of enriching the mixture during sudden acceleration.

8731.　　　**M04**
The primary purpose of the air bleed openings used with continuous flow fuel injector nozzles is to

A — provide for automatic mixture control.
B — lean out the mixture.
C — aid in proper fuel vaporization.

8730. Answer A. ITP-P2
Some Teledyne Continental fuel injection systems employ an altitude compensating aneroid valve to prevent an overly rich mixture during sudden acceleration. To accomplish this, an evacuated bellows responds to upper deck pressure to control the size of a variable orifice. When the throttle is suddenly opened, the aneroid holds the orifice open until the volume of air flowing into the éngine increases. Answer (B) is incorrect because detonation is prevented at high altitudes by not over leaning the fuel/air mixture. Answer (C) is wrong because an accelerating pump, not the altitude compensating valve, enriches the fuel mixture during sudden acceleration.

8731. Answer C. AC 65-12A
Some continuous flow fuel injector nozzles have air bleed holes that allow air to mix with fuel to help vaporize the fuel. Answer (A) is incorrect because mixture control is accomplished by the fuel control. Answer (B) is wrong because the amount of air admitted by the air bleeds is insufficient to lean the mixture.

ENGINE FUEL SYSTEMS

There are several components contained in a basic fuel system, including engine-driven fuel pumps, fuel strainers, transfer pumps, relief valves, and bypass valves. This chapter provides information on the basic operating principles of these components as well as how to properly inspect, service, and troubleshoot each. The FAA exam questions taken from this chapter include:

8732, 8733, 8734, 8735, 8736, 8737, 8738, 8739, 8740, 8741, 8742, 8743, 8744, 8745, 8746, 8747, 8748, 8749, 8750, 8751, 8752, 8753, 8754, 8755, 8756, 8757, 8758, 8759, 8760, 8761, 8762, 8763, 8764, 8765, 8766, 8767, 8768, 8769, 8770, 8771.

8732.　　　N01

During what period does the fuel pump bypass valve open and remain open?

A — When the fuel pump pressure is greater than the demand of the engine.
B — When the boost pump pressure is greater than fuel pump pressure.
C — When the fuel pump output is greater than the demand of the carburetor.

8732. Answer B . AC 65-9A

When an aircraft's boost pump pressure exceeds that of the primary fuel pressure pump, a bypass valve in the pressure pump opens and allows fuel to flow directly to the engine. This occurs during start, when the pressure pump is not operating, and any time the engine driven fuel pump becomes clogged or fails. Answer (A) is incorrect because fuel pump pressure has no effect on the fuel pump bypass valve. Answer (C) is wrong because a relief valve will bypass fuel when the pump output is greater than the carburetor's demand.

8733.　　　N01

Which of the following statements concerning a centrifugal-type fuel boost pump located in a fuel supply tank is NOT true?

A — Air and fuel vapors do not pass through a centrifugal-type pump.
B — Fuel can be drawn through the impeller section of the pump when it is not in operation.
C — The centrifugal-type pump is classified as a positive displacement pump.

8733. Answer C. AC 65-9A

A positive displacement pump provides a fixed quantity of fuel per pump revolution. With a centrifugal-type fuel boost pump, once the pressure builds to a predetermined pressure, fuel bypasses the impeller and remains in the fuel tank. Therefore, the pump does not continually displace fuel and is not a positive displacement pump. Since the question asked for the statement that is not true, answer (C) is the correct choice.

8734.　　　N01

Where is the engine fuel shutoff valve usually located?

A — Aft of the firewall.
B — Adjacent to the fuel pump.
C — Downstream of the engine-driven fuel pump.

8734. Answer A. FAR 23.995

According to the FAR 23.995, the engine fuel shutoff valve may not be located on the engine side of the firewall. Therefore, answer A is correct. Answers (B) and (C) are incorrect because they identify areas that are located on the engine side of the firewall.

8735.   N01
Boost pumps in a fuel system

A — operate during takeoff only.
B — are primarily used for fuel transfer.
C — provide a positive flow of fuel to the engine pump.

8736.   N01
(Refer to figure 7.) What is the purpose of the fuel transfer ejectors?

A — To supply fuel under pressure to the engine-driven pump.
B — To assist in the transfer of fuel from the main tank to the boost pump sump.
C — To transfer fuel from the boost pump sump to the wing tank.

8735. Answer C. AC 65-9A
The primary purpose of a fuel boost pump is to provide a positive flow of fuel to the engine driven pump. Answer (A) is incorrect because boost pumps are used during landing, when experiencing turbulence, and in emergency situations as well as during takeoff. Answer (B) is wrong because, although some boost pumps are used to transfer fuel, this is not their primary function.

8736. Answer B. AC 65-12A
A fuel transfer ejector helps transfer fuel from the main tank to the boost pump sump by creating a low pressure area at the fuel pick-up point. By pumping fuel past the venturi in the injector, a low pressure area is created that drains fuel into the line that feeds the boost pump sump. Answer (A) is wrong because ejectors do not supply fuel under pressure, and answer (C) is incorrect because transfer ejectors transfer fuel from the wing tank to the boost pump sump, not from the boost pump sump to the wing tank.

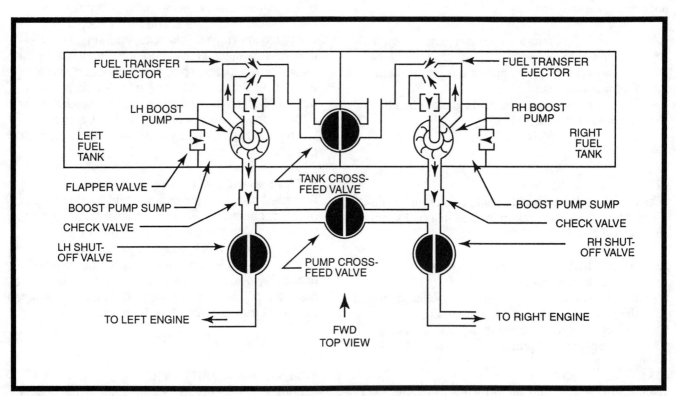

Figure 7.— Fuel System.

8737.   N01
What is the purpose of an engine-driven fuel pump
bypass valve?

A — To divert the excess fuel back to the main tank.
B — To prevent a damaged or inoperative pump from
    blocking the fuel flow of another pump in series
    with it.
C — To divert the excess fuel from the pressure side of
    the pump to the inlet side of the pump.

8738.   N01
Most large aircraft reciprocating engines are equipped
with which of the following types of engine-driven fuel
pumps?

A — Rotary-vane-type fuel pump.
B — Centrifugal-type fuel pump.
C — Gear-type fuel pump.

8739.   N01
When an electric primer is used, fuel pressure is built
up by the

A — internal pump in the primer solenoid.
B — suction at the main discharge nozzle.
C — booster pump.

8740.   N01
The fuel pump relief valve directs excess fuel to the

A — fuel tank return line.
B — inlet side of the fuel pump.
C — inlet side of the fuel strainer.

8741.   N01
Which type of pump is commonly used as a fuel pump
on reciprocating engines?

A — Gear.
B — Impeller.
C — Vane.

8737. Answer B. AC 65-9A
When an aircraft's boost pump pressure is greater than
that of the main pressure pump, a bypass valve in the
pressure pump opens and allows fuel to flow directly to
the engine. This prevents a damaged or inoperative
pump from blocking fuel flow to the engine (answer B).
Answers (A) and (C) are incorrect because diverting
fuel back to the main tank or back to the inlet side of
the pump could starve the engine of fuel.

8738. Answer A. AC 65-9A
The purpose of the engine-driven fuel pump is to
deliver a continuous supply of fuel at the proper pressure at all times during engine operation. Therefore, a
positive displacement pump must be used. One type of
positive displacement pump that is widely used is the
rotary-vane-type fuel pump (answer A). Answer (B) is
incorrect because centrifugal-type fuel pumps are not
positive displacement, and answer (C) is wrong
because gear-type pumps are not commonly used as
fuel pumps.

8739. Answer C. AC 65-9A
One of the many purposes of a boost pump is to supply fuel under pressure for priming prior to starting an
engine. Answer (A) is wrong because the primer solenoid does not contain its own pump, and answer (B) is
incorrect because, when the engine is not running,
there is no suction at the main discharge nozzle.

8740. Answer B. AC 65-9A
Engine-driven fuel pumps typically discharge more fuel
than an engine requires. Therefore, fuel systems must
incorporate a relief valve to prevent the build up of
excessive fuel pressures at the carburetor. A typical
fuel pump relief valve is spring-loaded and, when
opened, allows excess fuel to flow back to the inlet
side of the fuel pump. Answer (A) is wrong because
fuel tanks rarely utilize return lines, and answer (C) is
incorrect because fuel is routed to the inlet side of the
fuel pump, not the inlet side of the strainer.

8741. Answer C. AC 65-9A
The purpose of the engine-driven fuel pump is to
deliver a continuous supply of fuel at the proper pressure at all times during engine operation. Therefore, a
positive displacement pump must be used. One type of
positive displacement pump that is widely used is the
rotary-vane-type fuel pump (answer C). Answer (A) is
incorrect because gear-type pumps do not efficiently
pump low-viscosity fluids such as fuel. Answer (B) is
wrong because impeller pumps are not positive displacement pumps and, therefore, are used as boost
pumps rather than primary fuel pumps.

8742.   N01

The purpose of the diaphragm in most vane-type fuel pumps is to

A — maintain fuel pressure below atmospheric pressure.
B — equalize fuel pressure at all speeds.
C — compensate fuel pressures to altitude changes.

8743.   N01

The primary condition(s) that allow(s) microorganisms to grow in the fuel in aircraft fuel tanks is (are)

A — warm temperatures and frequent fueling.
B — the presence of water.
C — the presence of dirt or other particulate contaminants.

8744.   N02

It is desirable that fuel lines have a gentle slope upward or downward and not have sharp curves or sharp rises and/or falls in order to

A — prevent vapor lock.
B — prevent stagnation or "pooling" of fuel in the fuel lines.
C — minimize the generation of static electricity by decreasing fluid friction in the lines.

8745.   N02

The fuel systems of aircraft certificated in the standard classification must include which of the following?

A — An engine-driven fuel pump and at least one auxiliary pump per engine.
B — A positive means of shutting off the fuel to all engines.
C — A reserve supply of fuel, available to the engine only after selection by the flightcrew, sufficient to operate the engines at least 30 minutes at METO power.

8742. Answer C. AC 65-9A

In a compensated vane-type fuel pump, the fuel pressure delivered to the carburetor inlet varies with altitude and atmospheric pressure. This is done by allowing spring tension and either atmospheric or carburetor inlet air pressure to act on a diaphragm which controls the pump's relief valve. As the amount of pressure acting on the diaphragm varies, the pressure at which the relief valve bypasses fuel back to the pump's inlet varies. Answer (A) is incorrect because maintaining fuel pressure below atmospheric pressure would allow air to enter the inlet side of the pump, causing cavitation. Answer (B) is wrong because the relief valve is adjusted to maintain a certain fuel pressure at all speeds.

8743. Answer B. AC 65-9A

There are over 100 different varieties of microorganisms which can live in the free water which accumulates in the sumps of aircraft fuel tanks. Because they thrive in water, the best way to prevent their growth is to eliminate the water through proper fuel handling procedures. Answers (A) and (C) are incorrect because neither warm temperatures, frequent fueling, nor the presence of particulate contaminants allow microorganisms to grow in the absence of water.

8744. Answer A. AC 65-12A

To reduce the possibility of vapor lock, fuel lines are kept away from heat sources, are sometimes wrapped with insulation, and are installed in a smooth, flowing manner with no sharp bends. Answer (B) is wrong because stagnation and "pooling" of fuel in the fuel lines is not a problem. Answer (C) is incorrect because the way a fuel line is installed has little to do with how much static electricity is generated by the flow of fuel.

8745. Answer B. FAR 23.1189

According to FAR 23.1189, aircraft that are certified in the normal category must have a positive means of shutting off the fuel to all engines. Answer (A) is incorrect because there is no requirement that each engine have an engine-driven fuel pump or auxiliary fuel pump. Answer (C) is wrong because the reserve fuel supply is determined by the pilot during flight planning and is not a factor in designing a fuel system.

8746.   N02

Where should the main fuel strainer be located in the aircraft fuel system?

A — Downstream from the wobble pump check valve.
B — At the lowest point in the fuel system.
C — At any point in the system lower than the carburetor strainer.

8746. Answer B. AC 65-9A

The main fuel strainer in an aircraft's fuel system is installed so that fuel flows through it before reaching the engine-driven pump. Furthermore, the strainer is typically located at the lowest point in the fuel system so that water and other debris can collect in the strainer, where they can be drained from the system. Answer (A) is incorrect because locating the main fuel strainer downstream from the wobble pump would allow contaminants to enter the pump and damage it. Answer (C) is wrong because the main fuel strainer must be located at the lowest point in the system to allow collection and draining of water and other contaminants.

8747.   N02

Where physical separation of the fuel lines from electrical wiring or conduit is impracticable, locate the fuel line

A — below the wiring and clamp the line securely to the airframe structure.
B — above the wiring and clamp the line securely to the airframe structure.
C — inboard of the wiring and clamp both securely to the airframe structure.

8747. Answer A. AC 43.13-1A

Every effort should be made to physically separate electric wiring and lines carrying flammable fluids. However, when separation is impractical, electrical wire should be located above the flammable fluid line and both the electrical line and fluid line should be securely clamped to structure. Answers (B) and (C) are wrong because locating the fuel line above or beside electrical wiring could allow fuel to come in contact with the wiring and ignite.

8748.   N02

What is a characteristic of a centrifugal-type fuel boost pump?

A — It separates air and vapor from the fuel.
B — It has positive displacement.
C — It requires a relief valve.

8748. Answer A. AC 65-9A

The swirling action of a centrifugal boost pump impeller separates air and vapor from fuel before it enters the fuel line to the carburetor. By removing air and vapor, the possibility of vapor lock greatly decreases. Answer (B) is wrong because centrifugal-type boost pumps do not deliver a positive displacement, and answer (C) is incorrect because centrifugal-type pumps do not need relief valves.

8749.   N02

The Federal Aviation Regulations require the fuel flow rate for gravity systems (main and reserve) to be

A — 125 percent of the takeoff fuel consumption of the engine.
B — 125 percent of the maximum, except takeoff, fuel consumption of the engine.
C — 150 percent of the takeoff fuel consumption of the engine.

8749. Answer C. FAR 23.955

According to FAR 23.955, the fuel flow rate of a gravity-fed system must be at least 150 percent of the takeoff fuel consumption of the engine. Both answers (A) and (B) are incorrect because they indicate values less than 150 percent.

8750.   N02

Fuel boost pumps are operated

A — to provide a positive flow of fuel to the engine.
B — during takeoff only.
C — primarily for fuel transfer to another tank.

8750. Answer A. AC 65-9A

The primary function of a fuel boost pump is to supply a positive flow of fuel to the engine-driven fuel pump. Secondary functions include supplying positive fuel flow to the engine (answer A) when the engine-driven pump fails, and transferring fuel. Answer (B) is incorrect because fuel boost pumps are used more than just for takeoff. Answer (C) is incorrect because, although fuel boost pumps are used to transfer fuel, it is not a primary function.

8751.   N02

A pilot reports that the fuel pressure fluctuates and exceeds the upper limits whenever the throttle is advanced. The most likely cause of the trouble is

A —- a ruptured fuel pump relief-valve diaphragm.
B — a sticking fuel pump relief valve.
C — an air leak at the fuel pump relief-valve body.

8751. Answer B. AC 65-9A

During normal operation, the fuel pump delivers more fuel than the engine needs and, therefore, a fuel pump relief valve must be used to prevent excessive pressures from reaching the carburetor inlet. The relief valve is held closed by spring tension and, once opened by excessive fuel pressure, directs fuel back to the pump inlet. If a relief valve sticks closed when an engine accelerates, excessive fuel pressure will build until the relief valve opens. Therefore, a sticking fuel pump relief valve will cause fluctuating fuel pressure readings and, if the relief valve sticks enough, excessive pressure readings. Answer (A) is incorrect because a diaphragm failure allows air to enter the fuel and results in fuel leakage or cavitation, not high fuel pressure. Answer (C) is wrong because an air leak at the fuel pump relieve-valve body will result in lower-than-normal fuel pressure.

8752.   N02

A fuel strainer or filter must be located between the

A — boost pump and tank outlet.
B — tank outlet and the fuel metering device.
C — boost pump and engine-driven fuel pump.

8752. Answer B. FAR 23.997

According to FAR 23.997, there must be a fuel strainer or filter between the fuel tank outlet and the engine-driven pump or fuel metering device. Answers (A) and (C) are incorrect because fuel strainers are not required in either of these areas.

8753.   N02

Fuel pump relief valves designed to compensate for atmospheric pressure variations are known as

A — compensated-flow valves.
B — pressurized-relief valves.
C — balanced-type relief valves.

8753. Answer C. AC 65-9A

Fuel pump relief valves designed to compensate for atmospheric pressure variations operate on the principle that, within the valve, a balance between fuel pressure and atmospheric or carburetor inlet air pressure is maintained. Thus, these valves are often referred to as balanced-type relief valves. "Compensated-flow valves" (answer A) and "pressurized-relief valves" (answer B) are terms that are not commonly applied to fuel pump relief valves.

8754.   N02

Fuel lines are kept away from sources of heat, and sharp bends and steep rises are avoided to reduce the possibility of

A — liquid lock.
B — vapor lock.
C — positive lock.

8754. Answer B. AC 65-12A

To reduce the possibility of vapor lock, fuel lines are kept away from heat sources, are sometimes wrapped with insulation, and installed in a smooth, flowing manner with no sharp bends. Answer (A) is wrong because liquid lock occurs when oil or fuel enters the lower cylinders of a radial or inline engine and prevents engine rotation. Answer (C) is incorrect because "positive lock" is not a term used in aviation maintenance.

8755.   N02

Fuel crossfeed systems are used in aircraft to

A — purge the fuel tanks.
B — jettison fuel in an emergency.
C — maintain aircraft stability.

8755. Answer C. AC 65-9A

The purpose of a fuel crossfeed system is to allow fuel from any tank to be fed to any engine. Unfortunately, this is not a choice. In our opinion, the correct answer to this question is (C), even though a fuel transfer system is used to maintain a balanced fuel load and aircraft stability. Answer (A) is incorrect because fuel tank purging is a venting procedure that is performed when an aircraft is on the ground. Answer (B) is wrong because, although some crossfeed system components may be used to jettison fuel in an emergency, this is not what an entire crossfeed system is designed to do.

8756.   N02

If an engine equipped with a float-type carburetor backfires or misses when the throttle is advanced, a likely cause is that the

A — float level is too high.
B — main air bleed is clogged.
C — accelerating pump is not operating properly.

8756. Answer C.

When a carburetor's throttle valve is opened quickly, a large volume of air rushes into the carburetor. To prevent an excessively lean mixture from developing when this occurs, float-type carburetors employ an accelerator pump that injects a momentary burst of fuel into the engine to maintain the proper fuel/air mixture. If an accelerator pump does not operate properly, an excessively lean mixture that can lead to backfiring and missing will result when the throttle is advanced rapidly. Answer (A) is wrong because a float level that is too high would cause a rich mixture, which does not cause missing or backfiring. Answer (B) is wrong because a clogged main air bleed would result in poor mixing of fuel and air which could result in afterfiring, not backfiring.

8757.   N02

A fuel pressure relief valve is required on

A — engine-driven diaphragm-type fuel pumps.
B — engine-driven vane-type fuel pumps.
C — centrifugal fuel boost pumps.

8757. Answer B. AC 65-9A

Since an engine-driven vane-type fuel pump discharges more fuel than an engine requires, there must be some way of routing excess fuel away from the carburetor inlet line to prevent excess pressure from building. This is accomplished by using a spring loaded relief valve that is adjusted to deliver fuel at the recommended pressure. Answers (A) and (C) are incorrect because engine-driven diaphragm-type fuel pumps and centrifugal boost pumps are not constant displacement pumps and, therefore, do not require relief valves.

8758.   N02

A rotary-vane pump is best described as a

A — positive-displacement pump.
B — variable-displacement pump.
C — boost pump.

8758. Answer A. AC 65-9A

Rotary-vane pumps used as main fuel supply pumps provide a fixed quantity of fuel per pump revolution. Therefore, rotary-vane pumps are positive displacement pumps. Answer (B) is incorrect because rotary-vane pumps supply a fixed quantity of fuel, not a varying quantity, and answer (C) is wrong because rotary-vane pumps are generally not used as boost pumps.

8759.   N02

Fuel pressure produced by the engine-driven fuel pump is adjusted by the

A — bypass valve adjusting screw.
B — relief valve adjusting screw.
C — engine-driven fuel pump adjusting screw.

8759. Answer B. AC 65-9A

Since engine-driven fuel pumps provide more fuel than an engine needs, they must employ some means of limiting the pressure they deliver to the carburetor. This is accomplished with a relief valve that directs fuel away from the carburetor inlet line when fuel pressure exceeds the carburetor's demand. This relief valve relies on spring tension that uses an adjusting screw to maintain the appropriate fuel pressure. Answer (A) is wrong because a bypass valve allows fuel to bypass the engine-driven fuel pump if it should become inoperative. Answer (C) is incorrect because there is no such thing as an engine-driven fuel pump adjusting screw.

8760.   N02

Kerosene is used as turbine engine fuel because

A — kerosene has very high volatility which aids in ignition and lubrication.
B — kerosene has more heat energy per gallon and lubricates fuel system components.
C — kerosene does not contain any water.

8760. Answer B. ASTM Spec. D-910, D-1655

Aviation gasoline (100LL) has a heat energy of 112,320 BTUs per gallon while kerosene (Jet A fuel) has a heat energy of 123,541 BTUs per gallon. In addition, kerosene's high viscosity allows it to act as a lubricant in pumps and fuel control units. Therefore, answer (B) is correct. Answer (A) is incorrect because kerosene-based jet fuels are significantly less volatile than gasoline. Answer (C) is wrong because kerosene can contain significant amounts of entrained water.

8761.   N02

What are the principal advantages of the duplex fuel nozzle used in many turbine engines?

A — Restricts the amount of fuel flow to a level where more efficient and complete burning of the fuel is achieved.
B — Provides better atomization and uniform flow pattern.
C — Allows a wider range of fuels and filters to be used.

8761. Answer B. AC 65-12A

The principal advantages of duplex fuel nozzles over simplex fuel nozzles are that duplex nozzles provide better fuel atomization and a more uniform flow pattern at low engine speeds. Answer (A) is incorrect because flow rates of simplex and duplex nozzles are not substantially different, and answer (C) is wrong because the type of fuel nozzle used in an engine has no bearing on the grades of fuel or types of filters used in the engine.

8762.   N02

It is necessary to control acceleration and deceleration rates in turbine engines in order to

A — prevent blowout or die-out.
B — prevent overtemperature.
C — prevent friction between turbine wheels and the case due to expansion and contraction.

8762. Answer A. AC 65-12A

Because of the large changes in airflow associated with changes in power settings, turbine engines do not respond well to rapid power changes. For example, too rapid an acceleration or deceleration could cause a compressor stall, which could lead to a rich blowout or lean dieout (answer A). Answer (B) is incorrect because temperature is primarily determined by the amount of fuel burned in an engine, not the rate of acceleration or deceleration. Answer (C) is wrong because clearance between the turbine wheels and case is controlled by directing cooling air through turbine blades and around the turbine case and is not affected by the rate at which an engine accelerates or decelerates.

8763.   N02

Which of the following turbine fuel filters has the greatest filtering action?

A — Micron.
B — Small wire mesh.
C — Stacked charcoal.

8763. Answer A. AC 65-12A

Of the filters listed, the micron filter has the greatest filtering action. Micron filters can be made of cloth or paper and remove foreign matter measuring from 10 to 25 microns which equates to particles between .000,010 and .000,025 inch in size. Answer (B) is wrong because wire mesh filters capture relatively coarse particles and do not effectively remove small contaminants. Answer (C) is incorrect because stacked charcoal filter elements are very effective at filtering chemical vapors or solutions, but do not remove particulate contamination.

8764.   N02

What is the purpose of the flow divider in a turbine engine duplex fuel nozzle?

A — Allows an alternate flow of fuel if the primary flow clogs or is restricted.
B — Creates the primary and secondary fuel supplies.
C — Provides a flow path for bleed air which aids in the atomization of fuel.

8764. Answer B. AC 65-12A

The flow divider in a duplex fuel nozzle divides the fuel supply into a primary and secondary flow that discharge through separate, concentric spray tips. Primary fuel flows at all power settings, while secondary fuel flows only when fuel pressure builds enough to unseat the flow divider. Answer (A) is incorrect because whether the primary is clogged or not, fuel will not flow to the secondary until the fuel pressure reaches 90 psig. Answer (C) is wrong because turbine engine fuel nozzles do not utilize bleed air.

8765.   N02

What causes the fuel divider valve to open in a turbine engine duplex fuel nozzle?

A — Fuel pressure.
B — Bleed air after the engine reaches idle RPM.
C — An electrically operated solenoid.

8765. Answer A. AC 65-12A

The flow divider in a turbine engine duplex fuel nozzle opens when the fuel pressure reaches approximately 90 psig. Once open, fuel is directed into the secondary chamber in the fuel nozzle and then discharges through the secondary tip into the combustion liner. Neither bleed air (answer B) nor an electrically operated solenoid (answer C) opens the flow divider valve.

8766.   N02

How often should float carburetors be overhauled?

A — At engine overhaul.
B — Annually.
C — At engine change.

8766. Answer A. ITP-P2

Although float carburetors typically have no required overhaul period, good operating practice dictates that a carburetor be completely overhauled when the engine is overhauled. Operating beyond this point can result in poor fuel metering, which could lead to detonation and subsequent damage to a freshly overhauled engine. Overhauling a carburetor on an annual basis (answer B) would be a wasteful and unnecessary expense. Answer (C) is incorrect because if a low-time engine must be changed due to a mechanical failure, it would be unnecessary to overhaul the carburetor.

8767.   N02

What is the final authority for the details of carburetor overhaul?

A — The local FAA safety inspector.
B — The Type Certificate Data Sheets for the engine.
C — The manufacturer's recommendations.

8768.   N02

Excessively rich or lean idle mixtures result in

A — too rapid completion of combustion.
B — incomplete combustion.
C — incomplete cylinder scavenging.

8769.   N02

Which statement is true regarding proper throttle rigging of an airplane?

A — The throttle stop on the carburetor must be contacted before the stop in the cockpit.
B — The stop in the cockpit must be contacted before the stop on the carburetor.
C — The throttle control is properly adjusted when neither stop makes contact.

8770.   N02

What precaution should be taken when putting thread lubricant on a tapered pipe plug in a carburetor float bowl?

A — Put the thread lubricant only on the first thread.
B — Do not use thread lubricant on any carburetor fitting.
C — Engage the first thread of the plug, then put a small amount of lubricant on the second thread and screw the plug in.

8767. Answer C. ITP-P2

A carburetor manufacturer's recommendations are FAA approved and represent the final authority for maintaining a carburetor. Only those alterations or repairs that are in the manufacturer's maintenance materials should be made. Answer (A) is incorrect because, while local FAA safety inspectors are responsible for approving all major repairs and alterations, they are unlikely to possess specific maintenance information for carburetor overhauls. Answer (B) is wrong because Type Certificate Data Sheets do not contain specific overhaul data.

8768. Answer B. ITP-P2

Excessively rich or lean idle mixtures typically result in incomplete combustion. For example, with an excessively rich mixture carbon deposits form on the spark plugs and cause subsequent plug fouling. Excessively lean mixtures, on the other hand, can burn so slowly that combustion can carry into the intake stroke and cause backfiring: Answer (A) is wrong because an excessively rich or lean mixture causes slower than normal combustion. Answer (C) is incorrect because cylinder scavenging is determined by engine speed, valve timing, and engine design and has nothing to do with an engine's idle mixture.

8769. Answer A. ITP-P2

Throttle and mixture controls must operate freely throughout their full range of travel, and the stops on the carburetor must be contacted before the cockpit control reaches its stop. Springback in the control system ensures that the carburetor control is fully actuated. Answer (B) is incorrect because if the stop in the cockpit is contacted before the stop on the carburetor, the engine's full operational range will not be obtainable. Answer (C) is wrong because it represents an impossible situation.

8770. Answer C. ITP-P2

The use of thread lubricant on a float bowl plug helps prevent thread damage and provide a better seal. However, it is important that no thread lubricant be allowed to enter the carburetor bowl since the lubricant is insoluble and, therefore, can plug the fuel jets. When applying a thread lubricant, begin by screwing the plug one turn into the float bowl and applying lubricant to the second thread. This helps ensure that no lubricant enters the carburetor interior. Answer (A) is wrong because lubricating only the first thread increases the likelihood of contamination and does not provide sufficient lubrication to the plug threads. Answer (B) is incorrect because thread lubricant is often required by carburetor manufacturers.

8771.   N02

Maximum power is normally considered to be developed in a reciprocating engine with an air/fuel mixture ratio of approximately

A — 8:1.
B — 12:1.
C — 15:1.

8771. Answer B. AC 65-12A

Valve timing and engine induction system design require a slightly rich mixture in order to produce maximum power. This mixture typically contains 12 parts air to every 1 part fuel, or 12:1. An 8:1 mixture (answer A) represents an excessively rich mixture that would cause spark plug fouling. Answer (C) is incorrect because a 15:1 ratio represents the optimum ratio for combustion where all the fuel and air is used in the combustion process.

INDUCTION AND ENGINE AIRFLOW SYSTEMS

Chapter 11 discusses the basic operating principles associated with engine induction systems. This includes information on carburetor air heat systems, heat exchangers, air intakes and induction manifolds, alternate air systems, turbochargers, and turbine engine airflow and temperature control systems. The following FAA exam questions are taken from this chapter:

8772, 8773, 8774, 8775, 8776, 8777, 8778, 8779, 8780, 8781, 8782, 8783, 8784, 8785, 8786, 8787, 8788, 8789, 8790, 8791, 8792, 8793, 8794, 8795, 8796, 8797, 8798, 8799, 8800, 8801, 8802, 8803, 8804, 8805, 8806, 8807, 8808, 8809, 8810, 8811, 8812, 8813.

8772.   O01

A method commonly used to prevent carburetor icing is to

A — preheat the intake air.
B — mix alcohol with the fuel.
C — electrically heat the venturi and throttle valve.

8772. Answer A. AC 65-12A

Induction system ice forms in float and pressure carburetors when water condenses out of the air in a carburetor's venturi and freezes. Therefore, the easiest way to prevent icing is to heat the intake air to the point where ice cannot form. Answer (B) is incorrect because mixing alcohol with the fuel is not a common method used to prevent carburetor icing, and although electrically heating a carburetor's venturi and throttle valve (answer C) could prevent carburetor icing, this method is not practical and, therefore, is not used.

8773.   O01

Carburetor icing is most severe at

A — air temperatures between 30 and 40 °F.
B — high altitudes.
C — low engine temperatures.

8773. Answer A. AC 65-9A

Normally aspirated engines using float-type carburetors are most susceptible to icing when operated in temperatures between 30 and 40 degrees Fahrenheit. The reason for this is that any time the air being brought into the carburetor is near freezing, the additional temperature drop created by the carburetor venturi can readily cause water vapor to condense and freeze. However, it is important to note that carburetor icing can occur when the outside temperature is as high as 70 degrees Fahrenheit. Answer (B) is incorrect because icing at high altitudes is less likely due to the air's low moisture content. Answer (C) is wrong because engine temperature has little effect on the temperature at the carburetor venturi where icing takes place.

8774.   **O01**

Into what part of a reciprocating engine induction system is deicing alcohol normally injected?

A — The supercharger or impeller section.
B — The airstream ahead of the carburetor.
C — The low-pressure area ahead of the throttle valve.

8774. Answer B. AC65-12A

In addition to a carburetor heat system, some large reciprocating engines utilize an alcohol deicing system. This system allows the pilot to spray alcohol into the inlet of the carburetor to remove ice and assist the warm air in keeping the carburetor free of ice. Answer (A) is incorrect because superchargers become hot during operation and introducing alcohol into a supercharger or impeller section could cause thermal shock which could severely damage the impeller. Answer (C) is wrong because if alcohol were injected in the venturi just ahead of the throttle valve, the alcohol would not have sufficient time to disperse and remove ice from the venturi before being sucked into the engine.

8775.   **O01**

Carburetor icing on an engine equipped with a constant-speed propeller can be detected by

A — a decrease in power output with no change in manifold pressure or RPM.
B — an increase in manifold pressure with a constant RPM.
C — a decrease in manifold pressure with a constant RPM.

8775. Answer C. AC 65-12A

On engines equipped with constant speed propellers, the engine's power output is indicated on the manifold pressure gauge. Therefore, induction system icing is readily detected by a reduction in manifold pressure and no change in rpm (answer C). Answer (A) is incorrect because manifold pressure is the primary indicator of engine power and must decrease as power output decreases. Answer (B) is wrong because an increase in manifold pressure implies that the engine is developing more power, and induction ice causes an engine to lose power.

8776.   **O01**

What part of an aircraft in flight will begin to accumulate ice before any other?

A — Wing leading edge.
B — Propeller spinner or dome.
C — Carburetor.

8776. Answer C. AC 65-12A

When the air temperature is above freezing and there is no visible moisture, a carburetor will be the first part of an aircraft to accumulate ice. The reason for this is that as fuel vaporizes and the air pressure drops in the venturi, the air temperature typically drops enough to cause water vapor to condense and freeze. Answers (A) and (B) are incorrect because, although ice will form on the aircraft structure first when flying in temperatures below freezing and in visible moisture, we believe the purpose of this question is to emphasize that carburetor ice can occur without visible warning.

8777.   **O01**

Carburetor icing may be eliminated by which of the following methods?

A — Alcohol spray and electrically heated induction duct.
B — Ethylene glycol spray and heated induction air.
C — Alcohol spray and heated induction air.

8777. Answer C. AC 65-12A

Heating the air in the inlet duct and spraying alcohol in the carburetor inlet are the two primary methods of eliminating carburetor ice. Answer (A) is wrong because, although some aircraft utilize electrically heated inlet ducts to prevent ice formation on the duct, electric heat is not used in a carburetor. Answer (B) is incorrect because ethylene glycol is used to deice aircraft exteriors, not to eliminate carburetor ice.

8778. **O01**

Where would a carburetor air heater be located in a fuel injection system?

A — At the air intake entrance.
B — None is required.
C — Between the air intake and the venturi.

8779. **O01**

An increase in manifold pressure when carburetor heat is applied indicates

A — ice was forming in the carburetor.
B — mixture was too lean.
C — overheating of cylinder heads.

8780. **O02**

During full power output of an unsupercharged engine equipped with a float-type carburetor, in which of the following areas will the highest pressure exist?

A — Venturi.
B — Intake manifold.
C — Carburetor air scoop.

8781. **O02**

The use of the carburetor air heater when it is not needed causes

A — a very lean mixture.
B — excessive increase in manifold pressure.
C — a decrease in power and possibly detonation.

8782. **O02**

As manifold pressure increases in a reciprocating engine, the

A — volume of air in the cylinder increases.
B — weight of the fuel/air charge decreases.
C — density of air in the cylinder increases.

8778. Answer B. AC 65-12A

Because fuel injection systems inject fuel directly into an engine's intake manifold, there is no need for a carburetor. Therefore, no carburetor air heater is required.

8779. Answer A. AC 65-12A

On engines equipped with constant speed propellers, engine power output is indicated on the manifold pressure gauge. Therefore, the onset of induction system icing is indicated by a reduction in manifold pressure. Another indication of the presence of carburetor ice is when manifold pressure increases after carburetor heat is applied. Neither an excessively lean mixture (answer B) nor overheating cylinder heads (answer C) cause manifold pressure to increase.

8780. Answer C. AC 65-12A

In the induction system of an unsupercharged engine, the air pressure from the venturi to the intake valve is always less than atmospheric pressure when the engine is running. Therefore, of the options given, the highest pressure exists in the carburetor air scoop where ram air enters the induction system.

8781. Answer C. AC65-12A

When carburetor heat is used, warm air is routed into the carburetor. Since warm air is not as dense as cool air, the application of carburetor heat when it is not needed results in a slight decrease in power and an increase in cylinder head temperature which could lead to detonation. Answer (A) is wrong because the application of carburetor heat enriches the mixture slightly, and answer (B) is incorrect because carburetor heat causes a decrease in manifold pressure.

8782. Answer C. AC 65-12A

The pressure of a gas and its density are directly proportional to each other. In other words, as the pressure of a gas increases, its density also increases. Therefore, as an engine's manifold pressure increases, the density of the fuel/air charge going to the cylinders increases proportionally. Answer (A) is incorrect because the volume of air in an engine's cylinders is constant and, therefore, is unaffected by manifold pressure. Answer (B) is wrong because the weight of the fuel/air charge increases as an engine's manifold pressure increases.

8783.   O02

Which of the following statements regarding volumetric efficiency of an engine is true?

A — The volumetric efficiency of an engine will remain the same regardless of the amount of throttle opening.

B — It is impossible to exceed 100 percent volumetric efficiency of any engine regardless of the type of supercharger used.

C — It is possible to exceed 100 percent volumetric efficiency of some engines by the use of superchargers of the proper type.

8783. Answer C. AC 65-12A

The volumetric efficiency of an engine is the ratio of the volume of fuel/air charge drawn into the cylinders to the engine's total piston displacement. If an engine draws in a fuel/air charge that equals the piston's displacement, volumetric efficiency is 100 percent. All unsupercharged engines have volumetric efficiencies less than 100 percent. However, by using a supercharger, it is possible to force a fuel/air charge with a greater volume than that of the cylinder displacement into a cylinder and achieve a volumetric efficiency greater than 100 percent. Answer (A) is wrong because one of the factors that effects volumetric efficiency is the amount the throttle is open. Answer (B) is incorrect because gases are compressible, and by compressing the fuel/air charge before it enters the cylinder it is possible to achieve volumetric efficiencies greater than 100 percent.

8784.   O02

Bootstrapping of a turbocharged engine is indicated by

A — a overboost condition of the engine on takeoff.

B — a transient increase in engine power.

C — a maximum increase in manifold pressure.

8784. Answer B. AC 65-12A

Bootstrapping occurs when a turbocharger system senses small changes in temperature or rpm and continually changes the turbocharger output in an attempt to establish an equilibrium. Bootstrapping typically occurs during part-throttle operation and is characterized by a continual drift or transient increase in manifold pressure. Answer (A) is wrong because an overboost occurs when an engine exceeds its maximum manifold pressure and answer (C) is incorrect because a maximum increase in manifold pressure is more typical of an overboost condition, not a bootstrapping condition.

8785.   O02

Which of the following would be a factor in the failure of an engine to develop full power at takeoff?

A — Improper adjustment of carburetor heat valve control linkage.

B — Excessively rich setting on the idle mixture adjustment.

C — Failure of the economizer valve to remain closed at takeoff throttle setting.

8785. Answer A. AC 65-12A

When carburetor heat is used, warm, less dense air is let into the engine and a drop in engine power output results. In addition, the warmer intake air causes cylinder head temperatures to increase, which can lead to detonation, especially during high-power operations. Therefore, if the carburetor heat valve is improperly adjusted and warm air is allowed to enter the engine during takeoff, less than full power will be developed. Answer (B) is incorrect because the idle mixture adjustment has no effect on engine operations at high power settings. Answer (C) is wrong because an economizer valve should be open at high power settings to enrich the fuel/air mixture.

8786.   O02

If the turbocharger waste gate is completely closed,

A — none of the exhaust gases are directed through the turbine.

B — the turbocharger is in the OFF position.

C — all the exhaust gases are directed through the turbine.

8786. Answer C. AC 65-12A

The waste gate in a turbocharging system controls the amount of exhaust gas that is routed to the turbocharger, which ultimately dictates the amount of air that is forced into the engine. When the waste gate is closed, all the exhaust gas is routed to the turbocharger. However, if the waste gate is completely open, no exhaust gases flow to the turbocharger.

8787.   O02
Boost manifold pressure is generally considered to be any manifold pressure above

A — 14.7″ Hg.
B — 50″ Hg.
C — 30″ Hg.

8788.   O02
What is the purpose of the density controller in a turbocharger system?

A — Limits the maximum manifold pressure that can be produced at other than full throttle conditions.
B — Limits the maximum manifold pressure that can be produced by the turbocharger at full throttle.
C — Maintains constant air velocity at the carburetor inlet.

8789.   O02
What is the purpose of the rate-of-change controller in a turbocharger system?

A — Limits the maximum manifold pressure that can be produced by the turbocharger at full throttle conditions.
B — Controls the rate at which the turbocharger discharge pressure will increase.
C — Controls the position of the waste gate after the aircraft has reached its critical altitude.

8790.   O02
What directly regulates the speed of a turbocharger?

A — Turbine.
B — Waste gate.
C — Throttle.

8787. Answer C. ITP-P2
A boosted manifold pressure is any pressure that is higher than atmospheric pressure or 29.92 inches of mercury. For practical purposes, this is rounded to 30 inches of mercury.

8788. Answer B. AC 65-12A
A density controller contains a nitrogen-filled bellows that responds to changes in pressure and temperature to control the position of the waste gate and prevent an overboost condition. Therefore, the density controller in a turbocharger system limits the manifold pressure produced by the turbocharger at full throttle. Answer (A) is incorrect because the density controller only limits manifold pressure at full power settings, not at other than full throttle settings. Answer (C) is incorrect because there is no need to regulate the air velocity at the carburetor inlet.

8789. Answer B. AC 65-12A
The rate-of-change controller in a turbocharger system controls the rate at which the turbocharger discharge pressure increases. If discharge pressure increases too rapidly, the controller unseats and bleeds oil pressure from the waste gate actuator, opening the waste gate and decreasing manifold pressure. Answer (A) is wrong because the density controller in the turbocharger system, not the rate-of-change controller, limits the maximum manifold pressure produced at full throttle conditions. Answer (C) is incorrect because the rate-of-change controller modulates the waste gate position at all times during turbocharger operation, not just at critical altitude or above.

8790. Answer B. AC 65-12A
The speed of a turbocharger is most directly affected by the amount of exhaust gas entering the turbocharger. The component that controls the amount of exhaust gas that is allowed to flow through the turbine is the waste gate. Answer (A) is incorrect because the turbine is the rotating element of a turbocharger and does not regulate its own speed. Answer (C) is wrong because, although the turbocharger indirectly responds to throttle position, the waste gate has the most immediate effect on turbocharger speed.

8791.   **O02**

What is the purpose of a turbocharger system for a small reciprocating aircraft engine?

A — Compresses the air to hold the cabin pressure constant after the aircraft has reached its critical altitude.

B — Maintains constant air velocity in the intake manifold.

C — Compresses air to maintain manifold pressure constant from sea level to the critical altitude of the engine.

8792.   **O02**

What are the three basic regulating components of a sea-level boosted turbocharger system?

1.   Exhaust bypass assembly.
2.   Compressor assembly.
3.   Pump and bearing casing.
4.   Density controller.
5.   Differential pressure controller.

A — 2, 3, 4.
B — 1, 4, 5.
C — 1, 2, 3.

8793.   **O02**

The differential pressure controller in a turbocharger system

A — reduces bootstrapping during part-throttle operation.

B — positions the waste gate valve for maximum power.

C — provides a constant fuel-to-air ratio.

8794.   **O02**

The purpose of a sonic venturi on a turbocharged engine is to

A — limit the amount of air that can flow from the turbocharger into the cabin for pressurization.

B — increase the amount of air that can flow from the turbocharger into the cabin for pressurization.

C — increase the velocity of the fuel/air charge.

8791. Answer C. AC 65-12A

As an aircraft gains altitude, the decrease in air density causes a decrease in engine power output. One way to help maintain sea level pressure within an engine is to use a turbocharger to compress the air before it enters the engine, thereby maintaining sea level air density and manifold pressure up to the turbocharger's critical altitude. Answer (A) is incorrect because cabin pressurization is a secondary function of some turbocharger systems, not their primary purpose. Answer (B) is wrong because it is neither desirable nor practical to maintain a constant air velocity in the intake manifold.

8792. Answer B. AC 65-12A

A typical sea-level boosted turbocharger system is automatically regulated by an exhaust bypass valve assembly, a density controller, and a differential pressure controller. Therefore, answer B is correct.

8793. Answer A. AC 65-12A

A differential pressure controller senses air pressure upstream and downstream of the throttle valve and repositions the waste gate to smooth out pressure fluctuations, or bootstrapping. Answer (B) is wrong because the differential pressure controller adjusts the waste gate to provide smooth operation, not maximum power. Answer (C) is incorrect because a differential pressure control has no effect on an engine's fuel/air mixture.

8794. Answer A. ITP-P2

In some aircraft, air for cabin pressurization is provided by the turbocharger. However, before it reaches the pressurization system it must first pass through a sonic venturi, which acts as a flow limiter. A sonic venturi accelerates air to the speed of sound, thereby creating a shock wave that limits the amount of airflow into the cabin. Since a sonic venturi limits airflow, it cannot increase the amount of air flowing from the turbocharger into the cabin (answer B). Answer (C) is incorrect because, although a sonic venturi appears the same as the venturi in a carburetor, it has nothing to do with the fuel/air mixture.

8795.   **O02**
What is used to drive a supercharger?

A — Exhaust gasses.
B — Gear train from the crankshaft.
C — Belt drive through a pulley arrangement.

8795. Answer B. AC 65-12A
A supercharger is driven by the crankshaft through a gear train. Answer (A) is wrong because superchargers driven by exhaust gases are called turbo-superchargers or just turbochargers. Answer (C) is wrong because no turbochargers or superchargers are currently driven by a belt and pulley arrangement.

8796.   **O02**
The purpose of a bellmouth compressor inlet is to

A — provide an increased ram air effect at low airspeeds.
B — maximize the aerodynamic efficiency of the inlet.
C — provide an increased pressure drop in the inlet.

8796. Answer B. AC 65-12A
A bellmouth inlet has smooth, rounded surfaces that create very little resistance to air flow. Because of this, bellmouth inlets are extremely efficient (answer B). Answer (A) is incorrect because bellmouth inlets are typically used on installations that operate at airspeeds below the point where ram effect is a factor. Answer (C) is wrong because bellmouth inlets cause no pressure drop at the engine inlet.

8797.   **O02**
What method(s) is/are used to provide clean air to the engines of helicopters and turboprop airplanes that have particle (sand and ice) separators installed?

A — Positive and negative charged areas to attract and/or repel particulates out of the airflow.
B — Air/moisture separators, and "washing" the air clean utilizing water droplets.
C — Sharp airflow directional change to take advantage of inertia and/or centrifugal force, and filters or engine inlet screens.

8797. Answer C. TEP2
Some aircraft utilize a variety of screens, inertia separators, or particle separators to remove foreign objects such as sand (answer C). One type of particle separator relies on sharp directional changes in airflow to keep foreign particles from entering the engine. The exact type of filter used depends on the airflow of the engine and the type of installation. Answer (A) is incorrect because this method of filtering is too expensive and bulky to be used on aircraft inlets. Answer (B) is wrong because no aircraft currently in use utilize water droplets to "wash" incoming air.

8798.   **O02**
The vortex dissipators installed on some turbine-powered aircraft to prevent engine FOD utilize

A — variable inlet guide vanes (IGV) and/or variable first stage fan blades.
B — variable geometry inlet ducts.
C — a stream of engine bleed air blown toward the ground ahead of the engine.

8798. Answer C. AC 65-12A
Vortex dissipators, sometimes called blow-away jets, destroy the low pressure vortex which forms between the ground and the engine inlet by blowing a stream of bleed air ahead of the engine during ground operations. By destroying this low pressure vortex, the engine is less likely to suck up and ingest foreign objects that can cause compressor blade damage. Answer (A) is incorrect because variable inlet guide vanes and variable first stage fan blades are used to control compressor airflow, not to prevent foreign object damage (FOD). Answer (B) is wrong because there are currently no variable geometry inlet ducts in common use on gas turbine engines.

8799.   **O02**
Vortex dissipator systems are generally activated by

A — a landing gear switch.
B — a fuel pressure switch anytime an engine is operating.
C — an engine inlet airflow sensor.

8799. Answer A. AC 65-12A
Vortex dissipator systems, or blow-away jets, destroy the low pressure vortex which forms between the ground and the engine inlet by blowing a stream of bleed air ahead of the engine during ground operations. These systems are typically activated by a landing gear switch. Answer (B) is wrong because it is not necessary to operate the vortex dissipator in flight. Answer (C) is incorrect because turbine engines are not equipped with inlet airflow sensors.

8800.   O02

Air pressure within the inlet of an installed turbojet engine being operated in place on the ground is

A — positive.
B — negative.
C — ambient.

8801.   O02

What indications may shift when a gas turbine engine anti-icing (bleed air) system is turned on?

1. Fuel flow.
2. EGT.
3. EPR.

A — 1 and 2.
B — 1, 2, and 3.
C — 2 and 3.

8802.   O02

The purpose of an engine/inlet anti-ice system is primarily to

A — remove ice from engine and/or inlet areas.
B — prevent ice formation in engine and/or inlet areas.
C — remove ice from engine and/or inlet areas and prevent ice formation in engine and/or inlet areas.

8803.   O03

If carburetor or induction system icing is not present when carburetor heat is applied with no change in the throttle setting, the

A — mixture will become richer.
B — manifold pressure will increase.
C — engine RPM will increase.

8804.   O03

When starting an engine equipped with a carburetor air heater, in what position should the heater be placed?

A — Hot.
B — Cold.
C — Neutral.

8800. Answer B. TEP2

When a gas turbine engine is operated in place on the ground, negative, or low pressure develops within its inlet because the engine inlet acts like a venturi and as the airflow accelerates through a venturi, air pressure decreases.

8801. Answer C. TEP2

When an anti-ice system utilizing engine bleed air is turned on, an indicator light will illuminate in the cockpit and the EGT will rise slightly. Furthermore, both the engine pressure ratio (EPR) and compressor rpm will shift due to the momentary change in compression delivered to the combustor.

8802. Answer B. TEP2

Anti-ice systems are used to prevent ice from forming, while de-ice systems remove ice that has already formed. Therefore, an engine/inlet anti-ice system is used to prevent ice formation in the engine and inlet areas (answer B). Using a turbine engine anti-ice system to de-ice the inlet could result in ice ingestion and compressor damage.

8803. Answer A. ITP-P2

When carburetor heat is turned on, warm, less dense air is drawn into the carburetor. Therefore, if the mixture is not adjusted, the same amount of fuel continues to mix with the air. The combination of less dense air with no change in the amount of fuel supplied produces a mixture that is richer than it was before carburetor heat was applied. The application of carburetor heat will cause the manifold pressure (answer B) or engine rpm (answer C) to decrease, not increase.

8804. Answer B. AC 65-12A

A carburetor air heater should be placed in the cold position when starting an engine. If placed in the hot position (answer A), damage to the carburetor heat air box could result if the engine backfires. Furthermore, since carburetor heat air is typically not filtered, starting an engine with the carburetor heat knob in the hot position increases the chance of ingesting dirt into the engine. Answer (C) is incorrect because carburetor air heat controls do not have a neutral position.

8805.   **O03**
The application of carburetor heat during engine operation will

A — decrease the weight of the fuel/air charge.
B — decrease the volume of air in the cylinder.
C — increase the density of air in the cylinder.

806.   **O03**
The application of carburetor heat will have which of the following effects?

A — The manifold pressure will be increased.
B — The mixture will become leaner.
C — The mixture will become richer.

8807.   **O03**
When operating an engine, the application of carburetor heat will have what effect on the fuel/air mixture?

A — Enriching the mixture because the AMC cannot make a correction for increased temperature.
B — Enriching the mixture until the AMC can make a compensation.
C — Leaning the mixture until the AMC can make a compensation.

8808.   **O03**
In addition to causing accelerated wear, dust or sand ingested by a reciprocating engine may also cause

A — silicon fouling of spark plugs.
B — sludge formation.
C — acid formation.

8805. Answer A. AC 65-12A
When carburetor heat is turned on, warm, less dense air is drawn into the engine. Since air density is directly proportional to the weight of a given volume of air, less dense air decreases the weight of the fuel/air charge. Answer (B) is wrong because the volume of air flowing to the cylinders does not change when carburetor heat is used. Answer (C) is incorrect because the density of the fuel/air charge declines when carburetor heat is used.

8806. Answer C.
When carburetor heat is turned on, warm, less dense air is drawn into the carburetor. Therefore, if the mixture is not adjusted, the same amount of fuel continues to mix with the air. The combination of less dense air with no change in the amount of fuel supplied produces a mixture that is richer than it was before carburetor heat was applied. Answer (A) is wrong because the application of carburetor heat causes manifold pressure to decrease, not increase. Answer (B) is incorrect because the same amount of fuel is mixed with less air, and the resulting mixture is richer.

8807. Answer B. AC 65-12A
When carburetor heat is turned on, warm, less dense air is drawn into the carburetor. However, if the mixture is not adjusted, the same amount of fuel continues to mix with the air. The combination of less dense air with no change in the amount of fuel supplied produces a mixture that is richer than it was before carburetor heat was applied. However, on carburetors equipped with an automatic mixture control (AMC) the mixture will only remain rich until the AMC can compensate. Answer (A) is incorrect because an AMC will respond to changes in temperature, and answer (C) is wrong because the fuel/air mixture becomes richer, not leaner.

8808. Answer A. ITP-P2
Silicon glazing occurs when sand or dust enters an engine's induction system and proceeds to the cylinders where the sand forms a glaze on the nose of spark plugs. Answer (B) is wrong because sludge is primarily caused by water contamination and by oxidation of the lubricating oil. Answer (C) is incorrect because the chemical compounds in sand are not capable of forming acid compounds.

8809.   **O03**

In an airplane equipped with an alternate air system, if the main air duct air filter becomes blocked or clogged, the

A — system will automatically allow warm, unfiltered air to be drawn into the engine.
B — flow of air into the engine will be slowed or cut off unless alternate air is selected.
C — system will automatically allow warm, filtered alternate air to be drawn into the engine.

8810.   **O03**

If a fire starts in the induction system during the engine starting procedure, what should the operator do?

A — Turn off the fuel switches to stop the fuel.
B — Continue cranking the engine.
C — Turn off all switches.

8811.   **O03**

On small aircraft engines, fuel vaporization may be increased by

A — cooling the air before it enters the engine.
B — circulating the fuel and air mixture through passages in the oil sump.
C — heating the fuel before it enters the carburetor.

8812.   **O03**

The action of a carburetor airscoop is to supply air to the carburetor, but it may also

A — cool the engine.
B — keep fuel lines cool and prevent vapor lock.
C — increase the pressure of the incoming air by ram effect.

8813.   **O03**

A carburetor air pre-heater is not generally used on takeoff unless absolutely necessary because of the

A — loss of power and possible detonation.
B — possibility of induction system overboost.
C — inability of the engine to supply enough heat to make a significant difference.

8809. Answer A. AC 65-12A

There are actually two correct answers to this question. The alternate air system on most aircraft is the carburetor heat box. With this type of system, if the main air duct becomes clogged, airflow to the engine will be slowed or cut off unless carburetor heat or alternate air is selected (answer B). However, some aircraft are equipped with an alternate air system that automatically opens when the main air filter becomes sufficiently blocked (answer A). Both systems allow warm, unfiltered air from inside the cowling to be drawn into the carburetor or fuel injection unit. In our opinion, the question is referring to an alternate air system that opens automatically which, therefore, makes (A) the correct answer.

8810. Answer B. AC 65-9A

If a fire breaks out in a reciprocating engine's induction system during a start attempt, you should continue to crank the engine to try and draw the fire into the engine (answer B). If the fire does not go out, the fuel selector valve and ignition should be shut off, the mixture placed in the idle cutoff position, and a fire extinguisher used to put out the fire. Answers (A) and (C) are wrong because the first thing you should do is continue cranking the engine.

8811. Answer B. ITP-P2

Many horizontally opposed engines have their carburetors mounted on the oil sump so the induction pipes pass through the sump and allow the fuel/air mixture to be heated to aid fuel vaporization. Answer (A) is incorrect because aviation gasoline becomes less volatile at lower temperatures and is more difficult to vaporize. Answer (C) is wrong because small aircraft engines to not utilize fuel heaters.

8812. Answer C. AC 65-12A

In addition to supplying air to the carburetor, a typical air scoop is positioned to increase intake air pressure by utilizing the ram effect supplied by the slipstream. Answer (A) is wrong because cooling air enters the engine compartment through openings in front of the engine cowling. Answer (B) is incorrect because vapor lock is prevented by avoiding sharp bends or rises in the fuel lines and by wrapping the fuel lines with insulation.

8813. Answer A. AC 65-12A

The use of carburetor heat results in less dense air entering the engine. This less dense air causes a decrease in engine power and leads to increased cylinder head temperatures that can cause detonation. Therefore, carburetor heat should only be used on takeoff when absolutely necessary. Answer (B) is wrong because preheated air is less dense, and therefore the possibility of an induction system overboost is unlikely when carburetor heat is used. Answer (C) is incorrect because an engine can supply enough heat to cause loss of power and possible detonation.

ENGINE COOLING SYSTEMS

Most aircraft engines are air cooled. However, in order to ensure that an engine is cooled evenly and efficiently baffles, cowl flaps, and augmentor tubes are commonly used. Therefore, as an aviation technician, you must understand the purpose of these components as well as know how to inspect and repair them. The FAA exam questions based on this chapter include:

8814, 8815, 8816, 8817, 8818, 8819, 8820, 8821, 8822, 8823, 8824, 8825, 8826, 8827, 8828, 8829, 8830, 8831, 8832, 8833, 8834, 8835, 8836, 8837, 8838, 8839, 8840, 8841, 8842, 8843, 8844, 8845.

8814.   P01
The primary purpose of baffles and deflectors installed around cylinders of air-cooled aircraft engines is to

A — create a low pressure area aft of the cylinders.
B — force cooling air into close contact with all parts of the cylinders.
C — increase the volume of air used to cool the engine.

8814. Answer B. AC 65-12A
Many reciprocating engines utilize cylinder baffles to help direct cooling air into close contact with all cylinder parts. Answer (A) is incorrect because baffles and deflectors direct airflow around the cylinders and do not create a low pressure area aft of the cylinders. Answer (C) is wrong because cowl flaps control the volume of cooling air admitted into the engine compartment.

8815.   P01
What is the purpose of an augmenter used in some reciprocating engine exhaust systems?

A — To reduce exhaust back pressure.
B — To aid in cooling the engine.
C — To assist in displacing the exhaust gases.

8815. Answer B. AC 65-12A
In an augmenter system, engine exhaust gases are discharged into a stainless steel augmentor tube. The flow of high velocity exhaust gases within the tube creates an area of low pressure at the augmentor inlet that draws additional air from within the cowl into the augmentor tube where is it discharged overboard with the exhaust. This process increases the airflow over the engine and aids in cooling. Answers (A) and (C) are incorrect because augmentor tubes only direct the exhaust gas, they do not displace it or reduce its back pressure.

8816.   P01
Aircraft reciprocating engine cylinder baffles and deflectors should be repaired as required to prevent loss of

A — power.
B — fin area.
C — cooling.

8816. Answer C. AC 65-12A
Cylinder deflectors and baffles are designed to force air over the cylinder cooling fins to ensure proper cooling. Therefore, if a cylinder baffle or deflector is damaged, it should be repaired as soon as possible to prevent a loss of cooling efficiency. Even a small amount of damage could cause a localized hot spot and an eventual engine malfunction. Answer (A) is wrong because cylinder baffles and deflectors have no direct effect on engine power. Answer (B) is incorrect because a damaged baffle or deflector does nothing to change the cooling fin area on the cylinders.

8817.   P01

Cracks in cooling fins that do not extend into the cylinder head, may be repaired by

A — filling the extremities of the crack with liquid metal.
B — removing the affected area and contour filing within limits.
C — welding and then grinding or filing to original thickness.

8818.   P01

Which of the following should a mechanic consult to determine the maximum amount of cylinder cooling fin that could be removed when cracks are found?

A — AC 43.13-1A.
B — Engine manufacturer's service or overhaul manual.
C — Engine Structure repair manual.

8819.   P01

A bent cooling fin on an aluminum cylinder head

A — should be sawed off and filed smooth.
B — should be left alone if no crack has formed.
C — should be stop drilled or a small radius filed at the point of the bend.

8820.   P01

Where are cooling fins usually located on air-cooled engines?

A — Exhaust side of the cylinder head, inside the pistons, and connecting rods.
B — Cylinder head, cylinder walls, and inside the piston skirt.
C — Cylinder head, cylinder barrel, and inside the piston head.

8821.   P01

How do cowl flaps aid in cooling a horizontally opposed aircraft engine?

A — Recirculates air through the engine cylinders.
B — Directs air through the engine cylinders.
C — Controls the amount of air flowing around the cylinders.

8817. Answer B. AC 65-12A

Cracks in the cooling fins of a cylinder are allowed, provided they are within the manufacturer's allowable limits. To repair a cracked cooling fin, you should remove the damaged fin then contour file the affected area. In general, neither filling the extremities of a crack with liquid metal (answer A) nor welding and grinding cylinder cooling fins (answer C) is considered an acceptable repair.

8818. Answer B. AC 65-12A

When performing repairs to a cylinder's cooling fins, the engine manufacturer's service or overhaul manual should be consulted to ensure the repair is within limits. Answer (A) is incorrect because AC 43.13-1A does not contain approved information regarding the removal of material from cylinder cooling fins. Answer (C) is wrong because engine manufacturers do not publish engine structure repair manuals.

8819. Answer B. AC 65-12A

If a cooling fin is inadvertently bent on an aluminum cylinder head and no crack forms, the fin should be left alone. Aluminum cooling fins are very brittle, and any attempt to straighten them could cause them to crack or break. Answer (A) is incorrect because a bent cooling fin does not need to be removed if it is not cracked. Answer (C) is wrong because stop drilling or filing a bent fin will hasten the formation of a crack.

8820. Answer C. AC 65-12A

On an air-cooled reciprocating engine, cooling fins are located on the cylinder head, cylinder barrel, and on the underside of the piston head. Neither connecting rods (answer A) nor piston skirts (answer B) require cooling fins to dissipate excess heat.

8821. Answer C. AC 65-12A

Cowl flaps are typically located on the bottom of an engine cowl and provide a means of controlling the amount of air that exits the cowl which, in turn, controls the amount of air flowing around the cylinders. For example, opening the cowl flaps increases the air exit area which effectively increases the amount of air that can circulate over the cylinder fins. Furthermore, the outside airstream flowing over an opened cowl flap creates a low pressure area which further assists in removing heat from the engine compartment. Answers (A) and (B) are incorrect because cooling air passes around each cylinder, not through the cylinders.

8822.   P01

The position of the cowl flaps during normal cruise flight conditions is

A — closed.
B — open.
C — one half open.

8823.   P01

Generally, a small crack just started in a cylinder baffle

A — requires repair by reinforcing, such as installation of a doubler over the area.
B — requires no action unless it grows or is branched into two cracks.
C — may be stop drilled.

8824.   P02

Which of the following assists in removing heat from the metal walls and fins of an air-cooled cylinder assembly?

A — An intercooler system.
B — A baffle and cowl arrangement.
C — An engine induction system.

8825.   P02

During ground operation of an engine, the cowl flaps should be in what position?

A — Fully closed.
B — Fully open.
C — Opened according to ambient conditions.

8822. Answer A. AC 65-12A

Cowl flaps are small doors at the rear of an engine cowling that are opened to vary the amount of cooling air that flows through the engine compartment. In normal cruise flight, the forward motion of the aircraft typically produces enough airflow over the engine that the cowl flaps can remain closed. Answers (B) and (C) are incorrect because the cowl flaps typically do not need to be open during normal cruise operations.

8823. Answer C. AC 65-12A

Cylinder baffles are sheet metal shields located in an engine compartment that channel air around the cylinders for cooling. If a small crack develops in a cylinder baffle it is acceptable to stopdrill the crack. Answer (A) is incorrect because small cracks in cylinder baffles are generally acceptable as long as they are stop drilled. Answer (B) is wrong because it is good maintenance practice to stop drill small cracks in cylinder baffles when they are first discovered to keep them from growing.

8824. Answer B. AC 65-12A

An engine's cowling and baffles are designed to channel air over the engine cylinders to aid in removing heat from the engine. The cowling is responsible for receiving impact air and making it flow around the engine while the baffles direct the air close to the cylinder fins to prevent hot spots from forming. Answer (A) is wrong because an intercooler system is typically used in a turbocharger installation to cool the turbocharged air before it enters the engine's induction system. Answer (C) is incorrect because an engines induction system does nothing to remove heat from the cylinder assembly.

8825. Answer B. AC 65-12A

Cowl flaps are small doors at the rear of an engine cowling that are used to vary the amount of cooling air that flows through the engine compartment. When an engine is operated on the ground, the airflow through the cowl is limited due to the lack of forward motion. Therefore, to keep the engine from overheating, the cowl flaps should be placed in the full open position to allow the maximum amount of cooling air to flow through the engine compartment. Answer (A) is wrong because if the cowl flaps were fully closed, insufficient cooling air would flow through the engine compartment and the engine could easily overheat. Answer (C) is incorrect because, once the engine is warm, all ground operations typically require maximum engine cooling regardless of ambient conditions.

8826.   P02

The component(s) in a turbine engine that operate(s) at the highest temperatures is/are the

A — first stage turbine nozzle guide vanes.
B — turbine disks.
C — exhaust cone.

8827.   P02

During an operational check of an electrically powered radial engine cowl flap system, the motor fails to operate. Which of the following is the first to be checked?

A — Flap actuator motor circuit breaker.
B — Cockpit control switch.
C — Flap actuator motor.

8828.   P02

(1) Some aircraft exhaust systems include an augmenter system to draw additional cooling air over the engine.
(2) Augmenter systems are used to create a low pressure area at the lower rear of the aircraft engine cowling.

Regarding the above statements,

A — only No.1 is true.
B — both No.1 and No.2 are true.
C — only No.2 is true.

8829.   P02

Which of the following defects would likely cause a hot spot on a reciprocating engine cylinder?

A — Too much cooling fin area broken off.
B — A cracked cylinder baffle.
C — Cowling air seal leakage.

8830.   P02

What part of an air-cooled cylinder assembly has the greatest fin area per square inch?

A — Cylinder barrel.
B — Rear of the cylinder head.
C — Exhaust valve port.

8826. Answer A. ITP-P2

In a turbine engine, the fuel/air mixture is burned in the combustors, then flows into the first stage turbine nozzle guide vanes. Therefore, of the choices given, the guide vanes operate at the highest temperatures in a turbine engine. Answers (B) and (C) are incorrect because the turbine disks and exhaust cone are downstream of the guide vanes and, therefore, the exhaust gases have cooled.

8827. Answer A. AC 65-9A

Any time an electrical component fails to operate, the first action should be to check the component's fuse or circuit breaker. Answers (B) and (C) are incorrect because you must first ensure that the cockpit control switch and the flap actuator motor are being supplied with power through the circuit breaker before you can check their operation.

8828. Answer A. AC 65-12A

Only statement (1) is correct. An augmentor system consists of tubes running from the engine compartment to the rear of the nacelle. The exhaust collectors feed exhaust gas into the inner augmentor tubes where the high-velocity flow creates an area of low pressure at the augmentor inlet. This low pressure draws additional air through the cowling to aid in cooling. Statement (2) is false because cowl falps, not exhaust augmentors, create a low pressure area at the lower rear of the engine cowl.

8829. Answer A. AC 65-12A

The cooling fins on reciprocating aircraft engines are designed with a precise surface area to dissipate a certain amount of heat. Therefore, if a large piece of cooling fin breaks off from a cylinder, a hot spot can develop. Although a cracked cylinder baffle (answer B) or a leaking cowling air seal (answer C) would reduce the efficiency of the engine's cooling system, neither would cause a localized hot spot on a cylinder.

8830. Answer C. AC 65-12A

The hottest area on a cylinder head is around the exhaust valve and, therefore, requires the greatest fin area per square inch. Answers (A) and (B) are wrong because neither the cylinder barrel nor rear of the cylinder head get as hot as the area around the exhaust port.

8831.   P02

Reciprocating engines used in helicopters are cooled by

A — the downdraft from the main rotor.
B — a fan mounted on the engine.
C — blast tubes on either side of the engine mount.

8832.   P02

The greatest portion of heat generated by combustion in a typical aircraft reciprocating engine is

A — converted into useful power.
B — carried out with the exhaust gases.
C — dissipated through the cylinder walls and heads.

8833.   P02

A broken cooling fin on a cylinder head

A — is cause for rejection of the head.
B — may be filed to smooth contours if damage and/or repair limits are not exceeded.
C — should be left alone.

8834.   P02

An engine becomes overheated due to excessive taxiing or improper ground runup. Prior to shutdown, operation must continue until cylinders have cooled, by running engine at

A — low RPM with oil dilution system activated.
B — idle RPM.
C — high RPM with mixture control in rich position.

8831. Answer B.

When operating a reciprocating engine-powered helicopter, ram air pressure from the rotor system (answer A) is usually not sufficient to cool the engine, particularly when the helicopter is hovering. Therefore, many helicopters utilize large engine-driven fans to maintain a strong flow of air around the engine. Answer (C) is wrong because blast tubes do not provide sufficient cooling for a hovering aircraft.

8832. Answer B. AC 65-12A

In a typical aircraft reciprocating engine, about 40 percent of the heat generated in the engine is carried out with the exhaust gas while approximately 30 percent is removed by the oil and the engine's cooling system. The remaining 30 percent is converted into useful power. Therefore, the majority of heat generated by combustion is carried out with the exhaust gases.

8833. Answer B. AC 65-12A

Although a broken cooling fin reduces cooling efficiency, it is not necessarily cause for rejection. For example, if the manufacturer's service limits have not been exceeded, the cooling fin may be filed to produce smooth contours and remain in service. Answer (C) is incorrect because broken cooling fins should at least be filed smooth unless otherwise specified by the manufacturer's service instructions.

8834. Answer B. AC 65-12A

After a flight and a few minutes of taxiing, an engine typically will not become excessively warm and, therefore, can be shut down almost immediately. However, if an engine becomes excessively hot as indicated by the cylinder head temperature gauge and the oil temperature gauge, you should allow the engine to cool at idle speed for a short time before shutdown. Answer (A) is wrong because an engine's oil dilution system reduces oil viscosity to facilitate starting in cold weather and should never be used when the engine is overheated. Answer (C) is incorrect because operating an overheated engine at high rpm will only make the problem worse.

8835.   P02

Cylinder head temperatures are measured by means of an indicator and a

A — resistance bulb sensing device.
B — wheatstone bridge sensing device.
C — thermocouple sensing device.

8835. Answer C. AC 65-15A

Cylinder head temperature is usually measured with a thermocouple sensing device. A thermocouple consists of a circuit with two dissimilar metal wires that are joined at both ends to form two junctions. When one junction is heated, the thermocouple generates an electric current that can be measured by a galvanometer. The hotter the high temperature junction, the greater the current produced. By calibrating the galvanometer in degrees, it becomes a thermometer. Answer (A) is incorrect because resistance bulb sensing devices are limited to measuring lower temperature ranges such as carburetor air, oil, and free air temperatures. Answer (B) is wrong because, although a wheatstone bridge circuit is used with some temperature sensing devices, it is not typically used with cylinder head temperature gauges.

8836.   P02

High cylinder head temperatures are likely to result from

A — a very lean mixture at high power settings.
B — fouled spark plugs.
C — a very rich mixture at high power settings.

8836. Answer A. AC 65-12A

At higher power settings, a very lean mixture does not allow any excess fuel into the engine to aid in cooling and, therefore, high cylinder temperatures typically result. Answer (B) is wrong because fouled spark plugs typically fire intermittently and result in lower cylinder temperatures. Answer (C) is incorrect because the excess fuel in a very rich mixture helps cool engine cylinders and maintain low cylinder head temperatures.

8837.   P02

The purpose of an intercooler when used with a turbocharger is to cool the

A — exhaust gases before they come in contact with the turbo drive.
B — turbocharger bearings.
C — air entering the carburetor from the turbocharger.

8837. Answer C. AC 65-12A

When air is compressed, its temperature rises. Therefore, some turbocharger systems utilize an intercooler that cools the compressed air before it enters the carburetor. Answer (A) is incorrect because the exhaust gases must be hot before they enter the turbocharger. Answer (B) is wrong because most turbocharger bearings are cooled with oil from the engine crankcase.

8838.   P02

Prolonged idling of an engine will usually result in

A — excessive cylinder head temperatures.
B — increased oil consumption.
C — foreign material buildup on spark plugs.

8838. Answer C. AC 65-12A

When an engine is operated for a long period at idle rpm, a rich fuel/air mixture must be used to keep cylinder head temperatures within acceptable limits. However, after prolonged operation, the excess fuel has a tendency to build up and foul out the spark plugs. Answer (A) is incorrect because cylinder head temperatures remain within limits at idle if a rich fuel/air mixture is used. Answer (B) is wrong because increased oil consumption is caused by worn pistons rings, worn valve train components, or improper break-in, but not by prolonged ground idling.

8839.   **P02**

The most common method and generally the best conduction of heat from the inside of a cylinder barrel to the cooling air is accomplished by

A — machining fins directly on the outside of the barrel.

B — shrinking on a jacket or muff of aluminum cooling fins around a steel cylinder sleeve.

C — machining fins directly on the outside of the barrel and shrinking on a jacket or muff of aluminum cooling fins around a steel cylinder sleeve (on different areas of the barrel).

8840.   **P02**

What is the function of a blast tube as found on aircraft engines?

A — A means of cooling the engine by utilizing the propeller backwash.

B — A tube used to load a cartridge starter.

C — A device to cool an engine accessory.

8841.   **P02**

Which statement is true regarding the air passing through the combustion section of a jet engine?

A — Most is used for engine cooling.

B — Most is used to support combustion.

C — A small percentage is frequently bled off at this point to be used for air-conditioning and/or other pneumatic powered systems.

8842.   **P02**

Which of the following results in a decrease in volumetric efficiency?

A — Cylinder head temperature too low.

B — Part-throttle operation.

C — Short intake pipes of large diameter.

8839. Answer A. AC 65-12A

Almost all reciprocating engine cylinder barrels have cooling fins machined directly onto their outside surfaces to help dissipate heat. These fins allow heat to be conducted away from the inside of the cylinder, allowing the use of stronger, lighter alloys. Answers (B) and (C) are incorrect because the expense and difficulty of machining cooling fins onto a jacket which is then shrunk onto the cylinder barrel outweighs the usefulness of these designs.

8840. Answer C. AC 65-12A

Many reciprocating engines use blast tubes to direct cooling air to inaccessible areas of an engine compartment. A blast tube is simply a small pipe or duct that channels air from the main cooling air stream onto heat-sensitive components such as spark plugs and alternators. Answer (A) is incorrect because in flight, propeller backwash supplies only a small portion of the cooling air in an engine compartment. Answer (B) is wrong because the cartridges used in cartridge starters are loaded into the starter breech by hand, not with a blast tube.

8841. Answer A. AC 65-12A

Approximately 25 percent of the air passing through a turbine engine's combustion chamber is used to support combustion while the other 75 percent is used to propel the turbine and cool the engine. Answer (B) is incorrect because only 25 percent of the air is used to support combustion. Answer (C) is wrong because bleed air is taken from the compreessor, not the combustion section.

8842. Answer B. AC 65-12A

Volumetric efficiency is the ratio of the volume of the fuel/air charge drawn into a cylinder to the actual volume of the cylinder. Therefore, anything that limits airflow through an engine's induction system will cause a decrease in volumetric efficiency. At part throttle operation, the partially closed throttle valve restricts airflow to the cylinders and, therefore, causes a decrease in volumetric efficiency. Neither a low cylinder head temperature (answer A) nor the use of short, large diameter intake pipes (answer C) has an adverse effect on volumetric efficiency.

8843. **P02**

The undersides of pistons are frequently finned. The principal reason is to

A — provide sludge chambers and sediment traps.
B — provide for greater heat transfer to the engine oil.
C — support ring grooves and piston pins.

8844. **P02**

What is the position of the cowl flaps during engine starting and warmup operations under normal conditions?

A — Full open at all times.
B — Full closed at all times.
C — Open for starting, closed for warmup.

8845. **P02**

Increased engine heat will cause volumetric efficiency to

A — remain the same.
B — decrease.
C — increase.

8843. Answer B. AC 65-12A

The majority of aircraft engine pistons are machined from aluminum alloy forgings. On some pistons, cooling fins are provided on the underside of the piston to facilitate the transfer of heat to the engine oil. Answer (A) is incorrect because sludge chambers are found in an engine's crankshaft, not in the pistons. Answer (C) is wrong because, although the use of fins may provide additional strength to the piston pin boss, this is not always the case.

8844. Answer A. AC 65-12A

Cowl flaps are used to control the amount of air that flows over an engine. During ground operations, many aircraft engines have a tendency to overheat due to the decreased airflow into the cowling. Therefore, during most ground operations the cowl flaps are typically left fully open to provide maximum cooling. Answers (B) and (C) are wrong because, if the cowl flaps were left closed, the engine could overheat.

8845. Answer B. AC 65-12A

Volumetric efficiency is the ratio of the volume of the fuel/air charge drawn into a cylinder to the actual volume of the cylinder. With high engine temperatures the air entering an engine heats up and becomes less dense before it enters the cylinders. Because of this, less oxygen reaches the engine's cylinders and volumetric efficiency decreases. Answers (A) and (C) are incorrect because volumetric efficiency will not remain the same or increase.

CHAPTER 13

ENGINE EXHAUST AND REVERSER SYSTEMS

Chapter 13 discusses the materials and components used in a typical exhaust system as well as the methods commonly used to inspect, service, and repair these components. In addition, information regarding the operation and use of turbojet thrust reverser systems are described in detail. The following FAA exam questions are based on this chapter:

8846, 8847, 8848, 8849, 8850, 8851, 8852, 8853, 8854, 8855, 8856, 8857, 8858, 8859, 8860, 8861, 8862, 8863, 8864, 8865, 8866, 8867, 8868, 8869, 8870, 8871, 8872, 8873, 8874, 8875, 8876, 8877, 8878, 8879, 8880.

8846.   Q01
Why is high nickel chromium steel used in many exhaust systems?

A — High heat conductivity and flexibility.
B — Corrosion resistance and low expansion coefficient.
C — Corrosion resistance and high heat conductivity.

8847.   Q01
Reciprocating engine exhaust system designs commonly used to provide for ease of installation and/or allow for expansion and contraction, may include the use of

1. spring loaded ball/flexible joints.
2. slip joints.
3. bellows.
4. flexible metal tubing.

A — 1, 2, 3, and/or 4.
B — 1, 2, and/or 4.
C — 1, 2, and/or 3.

8848.   Q01
One source commonly used for carburetor air heat is

A — turbocharger heated air.
B — alternate air heat.
C — exhaust gases.

8846. Answer B. ITP-P2
Exhaust system parts are subjected to corrosive exhaust gases and large changes in temperature. Therefore, the metals used in these areas must be able to resist corroding and have a low expansion coefficient. One metal that possesses these properties is nickel chromium steel (stainless steel). Answers (A) and (C) are incorrect because high heat conductivity is not a desirable characteristic for exhaust system components.

8847. Answer C. ITP-P2
Spring loaded ball/flexible joints and slip joints are commonly used to correct slight misalignments, allow movement and expansion, and simplify installation. Bellows, on the other hand, allow the exhaust components to expand and contract without causing buckling. Answers (A) and (B) are incorrect because flexible metal tubing is not used in aircraft exhaust systems.

8848. Answer C. AC 65-12A
Most light aircraft have a carburetor heat system that draws air from within the cowling and routes it through a shroud that surrounds the exhaust pipe. With this type of system, the hot exhaust gases provide a source of heat that adequately heats the intake air to prevent or remove carburetor ice. Answer (A) is wrong because turbocharged engines do not use carburetors and, therefore, do not require carburetor air heat. Answer (B) is incorrect because alternate air does not supply sufficient heat to remove accumulated ice from a carburetor throat.

8849.   Q01

The hot section of a turbine engine is particularly susceptible to which of the following kind of damage?

A — Galling.
B — Pitting.
C — Cracking.

8850.   Q01

What is the purpose of a slip joint in an exhaust collector ring?

A — It aids in alignment and absorbs expansion.
B — It reduces vibration and increases cooling.
C — It permits the collector ring to be installed in one piece.

8851.   Q01

Sodium-filled valves are advantageous to an aviation engine because they

A — are lighter.
B — dampen valve impact shocks.
C — dissipate heat well.

8852.   Q01

What type nuts are used to hold an exhaust system to the cylinders?

A — Brass or heat-resistant nuts.
B — High-temperature fiber self-locking nuts.
C — High-temperature aluminum self-locking nuts.

8853.   Q01

Repair of exhaust system components

A — is impossible because the material cannot be identified.
B — must be accomplished by the component manufacturer.
C — is not recommended to be accomplished in the field.

8849. Answer C. AC 65-12A

Because of the high heat encountered in the hot section of a turbine engine, cracks frequently develop on turbine blades, stator vanes, and exhaust system components. Answer (A) is incorrect because galling, a severe chafing caused by a slight movement between mated parts, rarely occurs in a turbine engine hot section. Answer (B) is wrong because, although pitting does occasionally occur in turbine engine hot sections it is not that common.

8850. Answer A. AC 65-12A

As an exhaust system heats up, the various system components expand. One way to allow for this expansion so adjacent components do not start buckling against each other is to use slip joints to join different components. Answer (B) is wrong because slip joints neither reduce vibration nor increase engine cooling. Answer (C) is incorrect because collector rings are installed piece by piece, not as a single assembly.

8851. Answer C. AC 65-12A

Metallic sodium is used in some valves because it is an excellent heat conductor. In a metallic sodium valve, the sodium melts at approximately 208 degrees Fahrenheit. When this happens, the reciprocating motion of the valve circulates the liquid sodium enabling it to carry away excess heat and reduce valve operating temperatures. Answer (A) is incorrect because sodium valves are not substantially lighter than solid valves. Answer (B) is wrong because, although sodium valves dampen impact shocks somewhat, their primary purpose is to assist heat transfer.

8852. Answer A. AC 65-12A

Engine manufacturers typically use brass or heat-resistant nuts to fasten exhaust system components to cylinder heads. Neither high-temperature fiber self-locking nuts (answer B) nor high-temperature aluminum self-locking nuts (answer C) are designed to withstand the high temperatures encountered on exhaust system components.

8853. Answer C. AC 65-12A

Although repair of exhaust system components can be accomplished, it requires special equipment and techniques that are not typically available in the field. Therefore, it is recommended that exhaust stacks, mufflers, and tailpipes be replaced with new or reconditioned components rather than being repaired. Answer (A) is incorrect because, although it may be difficult to identify the material in an exhaust system component, it is not impossible. Answer (B) is wrong because exhaust system repairs may be performed by qualified repair stations other than the component manufacturer.

8854.   Q01
On turbine-powered airplanes, thrust reversers are capable of producing between?

A — 35 and 50 percent of the rated thrust in the reverse direction.
B — 35 and 75 percent of the rated thrust in the reverse direction.
C — 35 and 65 percent of the rated thrust in the reverse direction.

8855.   Q02
On an aircraft that utilizes an exhaust heat exchanger as a source of cabin heat, how should the exhaust system be inspected?

A — X-rayed to detect any cracks.
B — Hydrostatically tested.
C — With the heater air shroud removed.

8856.   Q02
How should ceramic-coated exhaust components be cleaned?

A — With alkali.
B — By degreasing.
C — By mechanical means.

8857.   Q02
Which of the following indicates that a combustion chamber of a jet engine is not operating properly?

A — Clam shells stick in thrust reverse position.
B — Hot spots on the tail cone.
C — Warping of the exhaust duct liner.

8858.   Q02
Select a characteristic of a good weld on exhaust stacks.

A — The weld should be built up 1/8 inch.
B — Porousness or projecting globules should show in the weld.
C — The weld should taper off smoothly into the base metal.

8854. Answer A. TEP2
To satisfy the minimum braking requirements after landing, a thrust reverser should be able to produce reverse thrust that is between 35 and 50 percent of the full forward thrust for which the engine is capable. Both answers (B) and (C) are wrong because the percentages indicated exceed the amount of reverse thrust that is required.

8855. Answer C. AC 43.13-1A
Most exhaust systems that use a heat exchanger as a source of cabin heat can be inspected visually once the heater air shroud is removed. Although X-ray inspection (answer A) can detect cracks in exhaust system components, these defects are more easily and economically found by frequent and thorough visual inspection. Answer (B) is incorrect because hydrostatic tests are used only when a component has hidden or nonremovable parts that cannot be inspected visually.

8856. Answer B. AC 65-12A
Ceramic coated stacks are typically cleaned using degreasing agents. However, you should always consult the manufacturer's specifications before using any cleaning agents. Harsh alkali cleaners (answer A) can attack some ceramic materials and should not be used. Answer (B) is wrong because mechanical cleaning, such as bead blasting or wire brushing, will typically damage the ceramic coating.

8857. Answer B. AC 65-12A
A malfunctioning fuel nozzle or combustion chamber disrupts the normal flow of gases through the turbine and exhaust sections of a turbine engine. These defects can typically be detected by the presence of hot spots on the exhaust duct or tail cone. Answer (A) is incorrect because clam shell doors stuck in the reverse position indicate a problem with the reverser system, not the combustion chamber. Answer (C) is wrong because warping of the exhaust duct liner indicates a severe overtemperature condition has occurred.

8858. Answer C. AC 43.13A
When welding an exhaust stack, the completed weld should have a smooth seam of uniform thickness and the weld should taper smoothly into the base metal. Answer (A) is wrong because a good weld should be built up 1/4 to 1/2 the thickness of the welded material, and answer (B) is wrong because porousness indicates excessive heat was used while projecting globules are characteristic of a cold weld.

8859.   Q02

How do the turbines which are driven by the exhaust gases of a turbo-compound engine contribute to total engine power output?

A — By driving the crankshaft through suitable couplings.
B — By driving the supercharger, thus relieving the engine of the supercharging load.
C — By converting the latent heat energy of the exhaust gases into thrust by collecting and accelerating them.

8860.   Q02

How should corrosion-resistant steel parts such as exhaust collectors be blast cleaned?

A — Use steel grit which has not previously been used on soft iron.
B — Use super fine granite grit.
C — Use sand which has not previously been used on iron or steel.

8861.   Q02

Power recovery turbines used on some reciprocating engines are driven by the

A — exhaust gas pressure.
B — crankshaft.
C — velocity of the exhaust gases.

8862.   Q02

Reciprocating engine exhaust systems that have repairs or sloppy weld beads which protrude internally are unacceptable because they cause

A — base metal fatigue.
B — localized cracks.
C — local hot spots.

8863.   Q02

Ball joints in reciprocating engine exhaust systems should be

A — tight enough to prevent any movement.
B — disassembled and the seals replaced every engine change.
C — loose enough to permit some movement.

8859. Answer A. AC 65-12A

A turbocompound engine consists of a conventional reciprocating engine with a set of exhaust-driven turbines, sometimes called power recovery turbines (PRTs), that are coupled to the engine crankshaft through a fluid clutch. With a PRT system, additional power is recovered from the exhaust gases that would otherwise be pumped overboard. Answer (B) is wrong because power recovery turbines are not connected to an engine's supercharger system. Answer (C) is incorrect because power recovery turbines convert the velocity of the exhaust gas into torque which is transmitted to the engine's crankshaft.

8860. Answer C. AC 65-12A

To prevent dissimilar metal corrosion, corrosion-resistant steel parts should be blast cleaned using sand that has not previously been used on iron or steel. Answer (A) is wrong because steel grit will corrode if it becomes embedded in exhaust components. Answer (B) is incorrect because granite grit is not typically used in aircraft repair shops.

8861. Answer C. AC 65-12A

Some large reciprocating engines utilize power recovery turbines (PRTs) that are attached to the crankshaft to supplement engine power. A PRT is driven by high velocity exhaust gases and transmits its rotational energy to the engine's crankshaft through a fluid clutch. Answer (A) is incorrect because PRTs are driven by the velocity of the exhaust gases, not the pressure, and answer (B) is wrong because the power recovery turbine drives the crankshaft.

8862. Answer C. AC 65-12A

Repairs or sloppy weld beads on exhaust components that protrude into the exhaust gas flow can restrict the exhaust gas flow and cause localized hot spots. Answers (A) and (B) are incorrect because a poor weld does not cause base metal fatigue or localized cracks.

8863. Answer C. AC 65-12A

Flexible ball joints absorb movement between stationary and movable portions of an engine's exhaust system. Therefore, ball joints must be installed with a specified clearance to prevent binding when expanded by hot exhaust gas. Answer (A) is wrong because rigidly mounted ball joints will lead to stress and cracking of exhaust system components. Answer (B) is wrong because ball joints should be replaced on condition, not on a set schedule.

8864.   **Q02**

All of the following are recommended markers for reciprocating engine exhaust systems except

A — India ink.
B — lead pencil.
C — Prussian blue.

8864. Answer B. AC 65-12A

Exhaust system parts should never be marked with a lead pencil. The lead is absorbed by the metal when heated, creating a distinct change in the metal's molecular structure. This change softens the metal in the area of the mark. India ink (answer A) and Prussian blue (answer C) are recommended markers for exhaust system components.

8865.   **Q02**

How are combustion liner walls cooled in a gas turbine engine?

A — By secondary air flowing through the combustion chamber.
B — By the pattern of holes and louvers cut in the diffuser section.
C — By bleed air vented from the engine air inlet.

8865. Answer A. AC 65-12A

The airflow coming off the compressor is typically divided into primary and secondary flows. The primary flow is used to support combustion and drive the turbine while the secondary flow is used to cool the combustion and turbine sections. Answer (B) is wrong because holes and louvers are cut into the burner cans, not the diffuser section. Answer (C) is incorrect because air at the engine inlet is at ambient pressure and cannot be bled off for combustor cooling.

8866.   **Q02**

Augmenter tubes are part of which reciprocating engine system?

A — Induction.
B — Exhaust.
C — Fuel.

8866. Answer B. AC 65-12A

Augmenter tubes are exhaust system components that assist engine cooling and provide a source of heat for anti-icing and cabin heating.

8867.   **Q02**

Dislodged internal muffler baffles on a small reciprocating engine may

A — obstruct the muffler outlet and cause excessive exhaust back pressure.
B — cause the engine to run excessively cool.
C — cause high fuel and oil consumption.

8867. Answer A. AC 43.13-1A

Internal failures in a muffler, such as displaced baffles or diffusers, can restrict the flow of exhaust gases resulting in excessive exhaust back pressure that can lead to a partial or complete engine power loss. Answer (B) is incorrect because restrictions in an exhaust system reduce the system's ability to expel heat which leads to higher operating temperatures. Answer (C) is wrong because an obstructed exhaust system will not greatly effect fuel or oil consumption.

8868.   **Q02**

What is the purpose of an exhaust outlet guard on a small reciprocating engine?

A — To prevent dislodged muffler baffles from obstructing the muffler outlet.
B — To reduce spark exit.
C — To shield adjacent components from excessive heat.

8868. Answer A. AC 43.13-1A

Engine power loss and excessive back pressure caused by exhaust outlet blockage can be prevented by the installation of an exhaust outlet guard. A typical exhaust outlet guard extends approximately two inches inside the muffler outlet port, thereby preventing any debris from blocking the outlet. Answer (B) is wrong because spark arresters are not commonly used on aircraft reciprocating engines. Answer (C) is incorrect because heat sensitive components are wrapped in insulating material, or "lagged," to protect them from damage by exhaust system heat.

8869.   Q02

What could be a result of undetected exhaust system leaks in a reciprocating engine powered airplane?

A — Pilot/passenger incapacitation caused by carbon monoxide entering the cabin.
B — A rough-running engine with increased fuel consumption.
C — Too low exhaust back pressure resulting in the desired power settings not being attained.

8870.   Q02

How may reciprocating engine exhaust system leaks be detected?

A — An exhaust trail aft of the tailpipe on the airplane exterior.
B — Fluctuating manifold pressure indication.
C — Signs of exhaust soot inside cowling and on adjacent components.

8871.   Q02

Compared to normally aspirated engines, turbocharged engine exhaust systems operate at

A — similar temperatures and higher pressures.
B — higher temperatures and higher pressures.
C — similar temperatures and pressures.

8872.   Q02

Most exhaust system failures result from thermal fatigue cracking in the areas of stress concentration. This condition is usually caused by

A — the drastic temperature change which is encountered at altitude.
B — improper welding techniques during manufacture.
C — the high temperatures at which the exhaust system operates.

8873.   Q03

Thrust reversers utilizing a pneumatic actuating system usually receive operating pressure from

A — the engine bleed air system.
B — an on board hydraulic or electrical powered compressor.
C —high pressure air reservoirs.

8869. Answer A. AC 43.13-1A
Cabin heat in most light aircraft is provided by a shroud that routes air over the exhaust system. Therefore, any exhaust system leakage should be regarded as a severe hazard. An undetected exhaust system leak can allow carbon monoxide to enter the cabin and incapacitate the pilot and passengers. Answers (B) and (C) are incorrect because an exhaust system leak will not result in a rough running engine or loss of power.

8870. Answer C. AC 43.13-1A
Prior to any cleaning in an engine compartment, the exhaust system and surrounding areas should be thoroughly inspected. The cowling and nacelle areas adjacent to the exhaust system should be inspected for signs of heat damage or exhaust gas soot, indicating possible exhaust leaks. Answer (A) is wrong because an exhaust trail aft of the tailpipe indicates an excessively rich fuel/air mixture. Answer (B) is incorrect because exhaust system leaks will not affect manifold pressure in a normally aspirated aircraft engine.

8871. Answer B. ITP-P2
Turbocharged engine exhaust systems extract energy from the exhaust gas flow to compress the intake air before it enters the cylinders. Any time a gas is compressed, its temperature increases. Therefore, turbocharged engine exhaust systems typically operate at higher temperatures and higher pressures than normally aspirated systems.

8872. Answer C. AC 43.13-1A
Approximately one half of all exhaust system failures are traced to cracks or ruptures in the heat exchanger surfaces used for cabin and carburetor air heat sources. The high temperature of the exhaust system components along with the vibration from the engine promotes thermal and vibration fatigue cracking in areas of stress concentration. Answer (A) is incorrect because exhaust system components are not directly exposed to extremely cold temperatures and do not experience drastic temperature changes. Answer (B) is wrong because thermal fatigue cracking occurs in exhaust system components regardless of the quality of the welding.

8873. Answer A. TEP2
Turbine engine thrust reversers are typically operated hydraulically, using hydraulic system pressure, or pneumatically using compressor bleed air. Answers (B) and (C) are incorrect because the weight and expense of on board compressors or high pressure air reservoirs are not required when a bleed air source is readily available.

8874. Q03

Operating thrust reversers at low ground speeds can sometimes cause

1. sand or other foreign object ingestion.
2. hot gas re-ingestion.
3. compressor stalls.

A — 1, 2, and 3.
B — 1 and 2.
C — 2 and 3.

8875. Q03

Engines using cold stream, or both cold and hot stream reversing include

A — high bypass turbofans.
B — turbojets.
C — turbojets with afterburner.

8876. Q03

The purpose of cascade vanes in a thrust reversing system is to

A — form a solid blocking door in the jet exhaust path.
B — turn the exhaust gases forward just after exiting the exhaust nozzle.
C — turn to a forward direction the fan and/or hot exhaust gases that have been blocked from exiting through the exhaust nozzle.

8877. Q03

Turbojet and turbofan thrust reverser systems are generally powered by

1. fuel pressure.
2. electricity.
3. hydraulic pressure.
4. pneumatic pressure.
5. engine oil pressure.

A — 1, 3, and 5.
B — 2, 3, and 4.
C — 3, 4 and 5.

8874. Answer A. TEP2

Statements number (1), (2), and (3) are true. The operation of thrust reversers at low ground speeds or during power backs disrupts the air flow into the compressor, increasing the chance of compressor stall. Furthermore, exhaust gas from the thrust reversers can blow sand and other foreign objects into the compressor inlet, and cause hot exhaust gas to be re-ingested. Therefore, answer (A) is correct.

8875. Answer A. TEP2

Cold stream reversing describes a system that uses bypass air to produce reverse thrust. This is only possible with bypass turbofan engines. Answers (B) and (C) are incorrect because turbojets do not bypass air and, therefore, cannot use cold stream reversing.

8876. Answer C. TEP2

The two types of thrust reversers in common use are the aerodynamic reversers and the mechanical blockage reversers. Aerodynamic, or cascade, reversers consist of a set of cascade vanes located ahead of the exhaust discharge that turn the escaping exhaust gases forward, which, in turn, produces reverse thrust. Mechanical blockage reversers typically consist of clamshell doors that extend into the exhaust stream and divert the flow of exhaust gases forward to create reverse thrust. Answer (A) is wrong because mechanical blockage reversers, not cascade reversers, form a solid blocking door. Answer (B) is incorrect because cascade reversers turn the exhaust gases forward before they reach the exhaust duct.

8877. Answer B. TEP2

The most common type of actuators used on thrust reverser systems are pneumatic. However, electric and hydraulic actuators are also used in some applications. Therefore, answer (B) is correct. Neither fuel pressure nor engine oil pressure is used in thrust reverser systems because the high heat encountered in the exhaust duct could cause either of these to ignite.

8878.   **Q03**
The rearward thrust capability of an engine with the thrust reverser system deployed is

A — less than its forward capability.
B — equal to or less than its forward capability, depending on ambient conditions and system design.
C — equal to its forward capability.

8879.   **Q03**
Which statement is generally true regarding thrust reverser systems?

A — It is possible to move some aircraft backward on the ground using reverse thrust.
B — Engine thrust reversers on the same aircraft usually will not operate independently of each other (must all be simultaneously).
C — Mechanical blockage system design permits a deployment position aft of the exhaust nozzle only.

8880.   **Q03**
What is the proper operating sequence when using thrust reversers to slow an aircraft after landing?

A — Advance thrust levers up to takeoff position as conditions require, select thrust reverse, de-select thrust reverser, retard thrust levers to ground idle.
B — Retard thrust levers to ground idle, raise thrust reverser levers as required, and retard thrust levers to ground idle.
C — Select thrust reverse, advance thrust reverser levers no higher than 75% N1, and retard thrust reverser levers to idle at approximately normal taxi speed.

8878. Answer A. AC 65-12A
Reversers are capable of producing between 35 and 50 percent of an engine's rated thrust in the reverse direction. Therefore, answer (A) is correct. Answers (B) and (C) are incorrect because it would be difficult, if not impossible, for a reverser system to have reverse thrust capability equal to an engine's forward capability because the exhaust gas loses energy when it is turned by the reverser system.

8879. Answer A. TEP2
The thrust reverser systems on some aircraft do create enough reverse thrust to move the aircraft backwards. This is referred to as a power-back operation. However, creating that much reverse thrust burns a great deal of fuel and, therefore, is not very economical. Answer (B) is wrong because an individual reverse thrust control is mounted on each power lever, and the reversers operate independently of each other. Answer (C) is incorrect because some mechanical blockage systems deploy forward of the exhaust nozzle.

8880. Answer B. TEP2
Thrust reverse can only be selected with the thrust levers in the ground-idle position. Therefore, to obtain reverse thrust, you must first retard the thrust levers to ground idle, then raise the thrust reverser levers attached to the power levers as required. Once the aircraft has decelerated sufficiently, the thrust reverser levers are returned to the ground idle position. Answers (A) and (C) are incorrect because the power levers must be retarded to the ground idle position before reverse thrust can be selected.

CHAPTER 14

PROPELLERS

This chapter discusses the various types of propellers in use including fixed pitch, constant-speed, and feathering. In addition, information on the operating principles of propeller governors as well as how to remove, repair, install, and balance propellers. The following FAA exam questions are taken from this chapter:

8881, 8882, 8883, 8884, 8885, 8886, 8887, 8888, 8889, 8890, 8891, 8892, 8893, 8894, 8895, 8896, 8897, 8898, 8899, 8900, 8901, 8902, 8903, 8904, 8905, 8906, 8907, 8908, 8909, 8910, 8911, 8912, 8913, 8914, 8915, 8916, 8917, 8918, 8919, 8920, 8921, 8922, 8923, 8924, 8925, 8926, 8927, 8928, 8929, 8930, 8931, 8932, 8933, 8934, 8935, 8936, 8937, 8938, 8939, 8940, 8941, 8942, 8943, 8944, 8945, 8946, 8947, 8948, 8949, 8950, 8951, 8952, 8953, 8954, 8955, 8956, 8957, 8958, 8959, 8960, 8961, 8962, 8963, 8964, 8965, 8966, 8967, 8968, 8969, 8970, 8971, 8972, 8973, 8974, 8975, 8976, 8977, 8978, 8979, 8980, 8981, 8982, 8983, 8984, 8985, 8986, 8987, 8988, 8989, 8990, 8991, 8992, 8993, 8994, 8995, 8996.

8881.   R01

How is aircraft electrical power for propeller deicer systems transferred from the engine to the propeller hub assembly?

A — By slip rings and segment plates.
B — By slip rings and brushes.
C — By flexible electrical connectors.

8881. Answer B. AC 65-12A

A typical electric propeller deice system utilizes a set of brush blocks and slip rings to transfer electrical power from the engine to the rotating propeller assembly. The brush blocks are mounted on the engine case just behind the propeller while the slip rings are mounted on the back of the propeller hub assembly. Answer (A) is incorrect because segment plates are not used in propeller deice installations. Answer (C) is wrong because, it is impossible to hardwire from a stationary source to a rotating propeller.

8882.   R01

How is anti-icing fluid ejected from the slinger ring on a propeller?

A — By pump pressure.
B — By centripetal force.
C — By centrifugal force.

8882. Answer C. AC 65-12A

A slinger ring is a U-shaped circular channel mounted on the rear of a propeller hub assembly that incorporates a discharge for each propeller blade. When an anti-icing system is on, a pump forces anti-icing fluid into the slinger ring where centrifugal force discharges the fluid from the slinger ring through the discharge tubes and onto the propeller blades. Answer (A) is wrong because the centrifugal force created by the rotating propeller eliminates the need for a fluid pump to eject fluid on to the propeller. Answer (B) is incorrect because centripetal force acts toward the center of a body's rotation as opposed to centrifugal force, which acts outward.

8883.   R01

On most reciprocating multiengine aircraft, automatic propeller synchronization is accomplished through the actuation of the

A — throttle levers.
B — propeller governors.
C — propeller control levers.

8884.   R01

Propeller fluid anti-icing systems generally use which of the following?

A — Ethylene glycol.
B — Isopropyl alcohol.
C — Ethyl alcohol.

8885.   R01

What is a function of the automatic propeller synchronizing system on multiengine aircraft?

A — To control the tip speed of all propellers.
B — To control engine RPM and reduce vibration.
C — To control the power output of all engines.

8886.   R01

Ice formation on propellers, when an aircraft is in flight, will

A — decrease thrust and cause excessive vibration.
B — increase aircraft stall speed and increase noise.
C — decrease available engine power.

8887.   R01

What unit in the propeller anti-icing system controls the output of the pump?

A — Pressure relief valve.
B — Rheostat.
C — Cycling timer.

8888.   R01

Proper operation of electric deicing boots on individual propeller blades may best be determined by

A — feeling the boots to see if they are heating.
B — observing the ammeter or loadmeter for current flow.
C — checking the ammeter for flickering and feeling the boots for sequence of heating.

8883. Answer B. AC 65-12A

A propeller synchronization system provides a means of synchronizing engine rpm by varying the pitch of the propeller blades through a set of propeller governors (answer B). Answers (A) and (C) are incorrect because the operation of a propeller synchronization system is entirely automatic and requires no movement of the throttle levers or the propeller control levers.

8884. Answer B. AC 65-12A

Propeller fluid anti-icing systems typically use isopropyl alcohol because of its availability and low cost. Answer (A) is incorrect because ethylene glycol is typically used as a deicing fluid, not an anti-icing fluid. Answer (C) is wrong because ethyl alcohol is too expensive for use as an anti-icing agent.

8885. Answer B. AC 65-12A

A propeller sycnronization system provides a means of synchronizing engine rpm by varying the pitch of the propeller blades through the propeller governors. Synchronization reduces vibration and eliminates the annoying pulsating produced by unsynchronized propellers. Answer (A) is incorrect because, although it is desirable to keep propeller tip speeds below the speed of sound, this is accomplished by engine and propeller design, not the synchronization system. Answer (C) is wrong because propeller synchronizing systems do not control engine power.

8886. Answer A. AC 65-12A

Ice formations destroy a propeller's aerodynamic profile which, in turn, reduces thrust. Furthermore, the formation of ice can also cause an unbalanced condition that can induce excessive vibration. Answers (B) and (C) are incorrect because the formation of ice on a propeller has no effect on an aircraft's stall speed or available engine power.

8887. Answer B. AC 65-12A

A typical fluid anti-icing system consists of a tank to hold a supply of anti-icing fluid, a pump, and a control inside the cockpit. The control system typically consists of a rheostat that allows the pilot to control the pump output. Answers (A) and (C) are wrong because there is no pressure relief valve or cycling timer in most fluid anti-icing systems.

8888. Answer C. APC

About the only way to tell if an individual electric deicing boot is operating properly is to turn on the system and feel each boot in sequence while someone else watches the ammeter for proper sequencing (answer (C). Answer (A) is incorrect because it does not allow you to check the proper operating sequence, and answer (B) is wrong because a shorted heating element could give a false indication of proper operation.

8889.   R01

A propeller synchrophasing system allows a pilot to reduce noise and vibration by

A — adjusting the phase angle between the propellers on an aircraft's engines.
B — adjusting the plane of rotation of all propellers.
C — setting the pitch angle of all propellers exactly the same.

8890.   R02

Which of the following determines oil and grease specifications for lubrication of propellers?

A — Airframe manufacturers.
B — Engine manufacturers.
C — Propeller manufacturers.

8891.   R02

Grease used in aircraft propellers reduces the frictional resistance of moving parts and is easily molded into any form under pressure. This statement defines

A — antifriction and plasticity characteristics of grease.
B — antifriction and chemical stability of grease.
C — viscosity and melting point of grease.

8892.   R02

What type of imbalance will cause a two-blade propeller to have a persistent tendency to come to rest in a horizontal position (with the blades parallel to the ground) while being checked on a propeller balancing beam?

A — Vertical.
B — Horizontal.
C — Harmonic.

8889. Answer A. ITP-P2

Synchrophasing is a form of synchronization that allows the pilot to adjust the phase angle between the propellers to reduce propeller noise and vibration. With this type of system, a pulse generator is keyed to the same blade of each propeller. Each generator produces a signal that is compared to the signal emanating from the opposite generator. If the signals don't match, a signal is sent to the slave governor which establishes the phase angle selected by the pilot. Answer (B) is wrong because a propeller's plane of rotation is a fixed design feature and cannot be changed. Answer (C) is incorrect because, due to variations in engine power outputs and minor deviations in the ambient conditions around a propeller, equalizing propeller pitch angles would not necessarily reduce noise and vibration.

8890. Answer C. AC 65-12A

Propeller manufacturers are responsible for determining and publishing the oil and grease specifications as well as the proper lubrication procedures for the propellers they produce. Answers (A) and (B) are wrong because neither an airframe nor an engine manufacturer develops specifications for propellers.

8891. Answer A.

The reduction of frictional resistance refers to a lubricant's anti-friction characteristics, while the ease at which a lubricant is molded under pressure refers to a lubricant's plasticity characteristics. Answer (B) is incorrect because a lubricants ability to be easily molded does not refer to its chemical stability. Answer (C) is wrong because viscosity applies to fluids such as lubricating oils, not to grease.

8892. Answer A. AC 65-12A

When a propeller is placed in a vertical position on a balancing stand and it rotates to a horizontal position, it is said to be vertically imbalanced. Answer (B) is incorrect because if a propeller is horizontally imbalanced, the propeller rotates to a vertical position. Answer (C) is wrong because harmonic imbalance in a propeller blade is an uncorrectable vibration that is a function of blade design and is only apparent when the propeller is rotating.

8893.   R02
What is the purpose of an arbor used in balancing a propeller?

A — To support the propeller on the balance knives.
B — To level the balance stand.
C — To mark the propeller blades where weights are to be attached.

8893. Answer A. AC 65-12A
The basic components of a typical propeller static balance stand include the bushing, arbor, knife edges, and balancing stand. The bushings are placed in a propeller's engine shaft hole while the arbor is inserted through the bushings. The arbor is designed to support and permit free rotation of the propeller on the knife edges which rest on the balancing stand. Answer (B) is wrong because the balance stand is leveled by jackscrews on its base. Answer (C) is incorrect because blades are typically marked with a felt-tip marking pen, not the arbor.

8894.   R02
If a blade of a particular metal propeller is shortened because of damage to the tip, the remaining blade(s) must be

A — reset (blade angle) to compensate for the shortened blade.
B — returned to the manufacturer for alteration.
C — reduced to conform with the shortened blade.

8894. Answer C. AC 43.13-1A
All of the blades on a conventional propeller assembly must be precisely the same length, profile, and weight to prevent severe vibration. Therefore, if the shape or length of one blade is changed, the opposite blade must also be changed. Answer (A) is wrong because resetting blade angle will not compensate for one blade that is shorter and lighter than the other. Answer (B) is incorrect because propeller blades can be altered by any appropriately certified repair station.

8895.   R02
The application of more protective coating on one blade than the other when refinishing a wood propeller

A — has little or no effect on operating characteristics.
B — should never be done.
C — may be necessary to achieve final balancing.

8895. Answer C. AC 43.13-1A
Minor horizontal propeller imbalances on a wood propeller may be corrected by applying an additional protective coating to the light blade. Answer (A) is wrong because excess finish on one propeller blade can effect a propeller's operating characteristics. Answer (B) is incorrect because applying an additional protective coating to one blade is an acceptable means of achieving propeller balance.

8896.   R02
Apparent engine roughness is often a result of propeller unbalance. The effect of an unbalanced propeller will usually be

A — approximately the same at all speeds.
B — greater at low RPM.
C — greater at high RPM.

8896. Answer C. AC 65-12A
Centrifugal force increases as an object's rotational speed increases. As a result, vibration emanating from an unbalanced propeller increases with an increase in propeller rpm.

8897.   R02
Which of the following is used to correct horizontal unbalance of a wood propeller?

A — Brass screws.
B — Shellac.
C — Solder.

8897. Answer C. AC 43.13-1A
To correct a horizontal imbalance on a wooden propeller, a small amount of solder is melted onto the face side of the metal tip cap of the light blade and filed smooth. Brass screws (answer A) should not be attached to wood propellers unless recommended by the propeller manufacturer. Answer (B) is incorrect because shellac is typically not used on wooden propellers.

8898.   R03

Propeller aerodynamic (thrust) imbalance can be largely eliminated by

A — correct blade contouring and angle setting.
B — static balancing.
C — keeping the propeller blades within the same plane of rotation.

8899.   R04

A powerplant using a hydraulically controlled constant-speed propeller is operating within the propeller's constant-speed range at a fixed throttle setting. If the tension of the propeller governor control spring (speeder spring) is reduced by movement of the cockpit propeller control, the propeller blade angle will

A — increase, engine manifold pressure will increase, and engine RPM will decrease.
B — decrease, engine manifold pressure will increase, and engine RPM will decrease.
C — decrease, engine manifold pressure will decrease, and engine RPM will increase.

8900.   R04

Why is the pulley stop screw on a propeller governor adjustable?

A — To limit the maximum engine speed during takeoff.
B — To maintain the proper blade angle for cruising.
C — To limit the maximum propeller pitch for takeoff.

8901.   R04

During engine operation at speeds lower than those for which the constant-speed propeller control can govern in the INCREASE RPM position, the propeller will

A — remain in the full HIGH PITCH position.
B — maintain engine RPM in the normal manner until the HIGH PITCH stop is reached.
C — remain in the full LOW PITCH position.

8898. Answer A. AC 65-12A

Aerodynamic thrust imbalance results when one propeller blade produces more thrust then the other blade. This type of unbalance can largely be eliminated by making sure all propeller blades are contoured properly and that they all have the same blade angle setting. Answer (B) is wrong because static balancing procedures cannot detect incorrect blade contours or angle settings. Answer (C) is wrong because a propeller's plane of rotation is not adjustable.

8899. Answer A. AC 65-12A

On aircraft that utilize a constant-speed propeller, the pitch of the propeller blades is controlled by a governor consisting of an oil pump, pilot valve, speeder spring, and flyweights. When the propeller is in an on-speed condition, the centrifugal force exerted on the rotating flyweights is exactly balanced by the force exerted by the speeder spring and the propeller blade angle remains constant. If the speeder spring force is reduced through the use of the propeller control, the flyweights tilt outward into an over-speed position and the pilot valve allows oil to drain out of the propeller hub. This results in an increased blade angle, a reduction in rpm, and an increase in manifold pressure.

8900. Answer A. AC 65-12A

The pulley stop screw limits the amount of tension put on the governor speeder spring which, in turn, limits the maximum engine speed with full power applied. Answer (B) is wrong because the propeller governor maintains the proper blade angle in cruising flight, and answer (C) is incorrect because the pulley stop screw does not limit the maximum propeller pitch.

8901. Answer C. AC 65-12A

When an engine operates at speeds lower than those the governor can govern in the INCREASE RPM position, the propeller will remain in the full LOW PITCH position. This occurs because, at low engine speeds the governor senses an under-speed condition and directs oil to position the propeller blades in the low pitch position in an effort to reduce engine load and increase rpm. Answers (A) and (B) are incorrect because the governor moves the propeller blades to the HIGH PITCH position only when it senses an over-speed condition.

8902.   R04

When engine power is increased, the constant-speed propeller tries to function so that it will

A — maintain the RPM, decrease the blade angle, and maintain a low angle of attack.
B — increase the RPM, decrease the blade angle, and maintain a low angle of attack.
C — maintain the RPM, increase the blade angle, and maintain a low angle of attack.

8902. Answer C. AC 65-12A

When engine power is increased, the propeller governor senses an over-speed condition. In an over-speed condition, centrifugal force causes the governor flyweights to tip outward causing the pilot valve to allow oil to drain from the propeller hub. As the oil drains, the propeller blade angle increases so the selected rpm can be maintained (answer C). Answers (A) and (B) are incorrect because, when power is increased the governor must increase propeller blade angle to absorb the additional power output from the engine. Answer (B) is also wrong because the propeller governor will always try to maintain a constant rpm unless the prop lever position is changed.

8903.   R04

The propeller governor controls the

A — oil to and from the pitch changing mechanism.
B — spring tension on the boost pump speeder spring.
C — linkage and counterweights from moving in and out.

8903. Answer A. AC 65-12A

The propeller governor controls the flow of oil into and out of the pitch change mechanism in the propeller hub assembly. Answer (B) is incorrect because the prop control lever in the cockpit controls speeder spring tension. Answer (C) is wrong because a propeller governor does not control the in and out movement of the propeller linkage and counterweights.

8904.   R04

During the on-speed condition of a propeller, the

A — centrifugal force acting on the governor flyweights is greater than the tension of the speeder spring.
B — tension on the speeder spring is less than the centrifugal force acting on the governor flyweights.
C — centrifugal force of the governor flyweights is equal to the speeder spring force.

8904. Answer C. AC 65-12A

On aircraft that utilize a constant-speed propeller, the pitch of the propeller blades is controlled by a governor consisting of an oil pump, pilot valve, speeder spring, and flyweights. When the propeller is in an on-speed condition, the centrifugal force exerted on the rotating flyweights is exactly balanced by the force exerted by the speeder spring and the propeller blade angle remains constant. Answers (A) and (B) are incorrect because when speeder spring tension is less than the force of the governor flyweights, an over-speed condition exists.

8905.   R04

What actuates the pilot valve in the governor of a constant-speed propeller?

A — Engine oil pressure.
B — Governor flyweights.
C — Governor pump oil pressure.

8905. Answer B. AC 65-12A

The governor flyweights actuate the pilot valve in a constant-speed propeller governor. When the governor flyweights tilt outward, the pilot valve is raised and oil flows in to the propeller hub assembly. On the other hand, when the flyweights tilt inward, the pilot valve is lowered, and oil flows out of the propeller. Answers (A) and (C) are incorrect because neither governor pump oil pressure nor engine oil pressure actuate the pilot valve.

8906.   R04

What action takes place when the cockpit control lever for a hydromatic, constant-speed propeller is actuated?

A — Compression of the speeder spring is changed.
B — The governor booster pump pressure is varied.
C — The governor bypass valve is positioned to direct oil pressure to the propeller dome.

8907.   R04

What will happen to the propeller blade angle and the engine RPM if the tension on the propeller governor control spring (speeder spring) is increased?

A — Blade angle will decrease and RPM will decrease.
B — Blade angle will increase and RPM will decrease.
C — Blade angle will decrease and RPM will increase.

8908.   R04

How is the speed of a constant-speed propeller changed in flight?

A — By varying the output of the governor booster pump.
B — By advancing or retarding the throttle.
C — By changing the load tension against the flyweights in the governor.

8909.   R04

When the centrifugal force acting on the propeller governor flyweights overcomes the tension on the speeder spring, a propeller is in what speed condition?

A — On-speed.
B — Under-speed.
C — Over-speed.

8906. Answer A. AC 65-12A

The propeller control in the cockpit allows a pilot to change the propeller blade angle by adjusting the tension on the governor speeder spring. When spring tension is increased, the propeller blade angle decreases and when spring tension is decreased the blade angle increases. Answer (B) is incorrect because the output pressure of the governor boost pump is driven by the engine and changes with engine speed. Answer (C) is wrong because the governor pilot valve, not a bypass valve, directs oil to the propeller dome.

8907. Answer C. AC 65-12A

When the propeller control in the cockpit is moved forward, governor speeder spring tension increases and causes the governor flyweights to tilt inward. This causes the pilot valve to lower and port oil in the direction necessary to decrease the propeller blade angle and increase rpm (answer C). Answer (A) is wrong because when the propeller blade angle decreases, rpm increases, and answer (B) is wrong because an increase in spring tension results in a decrease in the propeller blade angle, not an increase.

8908. Answer C. AC 65-12A

To change the rotational speed of a constant-speed propeller in flight, the pilot adjusts the prop lever which varies the spring tension on the governor speeder spring. Moving the prop control forward increases spring tension which tilts the governor flyweights inward and lowers the pilot valve. On the other hand, moving the prop control aft decreases spring tension which allows the flyweights to tilt outward and raise the pilot valve. Answer (A) is wrong because governor boost pump output remains relatively constant in flight. Answer (B) is incorrect because small changes in throttle settings only changes an engine's power output, not its rpm.

8909. Answer C. AC 65-12A

An over-speed condition exists when an engine turns at a faster rpm than that selected. When this occurs, centrifugal force causes the governor flyweights to overcome the speeder spring tension and raise the pilot valve. This ports oil to the propeller dome which increases a propeller's blade angle. Answer (A) is wrong because in an on-speed condition, the tension on the speeder spring exactly balances the centrifugal force of the flyweights. Answer (B) is incorrect because the tension on the speeder spring overcomes the centrifugal force of the flyweights in an under-speed condition.

8910.   R04

What operational force causes the greatest stress on a propeller?

A — Aerodynamic twisting force.
B — Centrifugal force.
C — Thrust bending force.

8911.   R04

What operational force tends to increase propeller blade angle?

A — Centrifugal twisting force.
B — Aerodynamic twisting force.
C — Thrust bending force.

8912.   R05

How is a propeller controlled in a large aircraft with a turboprop installation?

A — Independently of the engine.
B — By varying the engine RPM except for feathering and reversing.
C — By the engine power lever.

8913.   R05

How does the aerodynamic twisting force affect operating propeller blades?

A — It tends to turn the blades to a high blade angle.
B — It tends to bend the blades forward.
C — It tends to turn the blades to a low blade angle.

8914.   R05

Which of the following best describes the blade movement of a propeller that is in the high RPM position when reversing action is begun?

A — Low pitch directly to reverse pitch.
B — Low pitch through high pitch to reverse pitch.
C — Low pitch through feather position to reverse pitch.

8910. Answer B. AC 65-12A

The greatest stress on a propeller is the centrifugal force created by the propeller's rotation. Depending on a blade's weight and rpm, centrifugal force can be greater than 25 tons. Both answers (A) and (C) are wrong because both aerodynamic twisting force and thrust bending force create substantially less stress on the propeller than centrifugal force.

8911. Answer B. AC 65-12A

A propeller blade is an airfoil and is subject to the same aerodynamic forces as any other airfoil. On all propeller blades, the center of lift, or center of pressure, is forward of the blade's center of rotation. Therefore, when a propeller blade is producing lift (thrust), the blade tends to rotate to a higher angle. This is called aerodynamic twisting force. Answer (A) is wrong because centrifugal twisting force tends to decrease propeller blade angle, and answer (C) is incorrect because thrust bending force does not affect a propeller's blade angle.

8912. Answer C. AC 65-12A

On turboprop engines, the fuel control unit and propeller governor are interconnected. Therefore, in flight, when a pilot moves the power lever, the fuel control and governor establish the correct combination of rpm, fuel flow, and propeller blade angle to provide the desired power output. Answer (A) is wrong because no constant speed propeller operates independently of the engine. Answer (B) is incorrect because, in flight, engine rpm is controlled automatically by the propeller governor.

8913. Answer A. AC 65-12A

A propeller blade is an airfoil and is subject to the same aerodynamic forces as any other airfoil. On all propeller blades, the center of lift, or center of pressure, is forward of the blade's center of rotation. Therefore, when a propeller blade is producing lift (thrust), the blade tends to rotate to a higher angle. This is called aerodynamic twisting force. Answer (B) is incorrect because thrust bending force tends to bend the propeller blades forward. Answer (C) is wrong because centrifugal twisting force tends to turn the blades to a low angle.

8914. Answer A. AC 65-12A

When a propeller control is in a high rpm position, there is a relatively low pitch on the propeller blades. When a propeller moves to reverse pitch, the blades rotate through the low blade angle and into a negative blade angle. Therefore, if a propeller blade is in a low pitch position when reverse pitch is selected, the blades will move directly to the reverse pitch position. Answers (B) and (C) are incorrect because the propeller does not go into high pitch or feather before it reverses.

8915. R05

Propellers exposed to salt spray should be cleaned with

A — steel wool.
B — fresh water.
C — soapy water.

8915. Answer B. AC 65-12A

If a propeller has been exposed to salt water, it should be flushed with fresh water until all traces of salt have been removed. This should be accomplished as soon as possible after the salt water has been splashed on a propeller. After flushing, all parts should be dried thoroughly. Answer (A) is wrong because steel wool can damage a propeller's protective finish and could cause dissimilar metal corrosion if used on an aluminum prop. Although soapy water (answer C) is used to clean propellers, a thorough rinsing with fresh water is the preferred method of treating a propeller that has been exposed to salt water.

8916. R05

How can a steel propeller hub be tested for cracks?

A — By anodizing.
B — By magnetic particle inspection.
C — By etching.

8916. Answer B. AC 65-12A

Of the choices given, magnetic particle inspection is the preferred method for inspecting a steel propeller hub for cracks. Answer (A) is wrong because anodizing is a method of surface treatment of aluminum alloys and is not used to detect cracks. Answer (C) is wrong because acid etching is an obsolete inspection method used on aluminum propeller blades.

8917. R05

Which of the following functions requires the use of a propeller blade station?

A — Measuring blade angle.
B — Indexing blades.
C — Propeller balancing.

8917. Answer A. AC 65-12A

When measuring a propeller's blade angle, a reference blade angle measuring station is always specified by the propeller manufacturer. Therefore, you must be familiar with and use a propeller blade station to measure a propeller's blade angle. Answer (B) is wrong because indexing refers to the process of aligning the counterweight brackets on some propellers and does not make use of blade stations. Answer (C) is incorrect because neither dynamic nor static propeller balancing methods require the use of blade stations.

8918. R05

The propeller blade angle is defined as the acute angle between the airfoil section chord line (at the blade reference station) and which of the following?

A — The plane of rotation.
B — The relative wind.
C — The axis of blade rotation during pitch change.

8918. Answer A. AC 65-12A

The propeller blade angle is the acute angle between the airfoil section chord line at the proper reference station and the propeller's rotational plane. The reference station is typically at a point approximately 75 percent of the distance from the hub to the tip. Answer (B) is wrong because the angle formed between the relative wind and the blade chord line is called angle of attack. Answer (C) is incorrect because the axis of blade rotation is the same as the axis of the crankshaft rotation and is not related to a propeller's blade angle.

8919. R05

During which of the following conditions of flight will the blade pitch angle of a constant-speed propeller be the greatest?

A — Approach to landing.
B — Climb following takeoff.
C — High-speed, high-altitude cruising flight.

8919. Answer C. AC 65-12A

To obtain the maximum amount of engine power during takeoff and climb a low propeller blade angle is used. However, during high-speed, high-altitude cruising flight, less engine power is needed and, therefore, the propeller blade angle is typically greater. Answer (A) is incorrect because on approach to landing, a low propeller blade angle is used so the engine can produce maximum power in the event a go-around or missed approach is required. Answer (B) is wrong because a relatively low blade pitch is used during a climb.

8920.   R05

The actual distance a propeller moves forward through the air during one revolution is known as the

A — effective pitch.
B — geometric pitch.
C — relative pitch.

8921.   R05

The pitch-changing mechanism of the hydromatic propeller is lubricated by

A — the pitch-changing oil.
B — using an approved-type grease in a grease gun at intervals prescribed by the propeller manufacturer.
C — thoroughly greasing, necessary only during propeller overhaul.

8922.   R05

What is the result of moving the throttle on a reciprocating engine when the propeller is in the constant-speed range with the engine developing cruise power?

A — Opening the throttle will cause an increase in blade angle.
B — The RPM will vary directly with any movement of the throttle.
C — Movement of the throttle will not affect the blade angle.

8923.   R05

Propeller blade stations are measured from the

A — index mark on the blade shank.
B — hub centerline.
C — blade base.

8924.   R05

The thrust produced by a rotating propeller is a result of

A — an area of low pressure behind the propeller blades.
B — an area of decreased pressure immediately in front of the propeller blades.
C — the angle of relative wind and rotational velocity of the propeller.

8920. Answer A. AC 65-12A

Effective pitch is the actual distance a propeller moves through the air in one revolution. Answer (B) is incorrect because geometric pitch represents the theoretical distance a propeller should move through the air in one revolution. Relative pitch (answer C) is not a commonly used term in aircraft maintenance.

8921. Answer A. AC 65-12A

The same oil that is used to change the pitch of a propeller blade is also used to lubricate the pitch-changing mechanism on a hydromatic propeller. No greases or other lubrication are required for the pitch-change mechanism.

8922. Answer A. AC 65-12A

When the throttle is opened on an engine which has a constant-speed propeller operating in the constant-speed range, the propeller governor increases the blade angle to absorb the additional engine power and maintain the desired rpm. Answers (B) and (C) are incorrect because throttle movement will cause the propeller governor to change the propeller blade angle to maintain a constant rpm.

8923. Answer B. AC 65-12A

Propeller blade stations are measured from the hub centerline. Each blade has its own set of stations starting from station zero at the hub centerline and increasing out to the blade tip.

8924. Answer B. AC 65-12A

A propeller is a rotating airfoil and creates thrust the same way an airplane's wing creates lift. When the propeller rotates, an area of decreased pressure forms in front of the propeller blade, while an area of constant or higher pressure forms in back of the propeller. The pressure differential between the front and back of the propeller is the source of thrust.

8925.   R05

Why is a constant-speed counterweight propeller normally placed in full HIGH PITCH position before the engine is stopped?

A — To prevent exposure and corrosion of the pitch changing mechanism.

B — To prevent hydraulic lock of the piston when the oil cools.

C — To prevent overheating of the engine during the next start.

8925. Answer A. AC 65-12A

Some constant-speed counterweight propellers use an exposed actuating piston to change the pitch of the propeller blade. Therefore, when shutting down an engine equipped with this type of propeller, the propeller should be placed in the full HIGH PITCH position so that the actuating piston is covered and somewhat protected from corrosion causing moisture by the propeller hub. Answer (B) is incorrect because the oil in the propeller hub does not cause hydraulic lock. Answer (C) is wrong because the propeller blade angle has little to do with a reciprocating engine overheating when started.

8926.   R05

The low pitch stop on a constant-speed propeller is usually set so that

A — the engine will turn at its rated takeoff RPM at sea level when the throttle is opened to allowable takeoff manifold pressure.

B — maximum allowable engine RPM cannot be exceeded with any combination of manifold pressure, altitude, or forward speed.

C — the limiting engine manifold pressure cannot be exceeded with any combination of throttle opening, altitude, or forward speed.

8926. Answer A. FAR 23.33

The low pitch stop on a constant-speed propeller is set so that the engine can develop its rated power at sea level at the rpm specified by the propeller manufacturer. If the low pitch stop is improperly set, the engine could fail to attain rated power. Answer (B) is wrong because, the low pitch stop will not prevent an overspeed condition, and answer (C) is incorrect because, although the propeller setting can limit maximum rpm, it has no effect on an engine's manifold pressure.

8927.   R05

The angle-of-attack of a rotating propeller blade is measured between the blade chord or face and which of the following?

A — Plane of blade rotation.

B — Full low-pitch blade angle.

C — Relative airstream.

8927. Answer C. AC 65-12A

Propeller angle of attack is the acute angle between the blade chord and the relative wind. Answer (A) is wrong because blade angle, not angle of attack, is the angle between the blade chord and plane of rotation. Answer (B) is incorrect because full low-pitch blade angle is not the same as the relative airstream.

8928.   R05

The centrifugal twisting moment of an operating propeller tends to

A — increase the pitch angle.

B — reduce the pitch angle.

C — bend the blades in the direction of rotation.

8928. Answer B. AC 65-12A

When an object rotates, its center of mass tends to align with its center of rotation. A propeller's center of mass is typically ahead of its center of rotation. Therefore, when a propeller rotates, centrifugal force tries to pull the propeller's center of mass in line with its center of rotation thereby decreasing the propeller's pitch angle. Answer (A) is incorrect because aerodynamic twisting force tends to increase the pitch angle of rotating propeller blades. Answer (C) is incorrect because there is no force that bends propeller blades in the direction of rotation.

8929.   R05

Which of the following is identified as the cambered or curved side of a propeller blade, corresponding to the upper surface of a wing airfoil section?

A — Blade back.

B — Blade chord.

C — Blade face.

8929. Answer A. AC 65-12A

The curved, or cambered side of a propeller blade is called the blade back and the flat side is called the blade face. Answer (B) is incorrect because blade chord is an imaginary line that connects a blade's leading edge to its trailing edge. Answer (C) is wrong because the flat side of the blade is called the blade face.

8930.   R05

Which of the following best describes the blade movement of a full-feathering, constant-speed propeller that is in the LOW RPM position when the feathering action is begun?

A — High pitch through low pitch to feather position.
B — High pitch directly to feather position.
C — Low pitch through high pitch to feather position.

8931.   R05

The holding coil on a hydromatic propeller feathering button switch holds a solenoid relay closed that applies power to the propeller

A — governor.
B — dome feathering mechanism.
C — feathering pump motor.

8932.   R05

What is the primary purpose of the metal tipping which covers the blade tips and extends along the leading edge of each wood propeller blade?

A — To increase the lateral strength of the blade.
B — To prevent impact damage to the tip and leading edge of the blade.
C — To increase the longitudinal strength of the blade.

8933.   R05

Blade angle is an angle formed by a line perpendicular to the crankshaft and a line formed by the

A — relative wind.
B — chord of the blade.
C — blade face.

8934.   R05

Propeller blade station numbers increase from

A — hub to tip.
B — tip to hub.
C — leading edge to trailing edge.

8935.   R05

The aerodynamic force acting on a rotating propeller blade operating at a normal pitch angle tends to

A — reduce the pitch angle.
B — increase the pitch angle.
C — bend the blades rearward in the line of flight.

8930. Answer B. AC 65-12A

When a propeller is set in the LOW RPM position, the blade pitch is high. Therefore, when feathering is begun, the propeller blades move directly from high pitch into the feather position. Answer (A) is wrong because the propeller blades do not move into low pitch before going to the feather position. Answer (C) is incorrect because in the LOW RPM position, the propeller blades are already in the high pitch position.

8931. Answer C. AC 65-12A

The holding coil on a feathering propeller keeps the feathering button in the depressed position and provides current to the propeller feathering pump motor. Answers (A) and (B) are incorrect because neither a hydromatic propeller governor nor the propeller dome feathering mechanism is electrically powered and, therefore, do not utilize a holding coil.

8932. Answer B. AC 65-12A

Metal tipping is applied to the leading edge and tip of wood propeller blades to prevent damage from small stones or debris which might strike the prop during ground operations. This tipping is attached to the blade with countersunk screws in the thick blade sections and with copper rivets in the thin sections. Answers (A) and (C) are incorrect because the metal tipping is installed for abrasion resistance and provides no lateral or longitudinal strength to the blade.

8933. Answer B. AC 65-12A

Blade angle is the acute angle formed by a line perpendicular to the crankshaft centerline and the chord of the blade at a specified reference station.

8934. Answer A. AC 65-12A

Propeller blade stations are measured from the hub centerline. Each blade has its own set of stations starting from station zero at the hub centerline and increasing out to the blade tip.

8935. Answer B. AC 65-12A

A propeller blade is an airfoil and is subject to the same aerodynamic forces as any other airfoil. On all propeller blades, the center of lift, or center of pressure, is forward of the blade's center of rotation. Therefore, when a propeller blade is producing lift (thrust), the blade tends to rotate to a higher angle. This is called aerodynamic twisting force. Answer (A) is wrong because aerodynamic twisting force tends to rotate the propeller blade to a higher pitch angle, not a low pitch angle. Answer (C) is incorrect because there is no aerodynamic force that bends propeller blades rearward in the line of flight.

8936. R05

Which of the following forces or combination of forces operates to move the blades of a constant-speed counterweight-type propeller to the HIGH PITCH position?

A — Engine oil pressure acting on the propeller piston-cylinder arrangement and centrifugal force acting on the counterweights.
B — Centrifugal force acting on the counterweights.
C — Prop governor oil pressure acting on the propeller piston-cylinder arrangement.

8937. R05

The purpose of permanently sealing and partially filling some models of McCauley propeller hubs with dyed oil is to

A — provide an always clean separate lubrication of the internal parts.
B — dampen pressure surges and prevent too rapid changes in propeller blade angle.
C — make the location of cracks readily apparent.

8938. R05

Which of the following best describes the blade movement of a feathering propeller that is in the HIGH RPM position when the feathering action is begun?

A — High pitch through low pitch to feather position.
B — Low pitch through reverse pitch to feather position.
C — Low pitch through high pitch to feather position.

8939. R05

The blade angle of a fixed-pitch propeller

A — is greatest at the tip.
B — is smallest at the tip.
C — increases in proportion to the distance each section is from the hub.

8936. Answer B. AC 65-12A

With counterweight-type propellers, centrifugal force acting on a set of counterweights tends to rotate the blades to a high pitch angle. Answers (A) and (C) are incorrect because oil pressure acting on the propeller piston-cylinder arrangement tends to drive the propeller blades to the LOW PITCH position.

8937. Answer C. ITP-P2

Some models of McCauley propellers use dyed oil to aid in the detection of cracks. The propeller hub is permanently sealed and partially filled with red-dyed oil. If red dye appears on the hub or blades, some component in the hub has failed and the propeller should be removed and serviced. Answer (A) is wrong because the primary purpose of dyed oil is to aid in crack detection, not to maintain a separate lubrication source. Answer (B) is incorrect because smooth operation of the propeller pitch changing mechanism is accomplished by the propeller governor and the propeller hub.

8938. Answer C. AC 65-12A

When a propeller is set in the HIGH RPM position, the blade pitch is low. Therefore, when the feathering action begins, the blades must rotate from low pitch through high pitch and then to the feather position. Answer (A) is wrong because in the HIGH RPM position, the propeller blade pitch is low, not high. Answer (B) is wrong because the propeller does not go through reverse pitch before reaching the feather position.

8939. Answer B. AC 65-12A

A propeller's blade angle decreases from the hub to the tip. This is necessary because the further a blade station is from the hub, the faster the airfoil moves through the air. Therefore, in order to maintain a relatively equal amount of thrust along the entire blade length, the blade angle must decrease from the hub to the tip. Answer (A) is incorrect because blade angle is greatest at the hub, not the tip. Answer (C) is wrong because blade angle decreases from the hub to the tip.

8940.   R05

During operational check of an aircraft using hydromatic full-feathering propellers, the following observations are made: The feather button, after being pushed, remains depressed until the feather cycle is complete, then opens. When unfeathering, it is necessary to manually hold the button down until unfeathering is accomplished.

A — Both feather cycle and unfeather cycle are functioning properly.
B — Both feather and unfeather cycles indicate malfunctions.
C — The feather cycle is correct. The unfeather cycle indicates a malfunction.

8941.   R05

Inspection of propeller blades by dye-penetrant inspection is accomplished to detect

A — cracks or other defects.
B — corrosion at the blade tip.
C — torsional stress.

8942.   R05

What controls the constant-speed range of a constant-speed propeller?

A — Engine RPM.
B — Angle of climb and descent with accompanying changes in airspeed.
C — The mechanical limits in the propeller pitch range.

8943.   R05

For takeoff, a constant-speed propeller is normally set in the

A — HIGH PITCH, high RPM position.
B — HIGH PITCH, low RPM position.
C — LOW PITCH, high RPM position.

8944.   R05

Where are the high and low pitch stops of a Hamilton Standard constant-speed or two-position counterweight propeller located?

A — In the hub and blade assembly.
B — In the counterweight assembly.
C — In the dome assembly.

8940. Answer A. AC 65-12A

When the feather button is pushed in a normally functioning full-feathering hydromatic propeller system, a holding coil keeps the button in the depressed position until the feather cycle is completed. Furthermore, when unfeathering, the feathering button must be held manually until the propeller blades unfeather and reach low pitch. Both answers (B) and (C) are wrong because no malfunction is indicated. Both answers (B) and (C) are wrong because no malfunction is indicated.

8941. Answer A. AC 43.13-1A

Dye-penetrant inspection is normally used to detect cracks or other defects that are open to the surface. Answer (B) is wrong because corrosion at the blade tip is typically visible and does not require dye penetrant while answer (C) is wrong because dye penetrant cannot detect torsional stresses.

8942. Answer C. AC 65-12A

Mechanical stops in the propeller hub limit the constant-speed range of a constant-speed propeller. Both answers (A) and (B) are incorrect because neither engine rpm nor changes in airspeed dictate the range of propeller pitch control.

8943. Answer C. AC 65-12A

To allow an engine to develop its rated takeoff power, a constant-speed propeller is normally set in the low pitch, high rpm position. This places the lightest load on the engine, allowing it to develop maximum power. Answer (A) is incorrect because, in the high RPM position the propeller blades are set at a low pitch, not a high pitch. Answer (B) is wrong because a HIGH PITCH, low rpm setting is typically used in cruise flight when full power is not needed.

8944. Answer B.

The high and low pitch stops of Hamilton Standard propellers are located in the counterweight assembly. However, in some of the more modern constant-speed propeller assemblies, the pitch stops are located in the dome assembly.

8945. R05

Which of the following statements about constant-speed counterweight propellers is also true when referring to two-position counterweight propellers?

A — Blade angle changes are accomplished by the use of two forces, one hydraulic and the other centrifugal.
B — Since an infinite number of blade angle positions are possible during flight, propeller efficiency is greatly improved.
C — The pilot selects the RPM and the propeller changes pitch to maintain the selected RPM.

8946. R05

Most engine-propeller combinations have one or more critical ranges within which continuous operation is not permitted. Critical ranges are established to avoid

A — severe propeller vibration.
B — low or negative thrust conditions.
C — inefficient propeller pitch angles.

8947. R05

Which of the following defects is cause for rejection of wood propellers?

A — Solder missing from screw heads securing metal tipping.
B — An oversize hub or bolthole, or elongated boltholes.
C — No protective coating on propeller.

8948. R05

An aircraft's propeller system beta range

A — is used to produce zero or negative thrust.
B — is used to achieve maximum thrust during take-off.
C — refers to the most fuel efficient pitch range to use at a given engine RPM.

8945. Answer A. AC 65-12A

The two-position and the constant-speed counterweight propellers both use hydraulic force to decrease blade angle and centrifugal force acting on counterweights to increase blade angle (answer A). The major difference between the two is that the constant-speed propeller utilizes a governor to boost the oil pressure to a higher level and automatically control the oil flow to and from the propeller, while the two-position propeller operates at engine lubrication system pressure with the oil flow controlled by a manual selector valve. Answer (B) is wrong because a two-position propeller does not have an infinite number of positions. Answer (C) is incorrect because, with a two-speed propeller, the pilot can only select a blade angle, not a specific rpm.

8946. Answer A. ITP-P2

Propellers are subject to aerodynamic vibrations when the blade tips travel at near sonic speeds. In addition, mechanical vibrations are transmitted from the engine to the propeller. At certain combinations of airspeed and engine rpm these vibrations can create harmonic stresses that could lead to metal fatigue and eventual propeller blade failure. Therefore, the Type Certificate Data Sheets for engine/propeller combinations identify any critical rpm ranges that are to be avoided to prevent severe vibration. Regulations require that these ranges be marked on the tachometer with a red arc. Answer (B) is incorrect because low or negative thrust conditions are part of normal propeller operation. Answer (C) is wrong because inefficient pitch angles do not jeopardize safety and, therefore, are not indicated.

8947. Answer B. AC 43.13-1A

Oversize or elongated bolt holes on a wooden propeller are typically cause for rejection. However, some oversize or worn bolt holes may be repaired by the use of metal inserts to restore the original diameter. This is a major repair and must be performed by a certificated repair station. Answers (A) and (C) describe defects that are considered minor and, therefore, are not cause for rejection.

8948. Answer A. AC 65-12A

Beta range refers to a reversing-type propeller that can operate in a zero or negative thrust range. During operation in beta range, propeller governor operation is locked out and all propeller control is accomplished with the power lever. Answer (B) is wrong because beta range produces zero or negative thrust, not maximum takeoff thrust, and answer (C) is wrong because there is no term that is commonly used to describe a propeller's most fuel efficient pitch range.

8949.   R05

The primary purpose of a cuff on a propeller is to

A — distribute anti-icing fluid.
B — strengthen the propeller.
C — increase the flow of cooling air to the engine nacelle.

8950.   R05

The purpose of a three-way propeller valve is to

A — direct oil from the engine oil system to the propeller cylinder.
B — direct oil from the engine through the govemor to the propeller.
C — permit constant-speed operation of the propeller.

8951.   R05

The primary purpose of a propeller is to

A — create lift on the fixed airfoils of an aircraft.
B — change engine horsepower to thrust.
C — provide static and dynamic stability of an aircraft in flight.

8952.   R05

A constant-speed propeller provides maximum efficiency by

A — increasing blade pitch as the aircraft speed decreases.
B — adjusting blade angle for most conditions encountered in flight.
C — increasing the lift coefficient of the blade.

8953.   R05

The centrifugal twisting force acting on a propeller blade is

A — greater than the aerodynamic twisting force and tends to move the blade to a higher angle.
B — less than the aerodynamic twisting force and tends to move the blade to a lower angle.
C — greater than the aerodynamic twisting force and tends to move the blade to a lower angle.

8949. Answer C. AC 65-12A

A blade cuff is a metal, wood, or plastic structure that is attaches to the shank of a propeller blade. The cuff surface transforms the round shank into an airfoil section and is designed primarily to increase the flow of cooling air to the engine nacelle. Answer (A) is wrong because a slinger ring distributes anti-icing fluid on propellers, and answer (B) is incorrect because blade cuffs are not structural parts and provide no strength to the propeller blades.

8950. Answer A. DSA-25

A three-way propeller valve is a selector valve used in a two-position propeller control system. The three-way valve directs oil from the engine lubrication system to the propeller to control a propeller blade's pitch angle. Answer (B) is wrong because a three-way propeller valve is not used on propellers that use a governor, and answer (C) is incorrect because a three-way valve does not permit constant-speed operation.

8951. Answer B. AC 65-12A

The primary purpose of a propeller is to convert engine horsepower to useful thrust. Modern propellers can convert up to 85 percent of an engine's brake horsepower to thrust horsepower. Answer (A) is wrong because, although the prop wash coming off a propeller can produce some lift on the fixed airfoils, it is not the primary purpose of a propeller. Answer (C) is incorrect because propellers provide neither static nor dynamic stability to an aircraft in flight.

8952. Answer B. AC 65-12A

A constant-speed propeller achieves maximum efficiency by allowing the pilot to adjust the propeller blade angle as necessary to produce the most efficient blade angle for most conditions encountered in flight. Answer (A) is incorrect because increasing blade pitch is just one way a constant-speed propeller provides maximum efficiency. Answer (C) is wrong because the coefficient on a constant-speed propeller is no greater than that of a fixed pitch propeller.

8953. Answer C. AC 65-12A

The centrifugal twisting force, sometimes called centrifugal twisting moment, acting on a propeller is greater than the aerodynamic twisting force and tries to decrease a propeller's blade angle. Answer (A) is incorrect because centrifugal twisting force tends to move the propeller blade to a lower angle, not a higher angle, and answer (B) is wrong because centrifugal twisting force is greater than aerodynamic twisting force.

8954.   R05

Geometric pitch of a propeller is defined as the

A — effective pitch minus slippage.
B — effective pitch plus slippage.
C — angle between the blade chord and the plane of
        rotation.

8954. Answer B. AC 65-12A

A propeller's geometric pitch is the theoretical distance that the propeller will move forward in one revolution. Effective pitch, on the other hand, is the actual distance that the propeller moves forward in one revolution. The difference between geometric pitch and effective pitch is called slippage. Therefore, effective pitch plus slippage is equal to geometric pitch (answer B).

8955.   R05

Propeller blade angle is the angle between the

A — chord of the blade and the relative wind.
B — relative wind and the rotational plane of the propeller.
C — chord of the blade and the rotational plane of the
        propeller.

8955. Answer C. AC 65-12A

Propeller blade angle is the acute angle formed by the propeller blade chord line and the rotational plane of the propeller. Answer (A) is wrong because the angle between the blade chord and the relative wind is called the angle of attack. Answer (B) is wrong because the angle between the relative wind and the propeller's rotational plane is not a factor in propeller operation.

8956.   R05

What operational force causes propeller blade tips to lag in the opposite direction of rotation?

A — Thrust-bending force.
B — Aerodynamic-twisting force.
C — Torque-bending force.

8956. Answer C. AC 65-12A

Torque bending force, in the form of air resistance, tends to bend cause a propeller's tips to lag in the direction of rotation. Answer (A) is wrong because thrust-bending force tends to pull the blade tips forward as the propeller pulls the aircraft through the air. Answer (B) is incorrect because aerodynamic-twisting force tends to turn the propeller blades to a higher blade angle.

8957.   R05

What operational force tends to bend the propeller blades forward at the tip?

A — Torque-bending force.
B — Centrifugal-twisting force.
C — Thrust-bending force.

8957. Answer C. AC 65-12A

Thrust bending force tends to bend the propeller tips forward as the propeller pulls an aircraft through the air. This force is comparable to the coning action of a helicopter rotor blade, except that the thrust bending force acts forward instead of upward. Answer (A) is wrong because torque bending force, in the form of air resistance, tends to cause the propeller tips to lag in the opposite direction of rotation. Answer (B) is incorrect because centrifugal-twisting force tries to force the propeller blades to a lower blade angle.

8958.   R05

What are the rotational speed and blade pitch angle requirements of a constant-speed propeller during take-off?

A — Low-speed and high-pitch angle.
B — High-speed and low-pitch angle.
C — High-speed and high-pitch angle.

8958. Answer B. AC 65-12A

During takeoff, a constant-speed propeller is set for high speed and a low pitch angle so the engine can develop its maximum rated power. Cruising flight, on the other hand, does not require maximum power so the propeller can be set for low speed and a high pitch angle (answer A). Answer (C) is wrong because most reciprocating engines cannot develop high speed with a high pitch angle.

8959.   R05
(1) A mechanic certificate with a powerplant rating authorizes the holder to repair deep scars, nicks, and dents on aluminum propeller blades.
(2) A mechanic certificate with a powerplant rating authorizes the holder to perform minor straightening of steel propeller blades.

Regarding the above statements,

A — only No.1 is true.
B — both No.1 and No.2 are true.
C — neither No.1 nor No.2 is true.

8960.   R05
(1) During takeoff, propeller thrust (pull) is greatest if the blade angle of attack is low and the engine power setting is high.
(2) With the aircraft stationary, propeller thrust is greatest if the blade angle of attack is high and the engine power setting is high.

Regarding the above statements,

A — only No.1 is true.
B — only No.2 is true.
C — both No.1 and No.2 are true.

8961.   R05
Longitudinal (fore and aft) clearance of constant-speed propeller blades or cuffs must be at least 1/2 inch (12.7 mm) between propeller parts and stationary parts of the aircraft. This clearance is with the propeller blades

A — at takeoff pitch (maximum thrust) angle.
B — feathered or in the most critical pitch configuration.
C — at the lowest pitch angle.

8962.   R05
Constant-speed non-feathering McCauley, Hartzell, and other propellers of similar design without counterweights increase pitch angle using

A — oil pressure.
B — spring pressure.
C — centrifugal twisting moment.

8963.   R05
Counterweights on constant-speed propellers are generally used to aid in

A — increasing blade angle.
B — decreasing blade angle.
C — unfeathering the propellers.

8959. Answer C. FAR 65.81
Neither statement (1) nor (2) is correct. A certificated mechanic may perform minor repairs or alterations to propeller blades. Deep scars, nicks, and dents on aluminum propeller blades and the straightening of propeller blades are major repairs. These repairs may be performed by a properly certificated repair station or the propeller manufacturer.

8960. Answer A. AC 65-12A
Only statement (1) is correct. During takeoff, when maximum power and thrust are required, the propeller blades are set to a low blade angle that allows the engine to turn at a high rpm.

8961. Answer B. FAR 23.925
Federal Aviation Regulations require that the longitudinal clearance between the propeller blades or cuffs and stationary parts of the airplane be at least one-half inch measured with the propeller in the most adverse pitch position. Since the most adverse pitch position typically occurs with a high blade angle, answers (A) and (C) are incorrect.

8962. Answer A. AC 65-12A
Most non-counterweight propellers use oil pressure to increase the propeller's blade angle. Answer (B) is incorrect because spring pressure is typically used to decrease a propeller's blade angle. Answer (C) is wrong because centrifugal twisting moment tends to move the propeller blades into low pitch, not high pitch.

8963. Answer A. AC 65-12A
On constant-speed propellers equipped with counterweights, centrifugal force acting on the counterweights is used to increase a propeller's blade angle. Answer (B) is wrong because the centrifugal force acting on counterweights tends to move the counterweights into the plane of rotation and increase a blade's pitch. Answer (C) is incorrect because unfeathering is typically accomplished by a spring or nitrogen charge.

8964.   R05

When lubricating a Hartzell propeller blade with grease, to prevent damage to the blade seals, the service manual may recommend on some models to

A — pump grease into both zerk fittings for the blade simultaneously.
B — remove the seals prior to greasing and reinstall them afterwards.
C — remove one of the two zerk fittings for the blade and grease the blade through the remaining fitting.

8965.   R05

The primary purpose of a feathering propeller is to

A — prevent further engine damage when an engine fails in flight.
B — prevent propeller damage when an engine fails in flight.
C — eliminate the drag created by a windmilling propeller when an engine fails in flight.

8966.   R06

What normally prevents a Hartzell Compact propeller from going to feather when the engine is shut down on the ground?

A — Propeller cylinder air pressure.
B — A latch mechanism composed of springs and lock pins.
C — Accumulator provided oil pressure.

8967.   R06

When running-up an engine and testing a newly installed hydromatic propeller, it is necessary to exercise the propeller by moving the governor control through its entire travel several times to

A — seat the blades fully against the low pitch stop.
B — free the dome of any entrapped air.
C — test the maximum RPM setting of the governor.

8964. Answer C. ITP-P2

Hartzell propellers have two grease fittings (zerks) on their hubs. When lubricating these propellers, one zerk should be removed while grease is pumped into the other zerk. This prevents pressure buildup in the grease chamber and helps avoid damaging the blade seals. Answer (A) is wrong because servicing both zerk fittings simultaneously could damage the propeller blade seals. Answer (B) is incorrect because removing the seals prior to greasing would require removal and disassembly of the propeller.

8965. Answer C. AC 65-12A

When an engine is shut down in flight, the propeller blades create a substantial amount of drag which decreases aircraft performance. Feathering propellers eliminate this drag by driving the propeller blades to a 90 degree angle. Although feathering a propeller prevents it from windmilling and causing further engine damage (answer A), the primary purpose of feathering is to eliminate drag. Answer (B) is wrong because propellers are typically not damaged when an engine fails in flight.

8966. Answer B. AC 65-12A

Hartzell Compact propellers utilize a latch stop called the automatic high pitch stop to hold the blades in a low angle when the engine is shut down on the ground. The latch mechanism is comprised of springs and lock pins that prevent the propellers from feathering once engine rpm falls below a predetermined value. Answer (A) is wrong because propeller cylinder air pressure is typically used to unfeather a propeller. Answer (C) is wrong because accumulator provided oil pressure is used in unfeathering.

8967. Answer B.

During the first run of a newly installed hydromatic propeller it is necessary to bleed any air that may be trapped in the propeller dome. This is accomplished by several full travel movements of the propeller piston, which forces air back to the engine sump where it is vented through the breather line.

8968.   R06

Which of the following occurs to cause front cone bottoming during propeller installation?

A — The front cone becomes bottomed in the front propeller hub cone seat before the rear propeller hub cone seat has engaged the rear cone.
B — The front cone enters the front propeller hub cone seat at an angle causing the propeller retaining nut to appear tight when it is only partially tightened.
C — The front cone contacts the ends of the shaft splines, preventing the front and rear cones from being tightened against the cone seats in the propeller hub.

8969.   R06

What is indicated when the front cone bottoms while installing a propeller?

A — Propeller-dome combination is incorrect.
B — Blade angles are incorrect.
C — Rear cone should be moved forward.

8970.   R06

How is the oil pressure delivery on a hydromatic propeller normally stopped after the blades have reached their full-feathered position?

A — Pulling out the feathering push button.
B — Electric cutout pressure switch.
C — Stop lugs in the teeth of the rotating cam.

8971.   R06

The primary purpose of the front and rear cones for propellers that are installed on splined shafts is to

A — position the propeller hub on the splined shaft.
B — prevent metal-to-metal contact between the propeller and the splined shaft.
C — reduce stresses between the splines of the propeller and the splines of the shaft.

8968. Answer C. AC 65-12A

Front cone bottoming occurs during the installation of a spline shaft propeller when the apex of the front cone contacts the ends of the shaft splines. This happens when the rear cone is too far back on the propeller shaft. When this occurs, neither front nor rear cone can be tightened into the propeller hub's cone seats. The only way to correct this is to move the rear cone forward. Answer (A) is incorrect because the front cone fully engages the front cone seat in the propeller in a normal installation. Answer (B) is wrong because the shape of the front cone and the front cone seat preclude the possibility of misalignment during installation.

8969. Answer C. AC 65-12A

Front cone bottoming occurs during the installation of a spline shaft propeller when the apex of the front cone contacts the ends of the shaft splines. This happens when the rear cone is too far back on the propeller shaft. When this occurs, neither front nor rear cone can be tightened into the propeller hub's cone seats. The only way to correct this is to move the rear cone forward. Neither an incorrect propeller-dome combination (answer A) nor incorrect blade angles (answer B) can cause front cone bottoming during propeller installation.

8970. Answer B. AC 65-12A

When the feather button is pushed in a full-feathering hydromatic propeller system, a holding coil keeps the button in the depressed position. The feather button energizes the feathering pump motor which takes oil from the engine supply tank and directs it to the propeller governor. The propeller governor ports this oil to the propeller piston and drives it to the full feather position. When the propeller is fully feathered, pressure in the inboard piston increases rapidly and the electric cutout switch automatically opens (answer B). This de-energizes the holding coil which releases the feather button. Answer (A) is wrong because a feathering push button does not have to be manually pulled out. Answer (C) is incorrect because the stop lugs on the rotating cam stop blade movement when the blades reach full feather, but do not stop oil pressure delivery.

8971. Answer A. AC 65-12A

The purpose of the cones for a spine shaft propeller installation is to support and align the propeller hub on the shaft. This is similar to the action of tapered bearings which position and support a wheel on an axle. Answer (B) is wrong because you want as much metal-to-metal contact as possible between the propeller and the splined shaft. Answer (C) is incorrect because the cones position the propeller on the splined shaft but have no effect on stress.

8972.   R06

Which of the following statements concerning the installation of a new fixed-pitch wood propeller is true?

A — If a separate metal hub is used, final track should be accomplished prior to installing the hub in the propeller.
B — NAS close-tolerance bolts should be used to install the propeller.
C — Inspect the bolts for tightness after the first flight and again after the first 25 hours of flying.

8972. Answer C. AC 43.13-1A

AC 43.13-1A specifies that when a fixed pitch wooden propeller has been installed, the bolts should be checked for tightness after the first flight, after the first 25 hours of flying, and at least every 50 flying hours thereafter. This is because the moisture content of the wood fibers can cause shrinkage after exposure to heat, causing the bolts to become loose. The fibers can also swell from humidity, which will cause the bolts to be too tight. Answer (A) is incorrect because it is not possible to establish final track without having the hub installed in the propeller. Answer (B) is wrong because, unless otherwise specified by the propeller manufacturer, new AN bolts should be used to install a wood propeller.

8973.   R06

If propeller cones or hub cone seats show evidence of galling and wear, the most likely cause is

A — the pitch change stops were located incorrectly, causing the cone seats to act as the high pitch stop.
B — the propeller retaining nut was not tight enough during previous operation.
C — the front cone was not fully bottomed against the crankshaft splines during installation.

8973. Answer B. AC 65-12A

A loose retaining nut on a spine shaft propeller installation allows movement between the propeller cones and the hub cone seats. If not corrected, this movement can lead to galling or wear on both the front and rear cones and the cone seats. Answer (A) is incorrect because the setting of the pitch change stops has no effect on the seating or condition of the cone seats. Answer (C) is wrong because the front cone should not bottom against the crankshaft splines.

8974.   R06

On aircraft equipped with hydraulically operated constant-speed propellers, all ignition and magneto checking is done with the propeller in which position?

A — High RPM.
B — Low RPM.
C — High pitch range.

8974. Answer A. AC 65-12A

Hydraulically operated constant-speed propellers should be placed in the high rpm, low pitch position for all ignition and magneto checking. This causes the propeller to operate as a fixed-pitch propeller and provides a standard rpm for determining the operating condition of the engine. Answers (B) and (C) are incorrect because operating an engine in the low rpm, high pitch range for ignition and magneto system checks will not permit an accurate check.

8975.   R06

Oil leakage around the rear cone of a hydromatic propeller usually indicates a defective

A — piston gasket.
B — spider-shaft oil seal.
C — dome-barrel oil seal.

8975. Answer B. ITP-P2

In a hydromatic propeller, the spider shaft oil seal prevents oil from leaking between the spider and the propeller shaft and out around the rear cone. Answer (A) is incorrect because there is oil pressure on both sides of the piston gasket, and any leakage remains within the piston dome and is not apparent on the propeller exterior. Answer (C) is wrong because leakage from the dome-barrel oil seal would show up on the front of the propeller hub.

8976.   **R06**

Maximum taper contact between crankshaft and propeller hub is determined by using

A — bearing blue color transfer.
B — a micrometer.
C — a surface gauge.

8976. Answer A. APC

Bearing blue color transfer, sometimes called Prussian blue, is used to determine the amount of surface contact between a tapered propeller shaft and the propeller hub. At least 70 percent surface contact is required. Neither a micrometer (answer B) nor a surface gauge (answer C) can determine taper contact because the two surfaces have nonuniform dimensions and their profiles do not match exactly.

8977.   **R06**

Propeller blade tracking is the process of determining

A — the plane of rotation of the propeller with respect to the aircraft longitudinal axis.
B — that the blade angles are within the specified tolerance of each other.
C — the positions of the tips of the propeller blades relative to each other.

8977. Answer C. AC 65-12A

Propeller blade tracking is the process of determining the blade tip positions relative to each other. A propeller out-of-track condition may indicate a bent propeller shaft or a blade that is bent. Checking a propeller's plane of rotation with respect to the aircraft's longitudinal axis (answer A) is used to diagnose vibration and is done dynamically with the engine operating. Answer (B) is wrong because blade tracking measures the position of the blade tips and does not consider blade angles.

8978.   **R06**

What is the basic purpose of the three small holes (No.60 drill) in the tipping of wood propeller blades?

A — To provide a means for inserting balancing shot when necessary.
B — To provide a means for periodically impregnating the blade with preservation materials.
C — To allow the moisture which may collect between the tipping and the wood to escape (vent the tipping).

8978. Answer C. AC 65-12A

The three small holes (No. 60 drill) in the metal tipping of a wooden propeller serve to ventilate and release moisture formed by condensation between the tipping and the wooden blade. Answer (A) is wrong because shot is not used to balance wood propellers. Answer (B) is incorrect because wood propellers are not impregnated for the purpose of preservation.

8979.   **R06**

A fixed-pitch wooden propeller that has been properly installed and the attachment bolts properly torqued exceeds the out-of-track allowance by 1/16 inch. The excessive out-of-track condition may be corrected by

A — slightly overtightening the attachment bolts adjacent to the most forward blade.
B — discarding the propeller since out-of-track conditions cannot be corrected.
C — placing shims between the inner flange and the propeller.

8979. Answer C. APC

Correction of an out-of-track condition on a fixed pitch wooden propeller is made by inserting paper or brass shims between the inner flange of the metal hub and the propeller boss. On flange type shaft propeller installations, the shim should be placed between the propeller boss and the propeller shaft flange. Answer (A) is wrong because propeller mount bolts should never be tightened beyond the manufacturer's recommended torque specifications. Answer (B) is incorrect because a propeller should not be discarded if the out-of-track condition can be corrected by the use of shims.

8980. R06

Manually feathering a hydromechanical propeller means to

A — block governor oil pressure to the cylinder of the propeller.
B — port governor oil pressure to the cylinder of the propeller.
C — port governor oil pressure from the cylinder of the propeller.

8981. R06

In what position is the constant-speed propeller control placed to check the magnetos?

A — Full decrease, low propeller blade pitch angle.
B — Full increase, high propeller blade pitch angle.
C — Full increase, low propeller blade pitch angle.

8982. R06

If a flanged propeller shaft has dowel pins

A — the manufacturer's maintenance manual must be consulted to find the proper propeller installation position.
B — the propeller can be installed in only one position.
C — check carefully for front cone bottoming against the pins.

8983. R07

Repairs of aluminum alloy adjustable pitch propellers are not permitted to be made on which of the following propeller blade areas?

A — Shank.
B — Face.
C — Back.

8980. Answer C. AC 65-12A

To manually feather a hydromechanical propeller, the propeller control lever is pulled into the feather position. This action ports governor oil pressure from the cylinder in the propeller hub assembly back to the engine and allows the force of springs, counterweights, or compressed air to drive the propeller to the feather position. Answer (A) is wrong because blocking governor oil pressure to the propeller cylinder freezes the blade angle, and answer (B) is incorrect because porting governor oil pressure to the propeller cylinder drives the propeller blades to the low pitch position.

8981. Answer C. AC 65-12A

Hydraulically operated constant-speed propellers should be placed in the high rpm, low pitch position when conducting any ignition or magneto checking. This results in a set blade angle that provides a standard rpm for determining the operating condition of the magneto. Answers (A) and (B) are incorrect because, if the propeller were set in the full decrease or high pitch range for ignition and magneto system checks, the governor would allow the propeller blade angle to change and maintain a set rpm. This would make it very difficult to identify a bad magneto during a magneto check.

8982. Answer B. AC 65-12A

A flanged propeller shaft with dowel pins allows propeller installation in only one position. Answer (A) is incorrect because it is self-evident that the propeller can be installed in only one position without consulting a maintanance manual. Answer (C) is wrong because centering cones are used on splined shaft installations.

8983. Answer A. AC 43.13-1A

The shank, or base of an adjustable pitch propeller is subject to more stress than any other portion of the propeller blade. Therefore, no repairs are permitted to the shanks of aluminum alloy adjustable pitch propeller blades. Answers (B) and (C) are incorrect because repairs to a propeller blade face and back are permitted provided the repair does not materially affect the strength, weight, or performance of the blade.

8984.   **R07**

The amount which an aluminum alloy propeller blade can be bent in face alignment and still be repairable by cold straightening is determined by the

A — linear distance from the blade tip to where the bend is located.
B — thickness of the blade section where the bend is located.
C — chord length of the blade where the bend is located.

8985.   **R07**

It is important that nicks in aluminum alloy propeller blades be repaired as soon as possible in order to

A — maintain equal aerodynamic characteristics between the blades.
B — eliminate stress concentration points.
C — equalize the centrifugal loads between the blades.

8986.   **R07**

Generally, unless otherwise specified by the manufacturer, repairs of nicks, scratches, gouges, etc. on aluminum propeller blades must be made

A — parallel to the length of the blade.
B — perpendicular to the blade axis.
C — so as to return the damaged area to the original dimensions.

8987.   **R07**

Minor surface damage located in a repairable area, but not on the leading or trailing edges of aluminum blades, may be repaired by first

A — filing with a riffle file.
B — filing with a half round or flat file.
C — rough sanding and applying a proper filler.

8988.   **R07**

After proper removal of aluminum blade damage, the affected surface should be polished with

A — fine steel wool.
B — very fine sandpaper.
C — powdered soapstone.

8984. Answer B. AC 43.13-1A

The one factor which determines the amount an aluminum propeller blade can be bent is the thickness of the blade section where the bend is located. For example, only bends not exceeding 20 degrees at 0.15-inch blade thickness to 0 degrees at 1.1-inch blade thickness may be cold straightened. Neither blade station (answer A) nor blade chord length at the bend (answer C) determines whether an aluminum alloy propeller blade can be repaired by cold straightening.

8985. Answer B. AC 43.13-1A

Rotating propellers are constantly subjected to high centrifugal loads and severe vibration. Therefore, any scratch, nick, or gouge can create a stress concentration that could develop into a crack and lead to fatigue failure. Answer (A) is incorrect because minor nicks have little effect on a blade's aerodynamic characteristics. Although propellers must be accurately balanced to minimize centrifugal loads and reduce vibration (answer C), small nicks do not materially change propeller balance.

8986. Answer A. AC 43.13-1A

Repairs of minor defects on aluminum propeller blades should be made parallel to the length of the propeller blade. Answer (B) is incorrect because repairs that are made perpendicular to the blade axis can lead to fatigue cracking. Answer (C) is wrong because it is impossible to return a damaged area to its original dimensions if material must be removed.

8987. Answer A. ITP-P2

Repairs on the face or back of a propeller blade are made with a spoon-like riffle file, which is used to dish out the damaged area. Answer (B) is incorrect because half round or flat files should not be used on the face or back of aluminum propeller blades since they have a tendency to remove too much material. Answer (C) is wrong because fillers are never used on aluminum propeller blades.

8988. Answer B. AC 43.13-1A

To make sure that all minor scratches or file marks are removed after a repair is made to an aluminum propeller blade you should polish the affected surface with very fine sandpaper. The sandpaper should be moved parallel to the length of the blade and, once the sanding is complete, the repaired area should be treated with an appropriate protective coating. Steel wool (answer A) should not be used on aluminum propeller blades because steel particles could become embedded in the propeller and cause dissimilar metal corrosion. Answer (C) is incorrect because powdered soapstone is typically used as a lubricant, not a polishing compound.

8989.   R07
When preparing a propeller blade for inspection it should be cleaned with

A — mild soap and water.
B — steel wool.
C — methyl ethyl ketone.

8990.   R07
What method would be used to inspect an aluminum propeller blade when a crack is suspected

A — use a bright light.
B — magnetic particle.
C — dye-penetrant.

8991.   R07
Removal of propeller blade tips within Type Certificate Data Sheet limits when correcting a defect is

A — a major alteration.
B — a major repair.
C — permitted under the privileges and limitations of a powerplant rating.

8992.   R07
Surface treatment to counter the effects of dye-penetrant inspection on a propeller is accomplished by

A — washing off with solvent.
B — wiping with alcohol.
C — rinse the blade in alodine solution.

8993.   R07
One of the advantages of inspecting an aluminum propeller utilizing dye-penetrant inspection is that

A — defects just below the surface are indicated.
B — it shows whether visible lines and other marks are actually cracks rather than scratches.
C — it indicates overspeed condition.

8989. Answer A. AC 65-12A
When preparing a propeller blade for inspection it should be cleaned with mild soap and water. Answer (B) is wrong because if you use steel wool to clean an aluminum propeller blade, steel particles could become embedded in the aluminum and lead to dissimilar metal corrosion. Methyl ethyl ketone (answer C) is a powerful solvent that can remove the protective coating on aluminum propeller blades and, therefore, should not be used for cleaning.

8990. Answer C. AC 43.13-1A
Of the choices given, dye-penetrant inspection is the most effective method of detecting cracks on an aluminum propeller blade. Although a bright light (answer A) is a valuable tool for assisting in visual inspection, it is not a reliable means of detecting small cracks. Answer (B) is incorrect because magnetic particle inspection is only effective on ferrous materials such as iron or steel.

8991. Answer B. FAR 43, Appendix A
According to FAR Part 43, Appendix A, shortening propeller blades, or retipping wooden blades, is a major repair. All propeller major repairs must be performed by an appropriately certificated repair station or the propeller manufacturer. Answer (A) is incorrect because a propeller major alteration involves changes in blade, hub, or governor design, or the installation of parts not approved for the propeller. Answer (C) is incorrect because a powerplant rating entitles a technician to perform only minor repairs or alterations to propellers.

8992. Answer A. AC 43.13-1A
After performing a dye-penetrant inspection on a propeller, all penetrant residue should be removed using a solvent approved by both the penetrant and propeller manufacturer. Answer (B) is wrong because alcohol may not remove all the penetrant and developer from the blade surface. Answer (C) is incorrect because an alodine solution is a protective surface treatment for aluminum alloys that does not effectively remove dye penetrant.

8993. Answer B. AC 43.13-1A
Dye penetrant inspections allow a properly trained technician to differentiate between cracks and scratches on aluminum propeller blades. Answer (A) is wrong because dye penetrant can only detect cracks or other defects that are open to the surface. Answer (C) is incorrect because overspeed damage typically produces no visible damage and, therefore, cannot be detected by dye-penetrant inspection.

8994.   R07

The primary reason for careful inspection and prompt repairing of minor surface defects such as scratches, nicks, gouges, etc. on aluminum alloy propellers is to prevent

A — corrosion.
B — unbalanced aerodynamics.
C — fatigue failure.

8995.   R07

Which of the following generally renders an aluminum alloy propeller unrepairable?

A — Any repairs that would require shortening and re-contouring of blades.
B — Any slag inclusions or cold shuts.
C — Transverse cracks of any size.

8996.   R07

Cold straightening a bent aluminum propeller blade may be accomplished by

A — the holder of a mechanic certificate with a power-plant rating.
B — an appropriately rated repair station or the manu-facturer.
C — a person working under the supervision of the holder of a mechanic certificate with both air-frame and powerplant ratings.

8994. Answer C. AC 43.13-1A

Rotating propellers are constantly subjected to high centrifugal loads and severe vibration. Therefore, any scratch, nick, or gouge can create stress concentra-tions that could develop into a crack and lead to fatigue failure. Answer (A) is incorrect because promptly repairing minor surface defects does little to prevent corrosion. Answer (B) is wrong because a minor sur-face defect will not result in a aerodynamic imbalance.

8995. Answer C. AC 43.13-1A

A transverse crack is a crack that is parallel to a pro-peller blade's chord. Transverse cracks of any size are not repairable and render a propeller unairworthy. Answer (A) is incorrect because blades can be short-ened and recontoured if damage does not exceed the manufacturer's specified limits. Answer (B) is wrong because slag inclusions or cold shuts may be permissi-ble if they fall within the manufacturer's limts.

8996. Answer B. AC 43.13-1A

Cold straightening a bent aluminum propeller blade is considered a major repair and, therefore, can only be performed by an appropriately rated repair station or the propeller manufacturer. Both answers (A) and (B) are incorrect because neither a powerplant or airframe rating entitles a technician to perform or supervise major repairs to propellers.

CHAPTER 15

AUXILIARY POWER UNITS

This chapter describes the operation of turbine-driven auxiliary power units (APUs). Included is a discussion of the basic operating principles as well as the methods and procedures used to inspect, service, and troubleshoot a typical (APU). The FAA exam questions based on this chapter include:

8997, 8998, 8999, 9000, 9001, 9002, 9003, 9004, 9005, 9006.

8997.   T01
Frequently, an aircraft's auxiliary power unit (APU) generator

A — is identical to the engine-driven generators.
B — supplements the aircraft's engine-driven generators during peak loads.
C — has a higher load capacity than the engine- driven generators.

8997. Answer A. TCAS
Depending on the aircraft, an auxiliary power unit drives one or two generators that are typically identical to the engine driven generators. Answer (B) is incorrect because an aircraft's engine-driven generators must be capable of handling all electrical loads unassisted. Answer (C) is wrong because the generators used in auxiliary power units typically have the same load capacity as the engine-driven generators.

8998.   T01
Fuel is normally supplied to an APU from

A — its own independent fuel supply.
B — the airplane's reserve fuel supply.
C — the airplane's main fuel supply.

8998. Answer C. TCAS
Fuel is normally supplied to the auxiliary power unit from one of the aircraft's main tanks. Answer (A) is wrong because auxiliary power units typically do not have their own independent fuel supply. Answer (B) is incorrect because aircraft typically do not have reserve fuel supplies separate from their main fuel supply.

8999.   T01
An APU is usually rotated during start by

A — a turbine impingement system.
B — a pneumatic starter.
C — an electric starter.

8999. Answer C. TCAS
Due to the size and relatively low starting torque, virtually all gas turbine auxiliary power units use an electric starting motor. Neither turbine impingement systems (answer A) nor pneumatic starters (answer B) are commonly used to start auxiliary power units.

9000.   T01
The function of an APU air inlet plenum is to

A — increase the velocity of the air before entering the compressor.
B — decrease the pressure of the air before entering the compressor.
C — stabilize the pressure of the air before it enters the compressor.

9000. Answer C. ATD
A plenum is an enlargement in a duct or chamber in a turbine engine's induction system that helps eliminate pulsations and stabilize the pressure of the incoming air flow. Answers (A) and (B) are incorrect because an air inlet plenum chamber neither decreases nor increases air pressure.

9001.   **T01**
When in operation, the speed of an APU

A — is controlled by a cockpit power lever.
B — remains at idle and automatically accelerates to rated speed when placed under load.
C — remains at or near rated speed regardless of the load condition.

9002.   **T01**
Generally, when maximum APU shaft output power is being used in conjunction with pneumatic power

A — pneumatic loading will be automatically modulated to maintain a safe EGT.
B — electrical loading will be automatically modulated to maintain a safe EGT.
C — temperature limits and loads must be carefully monitored by the operator to maintain a safe EGT.

9003.   **T01**
When necessary, APU engine cooling before shutdown may be accomplished by

A — unloading the generator(s).
B — closing the bleed air valve.
C — opening the bleed air valve.

9004.   **T01**
Usually, most of the load placed on an APU occurs when

A — an electrical load is placed on the generator(s).
B — the bleed air valve is opened.
C — the bleed air valve is closed.

9005.   **T01**
Fuel scheduling during APU start and under varying pneumatic bleed and electrical loads is maintained

A — manually through power control lever position.
B — automatically by the APU fuel control system.
C — automatically by an aircraft main engine fuel control unit.

9001. Answer C. TEP2
After an auxiliary power unit is started it will accelerate to its rated speed and remain at that speed regardless of the load imposed. As pneumatic or electrical loads change, the APU fuel control automatically meters fuel to maintain the rated speed. Answer (A) is wrong because the only cockpit controls for an APU system are a start switch, a shutdown switch, and a fire extinguisher control. Answer (B) is wrong because APU systems operate at 100 percent rpm at all times and do not decelerate to idle.

9002. Answer A. TCAS
Pneumatic power requirements impose the greatest load on an operating auxiliary power unit. Therefore, when maximum shaft output is used in conjunction with pneumatic bleed air, the pneumatic loading will be automatically modulated to keep the APU's exhaust gas temperature within its limits. Answer (B) is incorrect because aircraft electrical demands represent a minor load on the APU and will not cause a high EGT. Answer (C) is wrong because APU operation is completely automatic and requires no manual control.

9003. Answer B. TCAS
Providing bleed air for an aircraft's pneumatic system places the greatest load on an auxiliary power unit (APU). Therefore, if you close the bleed valve, most of the load on the APU will be removed and the APU will cool. Answer (A) is incorrect because electrical demands impose a minor load on an APU and, therefore, removing electrical loads has little effect on APU operating temperature. Answer (C) is wrong because opening the bleed air valve imposes a higher load on the APU and increases its operating temperature.

9004. Answer B. TCAS
Opening the pneumatic bleed valve places the greatest load on an auxiliary power unit and causes an almost immediate rise in the APU's exhaust gas temperature. Answer (A) is incorrect because electrical demands impose a minor load on an APU. Answer (C) is wrong because closing the bleed air valve removes most of the load on the APU and results in a drop in operating temperature.

9005. Answer B. TCAS
Fuel scheduling for an auxiliary power unit is controlled automatically during start and under load by the APU fuel control system. Answer (A) is incorrect because auxiliary power units are not equipped with power levers. Answer (C) is wrong because an aircraft's main engines operate independently of the auxiliary power unit.

9006.   T01

On APU's equipped with a free turbine and load compressor, the primary function of the load compressor is to

A — provide air for combustion and cooling in the engine gas path.
B — provide bleed air for aircraft pneumatic systems.
C — supply the turning force for operation of the APU generator(s).

9006. Answer B. TCAS

An auxiliary power unit consists of a gas turbine engine that drives an electrical generator to that provide electrical power and a load compressor that provides bleed air for the aircraft's pneumatic systems. Answer (A) is incorrect because an APU's engine compressor, not the load compressor, provides combustion and cooling air. Answer (C) is wrong because APU generators are driven directly by the APU gearbox.

SUBJECT MATTER KNOWLEDGE CODES

LIST OF REFERENCE MATERIALS AND SUBJECT MATTER KNOWLEDGE CODES

The publications listed in the following pages contain study material you need to be familiar with when preparing for aviation mechanic knowledge tests. All of these publications can be purchased through U.S. Government bookstores, commercial aviation supply houses, or industry organizations. The latest revision of the listed references should be requested. Additional study material is also available through these sources that may be helpful in preparing for aviation mechanic knowledge tests. All publications listed would be excellent for a mechanic to have in a personal reference library.

The following abbreviations are used to identify the reference(s) associated with the subject matter.

AVIATION MECHANIC POWERPLANT ABBREVIATIONS AND REFERENCES

ABS	Aircraft Basic Science — Glencoe Division, Macmillan/McGraw-Hill Publication Company	AGTP	Aircraft Gas Turbine Powerplants — Jeppesen Sanderson, Inc.
AC	Advisory Circular	CFR	Title 14, Code of Federal Regulations (Part or § [Section]) - GPO
AEE	Aircraft Electricity and Electronics — Glencoe Division, Macmillan/McGraw-Hill Publication Company	PSG	A&P Technician Powerplant Study Guide - Jeppesen Sanderson, Inc.

AMR	Aircraft Maintenance and Repair — Glencoe Division, Macmillan/McGraw-Hill Publication Company
AMT-G	Aviation Maintenance Technician Series General - Aviation Supplies & Acedemics, (ASA) Inc.
AP	Aircraft Powerplants — Glencoe Division, Macmillan/McGraw-Hill Publication Company
DAT	Dictionary of Aeronautical Terms — Aviation Supplies & Academics (ASA), Inc.
TCAS	Transport Category Aircraft Systems — Jeppesen Sanderson, Inc.
APC	Aircraft Propellers and Controls — Jeppesen Sanderson, Inc.
ATD	Aircraft Technical Dictionary — Jeppesen Sanderson, Inc.
JSGT	A & P Technician General Textbook — Jeppesen Sanderson, Inc.
JSPT	A & P Technician Powerplant Textbook — Jeppesen Sanderson, Inc.

Reciprocating Engines — AC 65-9A, AC 65-12A, CFR Part 43, AP, JSPT

A01	Inspect and repair a radial engine
A02	Overhaul reciprocating engine
A03	Inspect, check, service, and repair reciprocating engines and engine installations
A04	Install, troubleshoot, and remove reciprocating engines

Turbine Engines — AC 65-9A, AC 65-12A, AC 65-15A, CFR Part 33, AP, AGTP, JSPT

B01	Overhaul turbine engine
B02	Inspect, check, service, and repair turbine engines and turbine engine installations
B03	Install, troubleshoot, and remove turbine engines

Engine Inspection — AC 65-9A, AC 65-12A, AC 39-7B, AC 43.13-1A, CFR Part 23, CFR Part 33, CFR Part 43, CFR Part 65, ABS, AP, JSGT, JSPT

C01	Perform powerplant conformity and airworthiness inspections
DXX	Reserved
EXX	Reserved
FXX	Reserved
GXX	Reserved

Engine Instrument Systems — AC 65-12A, AC 65-15A, AC 20-88A, CFR Part 65, AMR, AP, AGTP, JSPT

H01	Troubleshoot, service, and repair electrical and mechanical fluid rate-of-flow indicating systems
H02	Inspect, check, service, troubleshoot, and repair electrical and mechanical engine temperature, pressure, and RPM indicating systems

Engine Fire Protection Systems — AC 65-9A, AC 65-12A, ABS, AMR, AP, JSPT

I01	Inspect, check, service, troubleshoot, and repair engine fire detection and extinguishing systems

Engine Electrical Systems — AC 65-9A, AC 65-12A, AC 65-15A, AC 43.13-1A, CFR Part 23, CFR Part 25, AEE, AP, JSGT, JSPT

J01	Repair engine electrical system components
J02	Install, check, and service engine electrical wiring, controls, switches, indicators, and protective devices

Lubrication Systems — AC 65-12A, AC 65-15A, CFR Part 33, AP, AGTP, JSPT

K01	Identify and select lubricants
K02	Repair engine lubrication system components
K03	Inspect, check, service, troubleshoot, and repair engine lubrication systems

Ignition and Starting Systems — AC 65-12A, AC 65-15A, AEE, AP, AGTP, JSPT

L01	Overhaul magneto and ignition harness
L02	Inspect, service, troubleshoot, and repair reciprocating and turbine engine ignition systems and components
L03	Inspect, service, troubleshoot, and repair turbine engine electrical starting systems
L04	Inspect, service, and troubleshoot turbine engine pneumatic starting systems

Fuel Metering Systems — AC 65-9A, AC 65-12A, AP, AGTP, JSPT

M01	Troubleshoot and adjust turbine engine fuel metering systems and electronic engine fuel controls
M02	Overhaul carburetor
M03	Repair engine fuel metering system components
M04	Inspect, check, service, troubleshoot, and repair reciprocating and turbine engine fuel metering systems

Engine Fuel Systems — AC 65-9A, AC 65-12A, AC 43.13-1A, CFR Part 23, AP, JSPT

N01	Repair engine fuel system components
N02	Inspect, check, service, troubleshoot, and repair engine fuel systems

Induction and Engine Airflow Systems — AC 65-9A, AC 65-12A, AC 43.13-1A, AP, AGTP, JSPT

O01	Inspect, check, troubleshoot, service, and repair engine ice and rain control systems
O02	Inspect, check, service, troubleshoot, and repair heat exchangers, superchargers, and turbine engine airflow and temperature control systems
O03	Inspect, check, service, and repair carburetor air intake and induction manifolds

Engine Cooling Systems — AC 65-12A, ABS, AP, JSPT

P01   Repair engine cooling system components

P02   Inspect, check, troubleshoot, service, and repair engine cooling systems

Engine Exhaust and Reverser Systems — AC 65-12A, AC 43.13-1A, JSPT

Q01   Repair engine exhaust system components

Q02   Inspect, check, troubleshoot, service, and repair engine exhaust systems

Q03   Troubleshoot and repair engine thrust reverser systems and related components

Propellers — AC 65-9A, AC 65-12A, AC 43.13-1A, CFR Part 43, CFR Part 65, AP, ATD, APC, JSPT

R01   Inspect, check, service, and repair propeller synchronizing and ice control systems

R02   Identify and select propeller lubricants

R03   Balance propellers

R04   Repair propeller control system components

R05   Inspect, check, service, and repair fixed pitch, constant speed and feathering propellers, and propeller governing systems

R06   Install, troubleshoot, and remove propellers

R07   Repair aluminum alloy propeller blades

Auxiliary Power Units — DAT, TCAS, ATD, AGTP

T01   Inspect, check, service, and troubleshoot turbine-driven auxiliary power units

NOTE: AC 00-2, Advisory Circular Checklist, transmits the status of all FAA advisory circulars (AC's), as well as FAA internal publications and miscellaneous flight information such as Aeronautical Information Manual (AIM), Airport/Facility Directory, knowledge test study guides, and other material directly related to a certificate or rating. To obtain a free copy of AC 00-2, send your request to:

U.S. Department of Transportation
General Service Section, M-483.3
Washington, D.C. 20590

APPENDIX

2

CROSS-REFERENCE LISTING OF QUESTIONS

Appendix 2 is a numerical listing of all the Aviation Mechanic Powerplant Knowledge questions. The listing includes the FAA question number, answer, and a listing of the chapter and the page where the question is located.

Example: 8131   C   2-5

This indicates that the answer to question 8131 is C, and the question is answered in Chapter 2, page 2-5 of the Study Guide.

QUESTION	ANSWER	PAGE	QUESTION	ANSWER	PAGE	QUESTION	ANSWER	PAGE
8001	B	1-1	8029	B	1-8	8057	A	1-14
8002	C	1-1	8030	B	1-8	8058	C	1-14
8003	C	1-2	8031	C	1-8	8059	B	1-14
8004	B	1-2	8032	A	1-9	8060	A	1-14
8005	C	1-2	8033	B	1-9	8061	C	1-15
8006	C	1-2	8034	C	1-9	8062	A	1-15
8007	B	1-3	8035	C	1-9	8063	B	1-15
8008	A	1-3	8036	C	1-9	8064	C	1-15
8009	C	1-3	8037	C	1-10	8065	C	1-15
8010	C	1-3	8038	B	1-10	8066	B	1-16
8011	A	1-4	8039	B	1-10	8067	C	1-16
8012	C	1-4	8040	B	1-10	8068	A	1-16
8013	C	1-4	8041	A	1-10	8069	B	1-16
8014	A	1-4	8042	C	1-11	8070	B	1-17
8015	C	1-5	8043	A	1-11	8071	A	1-17
8016	A	1-5	8044	C	1-11	8072	C	1-17
8017	B	1-5	8045	C	1-11	8073	B	1-17
8018	A	1-5	8046	C	1-11	8074	B	1-17
8019	B	1-6	8047	A	1-12	8075	C	1-17
8020	A	1-6	8048	B	1-12	8076	B	1-18
8021	A	1-6	8049	C	1-12	8077	C	1-18
8022	B	1-6	8050	A	1-12	8078	C	1-18
8023	C	1-7	8051	C	1-12	8079	A	1-18
8024	C	1-7	8052	A	1-13	8080	A	1-18
8025	A	1-7	8053	B	1-13	8081	A	1-19
8026	A	1-7	8054	C	1-13	8082	B	1-19
8027	B	1-7	8055	C	1-13	8083	C	1-19
8028	B	1-8	8056	A	1-13	8084	A	1-19

QUESTION	ANSWER	PAGE	QUESTION	ANSWER	PAGE	QUESTION	ANSWER	PAGE
8085	C	1-19	8131	C	2-5	8176	A	2-14
8086	A	1-20	8132	A	2-6	8177	A	2-15
8087	A	1-20	8133	C	2-6	8178	A	2-15
8088	A	1-20	8134	A	2-6	8179	A	2-15
8089	C	1-20	8135	A	2-6	8180	A	2-15
8090	B	1-20	8136	C	2-6	8181	B	2-16
8091	C	1-21	8137	C	2-7	8182	B	2-16
8092	C	1-21	8138	B	2-7	8183	B	2-16
8093	C	1-21	8139	C	2-7	8184	A	2-16
8094	C	1-21	8140	A	2-7	8185	C	2-16
8095	B	1-21	8141	B	2-8	8186	A	2-17
8096	C	1-22	8142	B	2-8	8187	C	2-17
8097	A	1-22	8143	B	2-8	8188	B	2-17
8098	A	1-22	8144	C	2-8	8189	C	2-17
8099	B	1-22	8145	B	2-8	8190	C	2-17
8100	C	1-22	8146	A	2-9	8191	C	2-18
8101	A	1-23	8147	C	2-9	8192	A	2-18
8102	C	1-23	8148	A	2-9	8193	B	2-18
8103	A	1-23	8149	C	2-9	8194	C	2-18
8104	C	1-23	8150	B	2-9	8195	A	2-18
8105	A	1-24	8151	B	2-10	8196	A	2-19
8106	C	1-24	8152	B	2-10	8197	A	2-19
8107	C	1-24	8153	C	2-10	8198	B	2-19
8108	C	2-1	8154	C	2-10	8199	C	2-19
8109	C	2-1	8155	C	2-10	8200	B	2-19
8110	B	2-1	8156	B	2-11	8201	C	2-20
8111	A	2-2	8157	C	2-11	8202	B	2-20
8112	C	2-2	8158	A	2-11	8203	A	2-20
8113	B	2-2	8159	B	2-11	8204	C	2-20
8114	A	2-2	8160	A	2-11	8205	A	2-20
8115	B	2-2	8161	A	2-12	8206	C	2-21
8116	B	2-3	8162	C	2-12	8207	A	2-21
8117	A	2-3	8163	C	2-12	8208	B	2-21
8118	C	2-3	8164	A	2-12	8209	A	2-21
8119	C	2-3	8165	C	2-12	8210	A	2-21
8120	A	2-3	8166	A	2-12	8211	B	2-22
8121	A	2-4	8167	C	2-13	8212	B	2-22
8122	C	2-4	8168	C	2-13	8213	C	2-22
8123	A	2-4	8169	A	2-13	8214	A	2-22
8124	B	2-4	8170	A	2-13	8215	C	2-23
8125	A	2-4	8171	A	2-13	8216	A	2-23
8126	B	2-5	8172	B	2-14	8217	B	2-23
8127	C	2-5	8173	B	2-14	8218	A	2-23
8128	C	2-5	8174	B	2-14	8219	C	2-24
8129	C	2-5	8175	C	2-14	8220	A	2-24
8130	C	2-5						

QUESTION	ANSWER	PAGE	QUESTION	ANSWER	PAGE	QUESTION	ANSWER	PAGE
8221	C	2-24	8267	C	4-3	8312	C	5-2
8222	C	2-24	8268	B	4-3	8313	A	5-2
8223	C	2-24	8269	B	4-3	8314	A	5-3
8224	C	2-25	8270	C	4-4	8315	A	5-3
8225	C	2-25	8271	B	4-4	8316	B	5-3
8226	B	2-25	8272	B	4-4	8317	C	5-3
8227	A	2-25	8273	B	4-4	8318	C	5-3
8228	A	3-1	8274	B	4-5	8319	C	5-4
8229	B	3-1	8275	A	4-5	8320	A	5-4
8230	B	3-1	8276	A	4-5	8321	B	5-4
8231	A	3-2	8277	B	4-5	8322	A	5-4
8232	C	3-3	8278	C	4-5	8323	A	5-4
8233	B	3-3	8279	B	4-5	8324	C	5-5
8234	A	3-3	8280	A	4-6	8325	A	5-5
8235	B	3-3	8281	C	4-6	8326	B	5-5
8236	B	3-3	8282	A	4-6	8327	B	5-6
8237	A	3-3	8283	B	4-6	8328	A	5-6
8238	B	3-4	8284	A	4-7	8329	C	5-6
8239	B	3-4	8285	A	4-7	8330	A	5-6
8240	A	3-4	8286	C	4-7	8331	B	5-7
8241	A	3-4	8287	B	4-7	8332	C	5-7
8242	C	3-4	8288	A	4-8	8333	B	5-7
8243	B	3-5	8289	B	4-8	8334	B	5-7
8244	C	3-5	8290	A	4-8	8335	B	5-8
8245	C	3-5	8291	C	4-8	8336	B	5-8
8246	B	3-5	8292	C	4-9	8337	A	5-8
8247	B	3-6	8293	C	4-9	8338	B	5-8
8248	C	3-6	8294	B	4-9	8339	B	5-8
8249	B	3-6	8295	A	4-9	8340	B	5-8
8250	A	3-6	8296	A	4-9	8341	C	5-9
8251	A	3-7	8297	B	4-10	8342	B	6-1
8252	B	3-7	8298	C	4-10	8343	C	6-1
8253	A	3-7	8299	C	4-10	8344	C	6-1
8254	C	3-7	8300	A	4-10	8345	B	6-2
8255	A	3-8	8301	C	4-11	8346	C	6-2
8256	C	3-8	8302	C	4-11	8347	C	6-2
8257	A	4-1	8303	C	4-11	8348	C	6-2
8258	B	4-1	8304	A	4-11	8349	A	6-2
8259	C	4-1	8305	C	4-11	8350	B	6-2
8260	A	4-2	8306	B	4-12	8351	C	6-3
8261	A	4-2	8307	C	4-12	8352	C	6-3
8262	B	4-2	8308	A	4-12	8353	A	6-3
8263	B	4-2	8309	B	4-12	8354	C	6-3
8264	B	4-2	8310	C	5-1	8355	A	6-3
8265	A	4-3	8311	B	5-1	8356	B	6-4
8266	B	4-3						

QUESTION	ANSWER	PAGE	QUESTION	ANSWER	PAGE	QUESTION	ANSWER	PAGE
8357	B	6-4	8403	C	6-15	8448	A	7-9
8358	C	6-4	8404	C	6-15	8449	A	7-9
8359	C	6-4	8405	C	6-16	8450	B	7-9
8360	A	6-4	8406	A	6-16	8451	C	7-10
8361	C	6-5	8407	C	6-16	8452	B	7-10
8362	A	6-5	8408	A	6-16	8453	A	7-10
8363	C	6-5	8409	B	6-16	8454	A	7-10
8364	C	6-5	8410	C	6-16	8455	C	7-11
8365	A	6-5	8411	C	7-1	8456	A	7-11
8366	B	6-6	8412	A	7-1	8457	A	7-11
8367	A	6-6	8413	B	7-1	8458	C	7-11
8368	C	6-6	8414	C	7-2	8459	C	7-12
8369	C	6-6	8415	B	7-2	8460	A	7-12
8370	C	6-6	8416	A	7-2	8461	B	7-12
8371	A	6-7	8417	C	7-2	8462	A	7-12
8372	C	6-7	8418	C	7-3	8463	B	7-12
8373	B	6-7	8419	A	7-3	8464	B	7-13
8374	C	6-7	8420	B	7-3	8465	C	7-13
8375	B	6-8	8421	B	7-3	8466	C	7-13
8376	C	6-8	8422	A	7-4	8467	A	7-13
8377	C	6-9	8423	A	7-4	8468	A	7-13
8378	C	6-9	8424	C	7-4	8469	C	7-14
8379	A	6-9	8425	B	7-4	8470	C	7-14
8380	C	6-9	8426	A	7-4	8471	B	7-14
8381	C	6-9	8427	B	7-4	8472	B	7-14
8382	B	6-10	8428	A	7-5	8473	A	7-15
8383	B	6-10	8429	A	7-5	8474	A	7-15
8384	B	6-10	8430	A	7-5	8475	A	7-15
8385	B	6-10	8431	B	7-5	8476	C	7-15
8386	C	6-11	8432	B	7-5	8477	C	7-15
8387	B	6-11	8433	A	7-6	8478	B	7-16
8388	C	6-11	8434	A	7-6	8479	A	7-16
8389	A	6-11	8435	B	7-6	8480	B	7-16
8390	B	6-11	8436	B	7-6	8481	B	7-16
8391	C	6-12	8437	B	7-7	8482	C	7-17
8392	B	6-12	8438	C	7-7	8483	C	7-17
8393	C	6-12	8439	A	7-7	8484	B	7-17
8394	B	6-12	8440	B	7-7	8485	C	7-17
8395	C	6-13	8441	B	7-8	8486	B	7-17
8396	B	6-14	8442	C	7-8	8487	C	7-18
8397	A	6-14	8443	C	7-8	8488	C	7-18
8398	B	6-14	8444	C	7-8	8489	A	7-18
8399	C	6-14	8445	C	7-8	8490	B	7-18
8400	A	6-15	8446	C	7-9	8491	A	7-19
8401	A	6-15	8447	C	7-9	8492	C	7-19
8402	C	6-15						

QUESTION	ANSWER	PAGE	QUESTION	ANSWER	PAGE	QUESTION	ANSWER	PAGE
8493	C	7-19	8539	B	8-9	8584	C	8-19
8494	C	7-19	8540	B	8-9	8585	C	8-19
8495	C	7-20	8541	B	8-10	8586	B	8-19
8496	C	7-20	8542	C	8-10	8587	B	8-20
8497	C	7-20	8543	C	8-10	8588	B	8-20
8498	A	7-20	8544	C	8-10	8589	B	8-20
8499	A	7-20	8545	B	8-10	8590	A	8-20
8500	B	7-21	8546	C	8-11	8591	A	8-21
8501	C	7-21	8547	A	8-11	8592	A	8-21
8502	C	7-21	8548	C	8-11	8593	B	8-21
8503	B	8-1	8549	B	8-11	8594	A	8-21
8504	A	8-1	8550	C	8-11	8595	A	8-22
8505	B	8-2	8551	A	8-12	8596	C	8-22
8506	A	8-2	8552	C	8-12	8597	C	8-22
8507	B	8-2	8553	A	8-12	8598	C	8-22
8508	C	8-2	8554	A	8-12	8599	C	8-22
8509	B	8-3	8555	C	8-12	8600	C	8-23
8510	A	8-3	8556	A	8-13	8601	C	8-23
8511	C	8-3	8557	C	8-13	8602	A	8-23
8512	C	8-3	8558	B	8-13	8603	A	8-24
8513	A	8-3	8559	B	8-13	8604	C	8-24
8514	B	8-4	8560	B	8-14	8605	A	8-24
8515	C	8-4	8561	C	8-14	8606	C	8-24
8516	A	8-4	8562	A	8-14	8607	C	8-25
8517	A	8-4	8563	A	8-14	8608	B	8-25
8518	B	8-5	8564	B	8-14	8609	A	8-25
8519	C	8-5	8565	A	8-15	8610	B	8-25
8520	B	8-5	8566	C	8-15	8611	C	8-25
8521	A	8-5	8567	B	8-15	8612	B	8-26
8522	B	8-5	8568	A	8-15	8613	A	8-26
8523	B	8-6	8569	A	8-16	8614	C	8-26
8524	B	8-6	8570	A	8-16	8615	C	8-26
8525	B	8-6	8571	B	8-16	8616	B	8-27
8526	B	8-6	8572	A	8-16	8617	A	8-28
8527	A	8-7	8573	A	8-16	8618	A	8-28
8528	B	8-7	8574	A	8-17	8619	B	8-28
8529	B	8-7	8575	A	8-17	8620	A	8-28
8530	C	8-7	8576	A	8-17	8621	C	8-29
8531	C	8-7	8577	B	8-17	8622	B	8-30
8532	C	8-8	8578	A	8-18	8623	A	8-30
8533	C	8-8	8579	A	8-18	8624	B	8-30
8534	B	8-8	8580	C	8-18	8625	C	8-30
8535	B	8-8	8581	C	8-18	8626	C	8-31
8536	A	8-8	8582	A	8-19	8627	A	8-31
8537	C	8-9	8583	C	8-19	8628	A	8-31
8538	A	8-9						

QUESTION	ANSWER	PAGE	QUESTION	ANSWER	PAGE	QUESTION	ANSWER	PAGE
8629	B	8-31	8675	C	9-11	8720	C	9-21
8630	B	8-31	8676	A	9-11	8721	C	9-21
8631	C	8-32	8677	C	9-11	8722	B	9-22
8632	B	8-32	8678	B	9-12	8723	C	9-22
8633	B	8-32	8679	A	9-12	8724	A	9-22
8634	B	9-1	8680	B	9-12	8725	B	9-22
8635	A	9-1	8681	C	9-12	8726	C	9-23
8636	B	9-1	8682	B	9-12	8727	A	9-23
8637	A	9-2	8683	C	9-13	8728	A	9-23
8638	B	9-2	8684	B	9-13	8729	C	9-23
8639	C	9-2	8685	C	9-13	8730	A	9-24
8640	B	9-2	8686	C	9-13	8731	C	9-24
8641	A	9-3	8687	B	9-13	8732	B	10-1
8642	C	9-3	8688	B	9-14	8733	C	10-1
8643	C	9-3	8689	A	9-14	8734	A	10-1
8644	A	9-3	8690	C	9-14	8735	C	10-2
8645	C	9-3	8691	C	9-14	8736	B	10-2
8646	C	9-4	8692	B	9-14	8737	B	10-3
8647	A	9-4	8693	A	9-15	8738	A	10-3
8648	B	9-4	8694	C	9-15	8739	C	10-3
8649	B	9-4	8695	A	9-15	8740	B	10-3
8650	B	9-5	8696	A	9-15	8741	C	10-3
8651	C	9-5	8697	C	9-15	8742	C	10-4
8652	B	9-5	8698	C	9-16	8743	B	10-4
8653	B	9-5	8699	C	9-16	8744	A	10-4
8654	C	9-6	8700	A	9-17	8745	B	10-4
8655	C	9-6	8701	A	9-17	8746	B	10-5
8656	A	9-6	8702	A	9-17	8747	A	10-5
8657	A	9-6	8703	C	9-17	8748	A	10-5
8658	B	9-7	8704	C	9-17	8749	C	10-5
8659	A	9-7	8705	C	9-18	8750	A	10-5
8660	C	9-7	8706	B	9-18	8751	B	10-6
8661	A	9-7	8707	C	9-18	8752	B	10-6
8662	B	9-8	8708	C	9-18	8753	C	10-6
8663	C	9-8	8709	A	9-19	8754	B	10-6
8664	B	9-8	8710	C	9-19	8755	C	10-7
8665	A	9-8	8711	C	9-19	8756	C	10-7
8666	C	9-9	8712	B	9-19	8757	B	10-7
8667	C	9-9	8713	B	9-19	8758	A	10-7
8668	A	9-9	8714	B	9-20	8759	B	10-8
8669	A	9-9	8715	A	9-20	8760	B	10-8
8670	C	9-10	8716	B	9-20	8761	B	10-8
8671	B	9-10	8717	A	9-20	8762	A	10-8
8672	B	9-10	8718	B	9-21	8763	A	10-9
8673	B	9-10	8719	A	9-21	8764	B	10-9
8674	A	9-11						

QUESTION	ANSWER	PAGE	QUESTION	ANSWER	PAGE	QUESTION	ANSWER	PAGE
8765	A	10-9	8811	B	11-10	8856	B	13-3
8766	A	10-9	8812	C	11-10	8857	B	13-3
8767	C	10-10	8813	A	11-10	8858	C	13-3
8768	B	10-10	8814	B	12-1	8859	A	13-4
8769	A	10-10	8815	B	12-1	8860	C	13-4
8770	C	10-10	8816	C	12-1	8861	C	13-4
8771	B	10-11	8817	B	12-2	8862	C	13-4
8772	A	11-1	8818	B	12-2	8863	C	13-4
8773	A	11-1	8819	B	12-2	8864	B	13-5
8774	B	11-2	8820	C	12-2	8865	A	13-5
8775	C	11-2	8821	C	12-2	8866	B	13-5
8776	C	11-2	8822	A	12-3	8867	A	13-5
8777	C	11-2	8823	C	12-3	8868	A	13-5
8778	B	11-3	8824	B	12-3	8869	A	13-6
8779	A	11-3	8825	B	12-3	8870	C	13-6
8780	C	11-3	8826	A	12-4	8871	B	13-6
8781	C	11-3	8827	A	12-4	8872	C	13-6
8782	C	11-3	8828	A	12-4	8873	A	13-6
8783	C	11-4	8829	A	12-4	8874	A	13-7
8784	B	11-4	8830	C	12-4	8875	A	13-7
8785	A	11-4	8831	B	12-5	8876	C	13-7
8786	C	11-4	8832	B	12-5	8877	B	13-7
8787	C	11-5	8833	B	12-5	8878	A	13-8
8788	B	11-5	8834	B	12-5	8879	A	13-8
8789	B	11-5	8835	C	12-6	8880	B	13-8
8790	B	11-5	8836	A	12-6	8881	B	14-1
8791	C	11-6	8837	C	12-6	8882	C	14-1
8792	B	11-6	8838	C	12-6	8883	B	14-2
8793	A	11-6	8839	A	12-7	8884	B	14-2
8794	A	11-6	8840	C	12-7	8885	B	14-2
8795	B	11-7	8841	A	12-7	8886	A	14-2
8796	B	11-7	8842	B	12-7	8887	B	14-2
8797	C	11-7	8843	B	12-8	8888	C	14-2
8798	C	11-7	8844	A	12-8	8889	A	14-3
8799	A	11-7	8845	B	12-8	8890	C	14-3
8800	B	11-8	8846	B	13-1	8891	A	14-3
8801	C	11-8	8847	C	13-1	8892	A	14-3
8802	B	11-8	8848	C	13-1	8893	A	14-4
8803	A	11-8	8849	C	13-2	8894	C	14-4
8804	B	11-8	8850	A	13-2	8895	C	14-4
8805	A	11-9	8851	C	13-2	8896	C	14-4
8806	C	11-9	8852	A	13-2	8897	C	14-4
8807	B	11-9	8853	C	13-2	8898	A	14-5
8808	A	11-9	8854	A	13-3	8899	A	14-5
8809	A	11-10	8855	C	13-3	8900	A	14-5
8810	B	11-10						

QUESTION	ANSWER	PAGE	QUESTION	ANSWER	PAGE	QUESTION	ANSWER	PAGE
8901	C	14-5	8937	C	14-13	8973	B	14-21
8902	C	14-6	8938	C	14-13	8974	A	14-21
8903	A	14-6	8939	B	14-13	8975	B	14-21
8904	C	14-6	8940	A	14-14	8976	A	14-22
8905	B	14-6	8941	A	14-14	8977	C	14-22
8906	A·	14-7	8942	C	14-14	8978	C	14-22
8907	C	14-7	8943	C	14-14	8979	C	14-22
8908	C	14-7	8944	B	14-14	8980	C	14-23
8909	C	14-7	8945	A	14-15	8981	C	14-23
8910	B	14-8	8946	A	14-15	8982	B	14-23
8911	B	14-8	8947	B	14-15	8983	A	14-23
8912	C	14-8	8948	A	14-15	8984	B	14-24
8913	A	14-8	8949	C	14-16	8985	B	14-24
8914	A	14-8	8950	A	14-16	8986	A	14-24
8915	B	14-9	8951	B	14-16	8987	A	14-24
8916	B	14-9	8952	B	14-16	8988	B	14-24
8917	A	14-9	8953	C	14-16	8989	A	14-25
8918	A	14-9	8954	B	14-17	8990	C	14-25
8919	C	14-9	8955	C	14-17	8991	B	14-25
8920	A	14-10	8956	C	14-17	8992	A	14-25
8921	A	14-10	8957	C	14-17	8993	B	14-25
8922	A	14-10	8958	B	14-17	8994	C	14-26
8923	B	14-10	8959	C	14-18	8995	C	14-26
8924	B	14-10	8960	A	14-18	8996	B	14-26
8925	A	14-11	8961	B	14-18	8997	A	15-1
8926	A	14-11	8962	A	14-18	8998	C	15-1
8927	C	14-11	8963	A	14-18	8999	C	15-1
8928	B	14-11	8964	C	14-19	9000	C	15-1
8929	A	14-11	8965	C	14-19	9001	C	15-2
8930	B	14-12	8966	B	14-19	9002	A	15-2
8931	C	14-12	8967	B	14-19	9003	B	15-2
8932	B	14-12	8968	C	14-20	9004	B	15-2
8933	B	14-12	8969	C	14-20	9005	B	15-2
8934	A	14-12	8970	B	14-20	9006	B	15-3
8935	B	14-12	8971	A	14-20			
8936	B	14-13	8972	C	14-21